HE WHO WEPT

An Epic Novel of Jeremiah

THOM LEMMONS

QUESTAR PUBLISHERS, INC.
Sisters, Oregon

HE WHO WEPT
© 1990 by Thom Lemmons

published by
QUESTAR PUBLISHERS, INC.
Sisters, Oregon

Printed in the United States of America

International Standard Book Number: 0-945564-35-X

to DR. JOHN WILLIS,
Professor of Old Testament
Abilene Christian University

Without his guidance and teaching,
this book would not have happened

ACKNOWLEDGMENTS

In preparing this novel I relied heavily
upon Dr. John Willis's lecture notes on Jeremiah.
Also most helpful was Dr. Anthony Ash's excellent commentary
on Jeremiah and Lamentations.

My thanks to Thomas Womack and Marlee Alex
for their (mostly) kind and (always) helpful criticism.

Finally, I thank my wife and children for their love and patience.
Working on a novel about Jeremiah does not predispose one
to moods of jubilation or optimism. Nevertheless, they
graciously suffered with me through the gestation period.

Names of Characters

Prophets:

Jeremiah (whose name means "Yahweh is exalted")
Jehiel ("God lives")
Nathan ("giver") — apprentice to Jehiel before becoming a
    prophet himself in the days of King Zedekiah
Habakkuk ("embrace")
Zephaniah ("Yahweh has hidden")

The House of Abiathar in Anathoth:

Hilkiah ("Yahweh is protection") — Jeremiah's father
Libnah ("whiteness") — Jeremiah's mother
Joash ("Yahweh supports") — Jeremiah's oldest brother
Lemuel ("God is bright") — another older brother
Zeruah — Jeremiah's sister
Hannah ("grace") — beloved of Jeremiah, later the wife of Lemuel
Haggith — wife of Joash
Othniel — son of Joash and Haggith, nephew of Jeremiah

Also in Anathoth:

Mahseiah ("Yahweh is a refuge") — grandfather of Baruch, and
    former scribe to the prophet Isaiah

Kings of Judah (in order of succession):

Josiah ("Yahweh supports") — grandson of King Manasseh, son
    and successor of King Amon
Jehoahaz ("Yahweh upholds") — middle son and successor of
    Josiah
Eliakim ("God sets up"; also known as **Jehoiakim**, "Yahweh sets
    up") — oldest son of Josiah; placed on the throne by
    Pharaoh Neco to replace his younger brother Jehoahaz
Jeconiah ("Yahweh establishes") — son and successor of Eliakim
    (Jehoiakim); Jeconiah is also referred to in the Bible as
    "Coniah" and "Jehoiachin"
Mattaniah ("gift of Yahweh"; also named **Zedekiah**, "Yahweh is
    righteousness") — younger brother of Eliakim (Jehoia-
    kim); made king by Nebuchadrezzar to replace his
    nephew Jeconiah

Rulers and Officials of Other Nations:

Nebuchadrezzar (Hebrew form of Sumerian "Nabu-Kudur-Usur") — first monarch of the Neo-Babylonian Empire

Nebuzaradan — commander of Nebuchadrezzar's army

Neco — Pharaoh of Egypt

Hophra — Pharaoh of Egypt, successor to Neco

Sakhri — counselor to the Pharaohs, and their ambassador

Ashpenaz — chief eunuch of Nebuchadrezzar, and supervisor of captured Hebrew youths

Sheshach — Nebuchadrezzar's emissary to Jerusalem

Priests of the Temple:

Pashhur ("free") — chief priest in the days of King Jehoiakim; later carried to Babylon

Zephaniah ("Yahweh has hidden") — successor to Pashhur as chief priest

Ezekiel ("God strengthens") — young priest, later carried to Babylon

Judah's Nobles, Princes, and Royal Officials:

Shaphan ("prudent, crafty") — scribe and counselor to King Josiah, and tutor to his sons

Hananiah ("Yahweh is gracious") — son of Azzur of Gibeon; first a prophet in Jerusalem; later counselor to King Zedekiah

Ahikam ("my brother has risen") — son of Shaphan; counselor to Josiah and Jehoahaz, later chief scribe to Jehoiakim

Elnathan ("God is giving") — nobleman in the courts of Kings Josiah, Jehoiakim, and Zedekiah; father-in-law of the slain prophet Uriah

Daniel ("God is my judge") — son of a noble family; taken captive to Babylon and there renamed **Belteshazzar**

Gemariah — son of Shaphan, brother of Ahikam; proctor in the Temple courts

Micaiah — son of Gemariah

Jehudi — counselor to King Jehoiakim

Jerahmeel — son of King Jehoiakim

Shephatiah ("Yahweh is judge") — nobleman in the court of King Zedekiah; imprisoner of Jeremiah

Gedaliah ("Yahweh is great") — son of Ahikam, chief scribe to King Zedekiah, later governor of Judah after Jerusalem's fall

Ebed-melech ("servant of the king") — Cushite eunuch of King Zedekiah's court

Ishmael ("God hears") — prince in the court of King Jehoiakim

also in Jerusalem:

Baruch ("blessed") — scribe who copied the words of Jeremiah

Squint — servant and friend of Baruch

Jabesh — soldier of Judah

Jasiel — soldier of Judah

Johanan ("Yahweh is gracious") — Judean military officer who survived the fall of Jerusalem

names for God:

Adonai — Hebrew for "Lord"

Adonai Elohim — "Lord of gods"

El Shaddai — "God, the All-sufficient One"

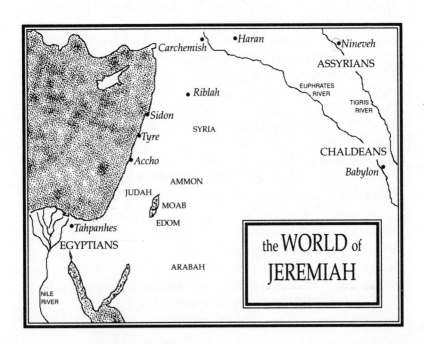

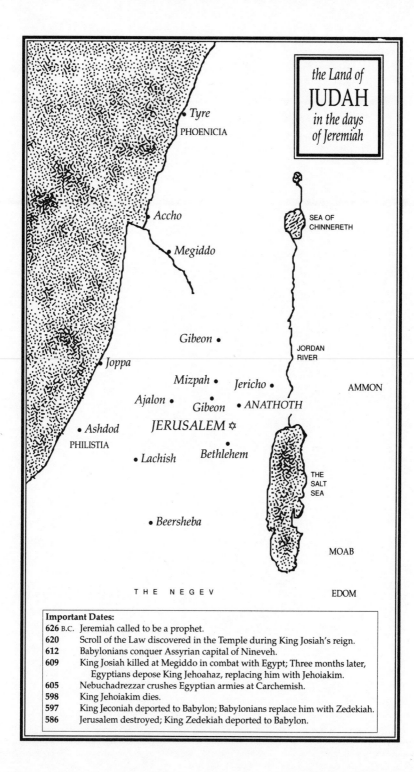

the Land of
JUDAH
in the days
of Jeremiah

Tyre
PHOENICIA

SEA OF
CHINNERETH

Accho

Megiddo

Gibeon •

JORDAN
RIVER

Joppa

Mizpah •   Jericho •   AMMON

Ajalon •   Gibeon   • ANATHOTH

Ashdod   JERUSALEM ✡

PHILISTIA

Lachish   Bethlehem

THE
SALT
SEA

Beersheba

MOAB

THE NEGEV   EDOM

Important Dates:
626 B.C. Jeremiah called to be a prophet.
620   Scroll of the Law discovered in the Temple during King Josiah's reign.
612   Babylonians conquer Assyrian capital of Nineveh.
609   King Josiah killed at Megiddo in combat with Egypt; Three months later,
            Egyptians depose King Jehoahaz, replacing him with Jehoiakim.
605   Nebuchadrezzar crushes Egyptian armies at Carchemish.
598   King Jehoiakim dies.
597   King Jeconiah deported to Babylon; Babylonians replace him with Zedekiah.
586   Jerusalem destroyed; King Zedekiah deported to Babylon.

HE
WHO
WEPT

The harvest is past,

the summer has ended…

and we are not saved.

JEREMIAH 8:20

PART I

The Calling

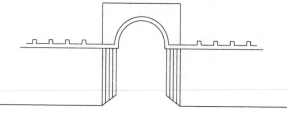

1

THE BLACK, FLOP-EARED GOAT skittered along the edge of
the flinty ravine, kicking pebbles haphazardly down the steep
banks into the shadows at the bottom of the gorge. Now and
again she paused, glancing about, testing the air before caper-
ing along her precarious way.

Edging along the narrow path behind the goat, nervously
eyeing the drop into the ravine, the young boy called out,
"Here, Whitefoot! Come back! You come back right now!"

The heedless animal, perhaps sensing the uncertainty of her
master, perhaps understanding in some brutish way the pleading tone of his voice, continued blithely along the edge of the
canyon, her single white fetlock flashing jauntily as she scampered farther down the rim of the chasm away from the annoying voice behind her.

Jeremiah heard the deep mumbling of thunder, felt the cool,
moist breeze on his back. This stupid goat would cause him to
get caught in the downpour threatened by the low, roiling
clouds moving in from the north and west. Yet he persisted, following her on an ever more narrow and treacherous trail.

Whitefoot was a pet, once a sickly kid he had saved from
death by pleading with his father not to kill her at birth. Now
he almost regretted his intercession.

"Whitefoot! Stop! We must get back to the shelter before the
rain starts!"

Suddenly Jeremiah felt the hair on the back of his neck
prickle. Without thinking, as if on command, he threw himself
to the rocky path — only an instant before a lightning bolt siz-
zled from the curdled sky.

On the rim of the gorge, a tamarisk tree was shredded at
once by the strike. A near-simultaneous crash of thunder roared

through the air. To Jeremiah it felt like a hammer blow, pounding his prone body into the earth.

The goat, panicked by the blast, lurched from the narrow path, her feet slipping over the edge of the canyon. Jeremiah watched in horror as Whitefoot slid down the wall of the crevice in a shower of pebbles, tumbling over and over. Her bleats of terror were silenced by dull thuds as she tumbled into the darkness at the bottom.

A dull knife of grief pressed hard against Jeremiah's throat. His eyes stung with tears. A blast of cold wind from the clouds drove pellets of rain, like tiny needles, into his skin. He pulled his cloak over his head and rose, sobbing, to pick his way back in the direction he had come.

When he reached the house, a gust of rain-laden wind slammed the door against the wall and hurled Jeremiah in a wet tangle inside. He folded onto the floor in a heap, his face in his hands, still moaning.

"Shut the door, little fool!" shouted Lemuel, Jeremiah's brother, older by three years. "What good is a house in a storm if you let rain in at the door?"

"Lemuel, be still," admonished Libnah, their mother, bustling into the room. She leaned against the blast to shut the door. "Son," she crooned, turning and going to her youngest child still crumpled on the floor. "Why all these tears?" She held him against her breast and rocked as he poured out an incoherent stream of wails and sniffling half-words. Lemuel, snorting in disgust, bounded from the room.

HILKIAH, PRIEST OF ANATHOTH, shifted uncomfortably on the stone wall dividing his field from that of his neighbor. The moisture in the air, lingering from the storms of the last few days, was causing his ill-mended knee to ache. Leaning his weight forward onto his cane, he raised slowly to his feet, swaying for a moment until gaining his balance. For the thousandth time he cursed that high-strung ass sold to him by a vagabond Amorite. The beast had thrown him — what, seven years ago was it? — and caused him unending misery.

As he turned toward his house, his eye fell upon a small knot of men atop a ridge to the west of the village, silhouetted by the evening sun. They were bowing before an altar to one of the baals, presumably presenting a thank offering for the rains of the past week. "Folly," mumbled Hilkiah into his kinky steel-gray beard. He began limping slowly back down the uneven path from the field to the house.

Since the days of Solomon, almost half a millennium ago, Hilkiah's clan had lived in Anathoth. They were descendants of the high priests, but since their ancestor Abiathar in the early days of Solomon's reign had unwisely backed Solomon's brother for the throne, they had lived here in genteel obscurity, within sight of Mount Moriah, two leagues to the south. They were never quite able to forget their fall from greatness.

Hilkiah's prosperity showed in his portliness and in the cut of his garments. Life had not been terribly hard on him. True, he did not enjoy the respect and power he might have if he had lived in the days of Hezekiah, or another of the rulers who feared Yahweh. Since the banishment of their ancestor, the clan had been forced to depend more upon their lands and herds, and less upon the tithe offerings they could have demanded had their family and their religion been more in favor. Yet things were not so bad.

Hilkiah did his best to maintain the ways of the past, for had not his fathers and grandfathers all been heirs of the traditions of Aaron? He instructed his sons in the Law as best he could. But it was now a different age. Many voices competed for the ears of the people. These days life was ordered much more by what passed in Nineveh than what occurred in the Temple or palace in Jerusalem. Discretion was the order of the day, and Hilkiah, despite his mutterings against the idolaters on the ridge, had mastered the art.

He arrived at his gate. Glancing a final time at the worshipers on the hillside, he shook his head as he turned to go in.

The house of Abiathar was a low, rambling affair constructed of stones quarried from beneath the hills of Benjamin where the village was situated. It had started as a single large chamber used for meals and sleeping. Through the centuries it had grown organically outward from this central room, taking on an alcove here, a hallway there, to accommodate sons and grandsons and their wives. The house was surrounded by a rock wall of about chest height and in a less-than-perfect state of repair.

Hilkiah limped from the gate in the wall to the door of his house.

The smells of roasted mutton, boiled lentils and freshly baked bread spread a warm, savory canopy inside. The household was gathered for the evening meal in the main room, where servants placed the food on the large board. Around it were cushions on which the family sat, awaiting the blessing of the head of the house. Hilkiah lowered himself carefully into his place and observed his brood while the final bustlings took place.

To his right sat his eldest son, Joash, and his wife. Joash was a strong and stable young man who had taken a wife only two summers past. He was assuming more and more of the operation of the lands, now that he was reaching suitable maturity. Joash was good and honest and industrious, but he had precious little interest in anything not directly useful in the pursuit of better-yielding crops and herds. Hilkiah had tried to interest his oldest boy in the lore of the clan's priestly heritage, but to no avail. Joash was, now and forever, a man of the soil. His eyes looked down, not up.

Beside Joash's wife sat Zeruah, Hilkiah's only daughter. A beautiful girl of thirteen years, Hilkiah had betrothed her last year to the son of Kenan, a wealthy landholder of the area. Hilkiah sighed; Kenan sacrificed to the asherim and the baals, but his dowry had been impressive, and he was, after all, an upstanding citizen of Anathoth. What else could one do? She was just entering her bloom; it was a good marriage for her, and, after all, to make such arrangements was a father's duty.

At the opposite end of the table sat Libnah, his wife. Hilkiah could not look on her without smiling — such was the happiness they had shared through the years. She had borne him fine sons and a lovely daughter, and was as faithful and patient a companion as any man could wish for. If she sometimes doted a bit too much on the baby...well, a woman could have worse faults.

Beside her sat Jeremiah, the youngest. The sight of the boy always wrinkled Hilkiah's brow with a puzzled expression.

Though still less than ten years old, barely old enough to read the scrolls for himself, little Jeremiah was a voracious reader and learner. Concepts which eluded older children were as natural as breathing to him, and his memory of the stories of Moses and the kings of Judah and Israel never ceased to astound his father.

Yet — he could do well to have a bit of the steadiness of his oldest brother. Jeremiah seemed to feel everything so intensely. Not for him the child's carefree ignorance of the ugly necessities of life. Once he had refused for three months to eat lamb when told it was needful to slaughter the animal to provide meat for the table. He was overly sensitive, this son Jeremiah. Hilkiah hoped it would not bring him to harm. Perhaps he would outgrow it with time.

And then, Lemuel. Hilkiah carefully studied the features of his middle son, but as usual the boy's half-lidded eyes and carefully neutral expression brushed aside inquiry. It concerned Hilkiah deeply that he did not trust this, his own son. But he did not know what to do about it.

It was time for the blessing. Hilkiah took up a loaf in one hand and a cup in the other.

"Blessed art Thou, Eternal our God, King of the Universe," he intoned as the family sat with heads bowed in reverence, real or feigned, "who hast brought forth grain from the ground, and given us the fruit of the vine to drink."

As he took his choices from the platter offered to him by the chief servant, Hilkiah turned to his oldest son. "Joash, did you make good progress in the plowing today?"

"Yes, Father. We should be ready to begin planting barley two days from now. The rains made the ground soft; it's working up well."

"Good. This would be a good year for a bountiful crop — the talk in the marketplace is of famine in the east. Famine and war."

"War, Father?" chirped Lemuel, evincing his first interest in the conversation.

"Yes. The traders speak of discontent in Babylon with the regime of Nineveh. Some say the Chaldeans begin to chafe under Ashurbanipal's leash. Others say Egypt stands only too ready to pounce on any weakness in Assyria. And here sits Judah, a lamb couched between wolves..."

"Not a lamb, Father!" complained Lemuel. "We could fight!"

"Really, my son? And against which foe would you direct your first assault?"

"That's simple. I'd send spies into Egypt and Assyria — maybe Babylon, too. I'd find out whose army was strongest, and wait until the right moment. Then I'd throw all my forces into the fight on the side of the winner. As my reward, the victorious king would give me whatever I asked for. Simple." The boy returned his attention to his food with a self-satisfied smirk. Hilkiah shuddered at the mixture of duplicity and naiveté in his son's scheme.

"Well, if war comes," announced Joash, "there will be a need for food, no matter who wins. And big talk doesn't grow food." He stared pointedly at Lemuel, who mumbled something into his hand and looked away.

"Father," breathed Haggith, Joash's wife, "do you really think Babylon will fight against Assyria — soon?" Her eyes were big with worry, and her hand strayed to the roundness of her belly.

"Softly, daughter, softly," soothed Libnah from her end of the table. "The old men in the marketplace have no other occupation with which to spend their days than endless chatter about wars and famines and other less pleasant things. In other times," she continued, locking eyes with her husband, "such talk did not so easily come to supper. Didn't the wise king say, 'A prudent man conceals his knowledge, but the foolish tell all they know?'"

Zeruah tittered, then clapped a hand over her mouth, staring from her mother to her father. Hilkiah cleared his throat and looked away into the corner of the chamber.

"See here, boy!" he harrumphed at a servant, "My cup is almost empty! Why must I feed you if you will not attend me?" The boy scampered after the wine pitcher.

"Father," said Jeremiah in a half-whisper into the awkward silence, "a bad thing happened when it rained."

"Yes, what was that?"

"My goat, Whitefoot — she...she...." His voice began to thicken, his lips twisted with emotion.

"His stupid she-goat ran off," scoffed Lemuel, "and got herself killed falling down the Ravine of the Vipers. She was probably so sick of Jeremiah's fawning over her, she did it just to get away."

"Lemuel!" said Hilkiah sternly. "You will be silent. Your brother may speak at this table without commentary from you.

"Now then, Jeremiah...what happened?"

The boy told, with frequent chest-heaving pauses, the story of Whitefoot's demise. When he reached the point of the lightning strike, Libnah gasped and clutched her fist to her chest. "Child! You said nothing of this before!"

2

IN THE PALACE on the slopes of Mount Moriah, another boy sat at table. He looked up from his food, and the muted conversations in the chamber fell silent. Josiah gave no thought to this, nor did he marvel at the reverence with which his words were received. He was king. This was a king's right. "Asaiah," he called, his reedy child's voice echoing in the now-hushed hall. The chamberlain approached and made obeisance.

"Yes, my lord king?"

Unlike Jeremiah, Josiah sat at the place of honor, and deference was paid to him as to the patriarch of the house. He was King of Judah and of Israel's Remnant, the Lord's Anointed, Heir to the Throne of David. It was a heavy title for such little shoulders to bear, but Josiah was growing into the role a bit at a time. After all, he had the frank acceptance of a child. If these men, who were supposed to know such things, told him his father was dead and he was now king — then it was so. He had not been close to Amon, his father, in any true familial sense. He knew more about his nurses and tutors than his sire.

He now addressed himself again to the chamberlain. "Send for Shaphan. I want him to tell me a story."

A few moments later Shaphan entered the hall with his careful, stoop-shouldered gait. As usual he carried a sheaf of parchment folded under one arm, and an ink-darkened stylus tucked, unnoticed, behind his ear. His beard was a wispy brown, just beginning to show traces of white at its edges. He bowed to Josiah, waiting impatiently at the head of the table.

"Come here, Shaphan. I want you to tell me the story of the northern kingdom."

Shaphan cocked his head quizzically. "My lord king! That is a sad tale for a dinner entertainment. Are you sure?"

"Yes! I want to hear it, because I don't want such bad things to happen to Judah! At least not while I'm king! Now tell me at once!" Josiah pounded a chubby fist on the table.

Shaphan paused and looked around at the king's attendants. So — the moment they had hoped for, prayed for, had come. All their planning, their careful control of Josiah's training and playmates, had begun to reach fruition. An ember of concern for the kingdom had kindled within the heart of this wide-eyed boy, who sat awaiting the beginning of the story. Would this spark within him become a flame of ardor for the ways of Yahweh? Or would Josiah continue the follies of his sire and grandsire?

The scribe glanced at Asaiah, who nodded almost imperceptibly, and at Achbor, the king's personal attendant, who gave the faintest wisp of a smile. Shaphan took a deep breath, and began:

"My lord king, in the days of Solomon, the great king of long ago, there was but one king in all Judah and Israel. Solomon, your forefather, reigned over all the territory from the bend of the great Euphrates at Tiphsah, to the tip of the Red Sea — a splendid kingdom indeed. In those days Jerusalem received the tribute of all the lands and nations. The ocean barges of the Phoenicians disgorged their bounty into Judah. The wild kings of the desert brought their most comely animals to Solomon, and heaped thousands of baskets of spices at his feet. Not even the rulers of Assyria and Egypt received greater honor than King Solomon, your forefather!"

Josiah's eyes were glistening with delight. Shaphan continued: "All this glory, all this honor, all this power, came to the great king from the hand of the Lord of Heaven, the God of Abraham, our most ancient father. May the Lord's name be blessed! And yet, my king — Solomon forgot the source of all his blessings, because his heart was turned toward other gods."

Now the face of the boy-king fell. He scowled at the floor for a moment, as Shaphan and the others held their breath.

"LET HIM SPEAK, Mother," admonished Hilkiah gently, looking into his wife's whitened face.

"That was wise of you, son," he said, turning back to

Jeremiah. "Throwing yourself to the ground very probably saved your life."

"Well..." Jeremiah began, squinting away from his father's gaze.

"Go on, boy — say what you are thinking."

"It's just that...when the lightning struck, I felt...I knew I wasn't going to die, because..." He paused at length, twining his fingers. "Because — there's something Adonai intends for me to do, and I haven't done it yet."

A howl of laughter burst from Lemuel. "Oh, that's right! This little baby who can't even shut the door when it's raining — this goat-lover — is a great man of God!"

Hilkiah rose from his place, grasped Lemuel by the shoulder, and pulled him to his feet. "Leave the table at once!" he commanded. "You may not mock your brother in my house!"

Lemuel sullenly shrugged his shoulder from his father's grasp. "Of course I'll leave," he said, turning to go. "My appetite has left me anyway." He skulked out of the room, glancing darkly back at Jeremiah.

Hilkiah and Libnah exchanged worried looks, and the rest of the meal passed in silence.

"AND JEROBOAM'S SONS after him became more and more wicked and faithless," finished Shaphan, "even though God sent many prophets and messengers to warn of the coming anger of God."

"Why wouldn't they listen to the prophets?"

"Ah, my lord king — the heart of a man can be as soft as a mother's tears or as hard as an armored fist. When a man's heart is closed he can shut out even the voice of the Almighty. And when the king's heart is closed..." Shaphan paused.

Josiah's frown deepened as he stared at the table top. He rose from his place, his face clouded. He paced slowly to a window which commanded a view of the city sloping west toward the Ephraim Gate. His little hands rested for a moment on the sill, his chin barely high enough to permit him to look outside. The small fingers clenched into fists as he looked out over this, his city. "And my grandfather..." came the high, tremulous voice of the child. "He was...bad?"

Shaphan waited before answering gently, "My lord, for most of his life — yes. Toward the end...perhaps—"

Josiah whirled angrily. "And my father?" he demanded. Tears began coursing down his cheeks.

"Your father Amon... He also was—"

"And for his faults he was slain?" It was half a shout, half a wail. "Did God tell the men to kill my father?"

Shaphan made no answer.

"It's not fair of God to make such demands on a king! Not fair! The king must live and die for his people — how can anyone carry such a burden? I don't want to be king! I can't! What if I make mistakes? Will they kill *me*, too?" The boy slumped down the wall below the window to sit on the floor, sobbing into his hands. "I'm only a child, a child..."

Slowly Shaphan went to him and lowered his angular frame to the floor beside his sovereign. He placed his hands on the boy's shoulders. "My lord," he murmured, "you are already king. You are the son and grandson of kings, and the true heir of David. Yours is not to choose nor reject the role, for the Lord has already chosen.

"But, my king," he continued, softly raising Josiah's tear-stained face to look into his own, "it does remain to you, and to you alone, to choose the sort of king you will be."

Josiah gazed for long moments into the kind, craggy face of the scribe. Gradually his sobs slowed, then stopped. Wiping his eyes with the back of his arm, he stood and looked out again at the city.

"I want to be a good king," announced the boy finally. "I don't want the same things to happen here that happened in Samaria."

He turned to face Shaphan. "Will you help me?" It was partly a command, partly a plea.

From his place on the floor, Shaphan looked into his king's eyes, smiled, and nodded.

The others in the room dropped to their knees.

3

JEREMIAH STRAIGHTENED and stood up, wincing as the nerves in his legs came back to tingling life. He was in the scanty shade of an acacia tree on a small ridge overlooking a brownish-green wold on which grazed a flock of Joash's sheep. He shaded his eyes and squinted into the glare of the afternoon sun, counting the flock. Yes, all still there.

A hot wind from the south blew the sparsely clad branches of the tree back and forth in jitters and jerks. Even the sheep were annoyed by the wind, yanking their heads up from grazing to bleat at every tumbling tuft of weed.

Jeremiah was ill at ease and didn't know why. Since awaking that morning he had felt somewhat distracted and a little queasy. The last time he remembered having this sensation was when his tutors came to examine the progress he had made in his lessons as a child. But he faced no examinations today — to his knowledge.

He squatted again, leaning his back against the acacia's trunk.

"Jeremiah!"

He jumped to his feet and turned — then held out his arms, laughing.

"Hannah! You gave me a start! I thought I was quite alone out here!"

The graceful, dark-eyed daughter of Gershom the miller smiled and held out her hands to touch his. "As always you were deep in your own mind and so oblivious to everything else! Had I been a troop of Assyrian cavalry you would have noticed no quicker," she chided.

"You do me great dishonor, maiden," he scolded in mock seriousness. "You imply that I slacken in my vigilance for the flock."

"Then I suppose you would be too offended to accept this"—
she reached into a pocket-fold of her mantle and brought out a
loaf of bread, glistening with butter —"from the hand of one
who accused you so unjustly." She pointed her chin at his left
shoulder, arching her eyebrows.

"Well, we mustn't be hasty," he said, snatching the loaf.
"Perhaps you meant no harm, after all."

They laughed and sat down together.

"Have you spoken yet to your father?" she asked, looking
expectantly into his face.

"I have," he said, taking an oversized bite from the loaf. He
chewed and gazed serenely out over the field.

"Well? Aren't you going to tell me?" she demanded.

"You know, this bread is good. Quite good, indeed! Did you
make it?"

"Jeremiah…"

"In fact, it's so good, that I…"

"Jeremiah!"

"…think I would marry the woman who made it."

"If you don't answer me this instant, I will never speak to
you again!"

"Yes."

"Are you going to answer me, or not?"

"Yes."

"Tell me!"

"Yes."

She jabbed his chest with her finger, punctuating each
word: "Tell—me—what—he—said—or—I'll…"

"Yes, *yes!*" he said, grabbing her wrist and laughing as he
fell backward. "My father said yes!"

Her mouth gaped into a little "O" of surprise, matched by
the shape of her eyes. Then she melted into a tumult of tears
and half-exclamations, alternately holding her face in her hands
and shining her countenance upon him in pride as bright as the
Judean sun.

Jeremiah smiled, finding it suddenly difficult to swallow.
He embraced her, his eyes brimming with tears. "Hannah," he
whispered. "I am to be betrothed to Hannah…she of the beautiful dark eyes and the silken skin. *Hannah.*"

"When?" she asked breathlessly. "When will Hilkiah speak to my father?"

"Slowly, my dear one, slowly," he said. "Don't forget; it is my father who must pay the dowry, but your father who must accept!"

"Oh, don't be silly," she chided. "Do you think you're the only one who has been at work here?"

"Hannah! Surely you have not said anything to Gershom! It is not seemly."

"No, no — nothing so crude as that," she said, shaking her head impatiently. "Sometimes, when you would drive your brother's flock through town on the way here, Mother and I would sit on the roof of the house. I would say things, and she would say things, and — perhaps..." Hannah smiled, coyly, glancing sideways at him.

"I see," he intoned, rubbing his chin thoughtfully. "Yes, I shall have to take care around you, I can see that. You are a wily one."

"Would you have it otherwise?" she asked, showing again the tilted chin, the deliciously arched eyebrows.

He grinned helplessly. "Of course not!"

He studied her face for a moment, then said, "When the harvest is in the barns, my father will speak to yours. But now I fear your mother will place in his ear a price too dear for the poor house of Abiathar to pay!"

"And what price might that be?"

He cupped her chin gently in his hand. "I can't imagine any dowry I would begrudge to win such a prize as you."

Their eyes melted and ran together.

The bleating of the sheep roused Jeremiah from his gaze. He jerked around to look toward the flock. "Oh, no! That stupid brown-necked ewe has wandered away again. I wish Joash would cull her for the stewpot!" He stood reluctantly, holding out a hand to help his beloved to her feet. "Thank you for the bread. And thank you for coming to see me. But you should go back, shouldn't you? It's not long until someone will miss you."

"You're right," she agreed hesitantly, "but I will miss you." She turned to go. "Perhaps this evening Mother and I will watch you bring in the flock."

She smiled and walked down the hill toward the path to Anathoth, with many a backward glance. He watched her go, her every movement tugging at him inwardly like the fingers of a harpist on the strings.

AFTER HE HAD CHASED the stubborn ewe back to the flock, Jeremiah returned and sat down under the acacia, wiping his forehead with the corner of his cloak. If anything, the afternoon had grown hotter. The wind from the south seemed to come straight from the brick kilns of Egypt.

He leaned back his head and stared up into the acacia's feathery branches — then blinked. He saw bobbing in the wind a branch of dark green almond leaves, clustered with ripe nuts.

The hair on the back of his neck began to prickle, and his heart came throbbing into his throat. He felt the touch of something he had only imagined before. "*Shaqed!*" he breathed. "The almond!"

A voice was within him which was not his own. Yet, as he heard it, he realized he had known it all his life: in the sighing of the wind, the rumble of the thunder, the glory of the lightning. It was this same Voice which had thrown him to the ground before the storm when he was a child.

"Yes," the Voice was saying, "it is *shaqed* you have seen, and I am *shoqed*, 'watching,' — watching over all that I have said, to bring it to pass."

Jeremiah fell on his face. He felt the wind on the back of his neck. It was shifting, suddenly cooling.

Now it was blowing from the north: a cold, cutting wind which seemed to carry within it the faraway sounds of battle and the faint smell of blood.

Try as he might, terrified though he was, he could not keep his face to the ground. Slowly he raised his eyes and looked to the north. The sky, too, had changed. Instead of a bright, hot, early summer blue, a low bank of gray covered the north. As he watched, the cloud bank began to swirl, wrapping around and upon itself to form a hollow, a bowl, a...

"What do you see now?" the Voice asked.

"I see...a boiling pot in the sky," he stammered, "overflowing from the north."

"You have seen well. For out of the north I will bring calamity upon this land. I will bring the people of the north, and they shall set their thrones at the gates of Jerusalem, and they shall conquer every city of Judah. And I will make known Judah's wickedness, for the people have forgotten Me. They have offered up sacrifice to gods which they have made with their own hands.

"But you must arise, Jeremiah, and get ready for the work I am giving you. Indeed, I have been preparing you for it all your life. I will make you like a fortified city, like a bronze wall. And whatever I say to you, you must tell them, whether they be priests, or princes, or kings. They will hate you, but do not fear them. I am Adonai, and I will deliver you from their hands."

Again Jeremiah dropped his face to the ground, afraid to move.

WHEN HE LOOKED UP again, the day was sunny and bright as before. The sky was cloudless. The sheep were quietly grazing. He turned to look up into the acacia tree, and saw nothing but wispy leaves.

That evening he drove the sheep back to the fold, never glancing right or left. Hannah waved to him from the doorway of her house, but he did not see her. She frowned after him for several moments, then closed her door, puzzled.

That night he tossed on his bed, his clothing drenched in sweat. He saw himself standing at the gate of a city. The walls towered up to heaven, and the gate was of a shiny metal, harder than iron. He knew he was to knock upon the gate, to deliver a message to those inside. But he did not know the words of the message.

"Sovereign Lord!" he cried out, "how can I speak to these people? I don't know what to say! I'm barely more than a child! It's too much for me!"

Then the Voice was within him: "Do not say, 'I am only a child.' For I have known you from all time: I knit you together within your mother's womb for this very purpose!" Jeremiah felt a touch on his lips, like fire and ice.

"Now I have given you the words you will speak. You will preach to kingdoms and rulers. Your words will break down walls, and build up cities. Your words will bring famine, and bounty."

The Voice now was silent. Jeremiah reached out and knocked on the gate. It swung slightly inward, and he stepped inside. The city, for as far as he could see, was full of dead bodies, swollen with putrefaction.

He awoke screaming.

4

"HOW PROCEEDS the work?" Josiah demanded, pacing back and forth in his chamber, his hands clasped behind him.

"The last of the unclean altars is to be pulled down today, my lord," answered Shaphan, "and the construction in the inner and outer sanctuaries should be completed within seven days. Then the purification can begin."

"Good." The king looked out the window toward the Temple grounds. "Now, Shaphan, I want you to take down what I am about to say."

"Very well, my king," said the old man, reaching for his ever-ready stylus and ink block.

"Write this in my chronicle, Shaphan: 'In his last days, Manasseh, king of Judah, repented of the evil he had done in the land, and caused the unclean altars and the asherim to be removed from the House of the Lord in Jerusalem...'"

Shaphan paused, raised his stylus from the parchment and looked up at Josiah, whose back was toward him. "Are you certain you wish it written so, my king?" he asked.

Josiah turned to face his teacher. "Yes, Shaphan. I have heard you say it yourself: Toward the end of his life, my grandfather seemed to feel remorse for departing so wickedly from the righteousness of his father Hezekiah.

"And it is my wish," Josiah continued firmly, "that he leave some legacy to future generations other than as the Polluter of Judah. I wish to cleanse the Temple, and I wish to do it in the name of my grandfather. It is little enough. But it is, nonetheless, my earnest desire." He looked intently into the eyes of the scribe for a long moment, until the older man nodded and began writing.

DOWN IN THE TEMPLE COURTYARD, a stone mason forced his chisel into a small crack in the mortar and raised his hammer. He pounded the iron wedge into the joint between the stones until the crevice was the breadth of a finger. Then he put aside the hammer and picked up the long iron bar with the wide, tapered end. He inserted it into the fissure and pried down and up with wider and wider motions, until with a grinding pop! the square-cut stone broke loose from the mortar and tumbled to the ground.

He signaled to the sledge team, who dragged their wooden pallet over and began to load the three stones he had dislodged to be carried out of the courtyard.

It was the middle of the month of Tammuz, and the hot summer sun beat down into the courtyard of Solomon's Temple with a pitiless glare, absorbed and magnified by the stones of the Temple wall. The mason wished, not for the first time, that King Josiah had waited until after the blazing days of summer to order this work done. He wondered: Forty years hence, would another king order this altar or one like it to be rebuilt on the same spot? From what he had observed of kings, he felt it not unlikely. But King Josiah had ordered this work — and besides, the pay was generous.

He wiped his face on his sleeve as he wandered onto the Temple portico. He glanced inside, where men were finishing out the new cedar beams for the outer sanctuary. The interior of the building was a beehive of activity, awash with the smooth redolence of cedar shavings. And everywhere the priests and Levites poked about, supervising, inspecting, and making a nuisance of themselves.

A small group of men emerged from the back of one of the chambers which lined the sides of the outer and inner sanctuaries. They walked along slowly, peering over each other's shoulders at a scroll carried by a Levite in their center. They came close to where the mason stood.

"Eliabah!" he called to the Levite in their midst. "What have you there?"

"We're not sure," the Levite murmured, continuing to scrutinize the vellum roll. "As we were preparing the wages for the day, we found this scroll on a back shelf of the vault. It appears to be quite old. See how brittle it is?" He broke off a slight corner of the brownish-yellow document.

"And from what we can tell," said one of the men with him, "the style is also quite archaic. I wouldn't be surprised if this were not a writing of one of the grandsons of Solomon — perhaps even that of the great king himself."

A mutter of awed agreement passed among them.

"What will you do with it?" asked the mason.

"We're taking it to Shaphan the scribe. He's very learned in such things, and will know what use to make of it."

They proceeded into the courtyard, left the Temple through the gate by the Bronze Basin, and strode toward the palace.

A FOOTMAN padded softly into the room, prostrated himself before the king, and went to Shaphan, murmuring a message of some length in his ear. Then the scribe glanced up at the king.

"What is it?" demanded Josiah.

"A book has been found in the vault of the Temple, my lord. It would appear to be a very old book. Perhaps I should examine it."

"Yes, of course! Do so at once, and report back to me."

The scribe and the messenger bowed to Josiah, who had already turned away to stare out the window again toward the Temple.

Leaving the king, Shaphan followed the footman to the council chamber where a group of priests and Levites stood around a table in the center of the room. On it was spread the old scroll. Hilkiah, one of the priests in charge of the Temple project, was bent over the parchment.

"What have we here, Hilkiah?" asked Shaphan. The group at the table made way at once for the king's scribe, who bent down beside Hilkiah.

"Hmmm. Yes," Shaphan said, moving his finger slowly from right to left along the neatly ordered lines of writing. He mouthed the words silently as he deciphered the script.

He lifted his eyes. "The style is old," he said aloud, "very old indeed."

Together he and Hilkiah leaned down even closer, examining the scroll yet more carefully. Finally Shaphan spoke again, his gaze still following the script: "An example, I believe, of the writing of...of..." His voice trailed off. His face blanched. He stopped reading, and the scribe and Hilkiah looked up at each other, their eyes wide.

"We must take this to the king," said Shaphan, "without delay."

Hilkiah nodded. Shaphan gathered up the parchment and hurried out.

"MY KING," said the scribe as he entered Josiah's chamber, barely pausing to make the slightest of bows, "it is as reported. The scroll is very old."

"Well, what does it say?"

"It is a book of laws, your majesty. The Laws of Moses."

The king stared at him for several heartbeats, open-mouthed.

"Can it be? The law has not been read in Judah since..."

"Since the time of Hezekiah, your great-grandfather, almost four-score years ago."

"Read it to me, at once!"

"Yes, my king." Shaphan tenderly opened the age-stiffened scroll. His eyes scanned the ancient, holy writing. He selected a place, cleared his throat, and with difficulty began to read:

"'And Moses called all Israel, and said unto them, "Hear, O Israel, the statutes and judgments which I speak in your ears this day, that ye may learn them, and keep, and do them. The Lord our God made a covenant with us in Horeb....The Lord talked with you face to face in the mount out of the midst of the fire, saying, 'I am the Lord thy God, which brought thee out of the land of Egypt, from the house of bondage. Thou shalt have no other gods before Me....'"'"

Shaphan was finding his voice, his words now resounding in the royal chamber: "'Hear, O Israel: The Lord our God is one Lord, and thou shalt love the Lord thy God with all thine heart, and with all thy soul, and with all thy might....

"'All the commandments which I command thee this day shall ye observe to do, that ye may live, and multiply, and go in and possess the land which the Lord thy God sware unto your fathers....'"

"'Beware that thou forget not the Lord thy God'"— he halted momentarily, his eyes looking ahead at words to come; then he resumed in a lower but stronger tone —"'in not keeping His commandments, and His judgments, and His statutes, which I command thee this day, lest when thou hast eaten and art full, and hast built goodly houses, and dwelt therein, and when thy herds and thy flocks multiply, and thy silver and thy gold is multiplied, and all that thou doest is multiplied, then thine heart be lifted up, and thou forget the Lord thy God, which brought thee forth from the house of bondage....'"

Now he read more slowly: "'And it shall be, if thou do at all forget the Lord thy God, and walk after other gods, and serve them, and worship them, I testify against you this day that ye shall surely perish. As the nations which the Lord destroyeth before your face, so shall ye perish, because ye would not be obedient unto the voice of the Lord your God.'"

Shaphan looked up. Josiah, king of Judah, was slumped against the wall, weeping. As the scribe looked on, the king reached up to his neck, took hold of the seam of the purple silk robe he wore, and ripped it.

As the king sobbed into his hands, the workmen outside labored on under the summer sun.

5

JEREMIAH KNOCKED at the door of the hovel. The old man opened it a fraction, his eyes glittering suspiciously back and forth as he searched for any sign of unexpected visitors. Satisfied that Jeremiah was alone, he grudgingly allowed the flimsy, weatherbeaten door to open just enough to admit the young man with the haunted eyes.

The old man was Mahseiah, and in better days he had been a scribe in Jerusalem. But in the days of King Manasseh he fled for his life from Zion, for the wicked king hunted down mercilessly all whom he suspected of collaboration with Isaiah, that annoying prophet who could not learn to be silent. Mahseiah had left in the middle of the night, carrying with him all his scrolls, his life's work. His son stayed behind, despite all Mahseiah's pleading — and paid for it with his life.

Now Mahseiah scraped out a living in this backwater village, copying legal agreements and deeds for those who wished a permanent record of their affairs. He trusted no one, associated with no one, befriended no one. He kept to himself by choice and by inclination.

When the door was shut again, he eyed the son of Hilkiah critically. This barely bearded boy had been pestering him incessantly these last weeks.

"Well, boy? You are here. Now what do you want?"

As he stood in the center of the tiny mud-and-wattle hut, Jeremiah's head bent at a rather uncomfortable angle to keep it from striking the roof. "I am told...that is to say...I have heard...I am interested in seeing some scrolls you may have in your possession..." His voice wandered into silence.

Mahseiah snorted impatiently. "Scrolls? Yes, I have scrolls! Hundreds of them! Hurry up, boy, you are tiring me!"

41

"The scrolls I wish to see concern... a certain prophet."

Mahseiah glared at Jeremiah. "I know no prophets! None! They are a thoroughly troublesome lot, and they bring no good to those they meet! Now if you will please leave—"

"No! Sir, I beg of you. I wish you no harm. And I desire most earnestly to read any words you may have about a man named Isaiah."

"What could you know about Isaiah? He lived long ago, and he is dead, so what concern is he of yours?"

"Yet I am told that you knew him — somewhat well. And I want to know about him," the boy persisted.

"Why? I have had more than enough trouble in my life because of that one, and I am not eager to bring up his name again. Why do you have such an interest in a dead prophet?"

Jeremiah sat down on the dirt floor before answering, and looked up helplessly at the old, wizened man.

"Because Adonai Elohim has placed his hand upon me. I, too, it seems, am to be a prophet. And there are things about Isaiah I must know." His eyes bored into Mahseiah's with the force of a pleading child.

The old man's abrasive shell melted from him, replaced by a cloak of great sadness. His shoulders sagged, and he sat cross-legged on the floor in front of Jeremiah. His eyes were lowered as he allowed thoughts into his mind which he had intended to banish forever.

"Yes, I knew the prophet Isaiah."

After several moments Jeremiah asked softly, "What was he like?"

Mahseiah appeared not to have heard. Just as Jeremiah was about to repeat his query, the old man glanced up.

"Like? What was he like? Well...he was like an ancient seer, and an innocent child. He was like a blazing coal from the altar, and like a spring of cold water from the mountains. He was like an old friend, and a stranger."

The scribe brooded, his eyes staring into a dark corner of his hut. "And I — even I, who wrote down his words for future generations — sometimes I felt...anger, and resentment. For the flame which burned within him singed even the righteous. Even good men felt shamed by his fervor for the Lord which

42

brooked no bridle, tolerated no compromise. He burned so brightly. And those of us who sought to see by his light came to know shame at the darkness within us.

"Do you know what it means, boy — to be a prophet?" the old man demanded, lancing Jeremiah with a sudden stare.

"I...no, sir, I suppose not. Not yet."

"Ah, well, you will, if your call be genuine," muttered the old man. "You will know the loneliness, the despair... You will see your words cut men's hearts, and though they may respect you, even fear you, rarely will they love you. You will hear the bleeding of your soul parodied by the street-corner charlatans, transformed into play-rhymes by children in the streets. You will be cursed with vision in a land of the blind."

"You speak almost as if you were Isaiah himself."

"Me?" Mahseiah gave a chuckle. "No, I'm not his equal, not by quite a stretch. I'm a scribe, not a prophet. Mine is not to see the writings in the heavens, but to scratch onto parchment the visions of others. To preserve, and to remember." For a moment his eyes were tunnels into the past. "Yes, to remember..."

He rose and went to a crudely fashioned oaken table near a wall. On it sat haphazard piles of ink blocks, new and old styluses, sheets of blank parchment, several tallow lamps. The table was draped by a dirty piece of cloth which hung to the floor. Laboriously the old man got down upon his knees, pulled aside the cloth, and reached into the darkness beneath the table. He pulled out an earthen jar, round and squat, dusty from long disuse. Pulling off the lid, he looked inside for a moment, and selected a scroll from among several. He slid back the scroll's protective sheath, grunted in satisfaction, replaced the jar under the table, and came back to where Jeremiah waited.

"Very well. Here is a scroll of some of the sayings of Isaiah, the prophet. Take this and read it. When you are finished, if you still believe God has called you to prophesy, come back. I have other scrolls you may find useful."

"Thank you, sir!" Jeremiah stood, gratefully taking the old leather case from Mahseiah's hand. "I will care for these words with my very life!"

The old man squinted up at him. "If your call is true, you will indeed. Take it then, and go."

TOO LATE, Jeremiah realized his route was carrying him past the home of Gershom the miller. He was about to seek another path when Hannah bounded from her doorway and ran to him.

He tucked the scroll more tightly under his arm.

"Jeremiah! Where have you been? I've been searching for you for three days! Have you been in hiding?" she chided.

"No, of course not," he said, with a nervous little laugh. "Why would you think so?"

"No special reason. Just the fact that you have not been in any of our usual meeting places."

"Hannah, we must be careful. We are not yet betrothed. If we were seen together too much, people would talk."

"Why this sudden concern? The opinion of others was not so much on your mind when I brought food to you in the fields. Have the eyes of the folk of Anathoth grown so much sharper now than then?" Her tone was no longer playful, and her eyes demanded answers he was loath to give.

"Hannah... I... There is much I must tell you..."

"Indeed!"

"...but now is not the time. I beg of you, go back in. I'm on an errand of some urgency, and I must hurry."

"A secret mission, perhaps? Who has commissioned you to this dark, dire errand?"

"Hannah..."

"No, I want to know!" She turned her head away, and asked quietly, "What woman could it be?"

"Hannah, stop it! I forbid you to speak so! Surely you do not think, after all we have meant to each other, that my eyes are so easily turned. No other woman could ever come between my heart and yours."

She faced him again, and looked deeply into his gaze. "Then what has come between us, beloved?" A tear started down her face.

After several swallows he managed to say, "Hannah... there is a thing I must do. I cannot tell you more now, for I do not understand it myself. But you must know that I would never willingly leave you."

She heard the confusion in his voice, saw the pain on his face mirroring the hurt and bewilderment of her own. And at that moment she knew, though she would not yet admit it, that she would never dwell in Jeremiah's house.

He continued looking silently into her eyes. "Perhaps," she said, "perhaps one day you will be able to speak your heart more fully. Until then, I..." She could not say more. She gripped his hand, then turned and ran back into her house, holding a hand over her mouth. Jeremiah looked after her for a moment, then continued homeward, a dull ache occupying the place where his heart had been.

THAT NIGHT another dream came to him.

He was leaving his house to go out into the fields for the day. Hannah, his wife, came to him smiling, carrying their child in her arms. The smiling boy, his head a mass of dark curls, reached for him. Gladly he took him in his arms and kissed him. Handing him back to Hannah, he kissed her, then left the house.

Then it was dark, and he was returning home. He heard a keening wail from within his house. He rushed inside. Hannah sat on the floor beside the child's crib, moaning and rubbing dirt on her face.

He raced to the crib and looked inside. There lay the boy. He looked as if he had been dead for a week: His eyes were dry sockets, open in a horrid, vacant stare; his mouth buzzed with flies. His little ribs jutted out in stark relief against the dry, cracked leather of his skin. His arms, stiffened, were locked in a reaching pose, as though he appealed to someone, anyone, to save him from such a fate.

Jeremiah jerked upright in his bed, panting with terror and revulsion.

Then the Voice was within him.

6

"SO, THEN, Peleg," said Hilkiah, "you say the Chaldeans of Babylon have finally struck the first blow against Nineveh?"

It was the week's Third Day, and by custom the old men of Anathoth gathered in the marketplace in the shade of a mulberry tree, to hear and tell news of Judah and the world beyond. The faces had changed little through the years, other than with age. The base of the mulberry's trunk was polished by the backs of the elders as they leaned or stood propped against it. This tree was, in fact, something of a local landmark. It had even found its way into the idiom of the area. If a younger man wished to chide his elders without appearing too insolent, he might say, in answer to some dubious statement or other, "Ah! And did you learn this at the mulberry?"

On this day, as it happened, there was reliable news of some importance being transmitted beneath the mulberry. Peleg, an old trader who had made many journeys through Anathoth, both from the east and the west, was lecturing the old men.

"Oh, yes, so they have," the old peddler answered Hilkiah's query. "They have cast the Assyrians out from the lower Tigris and Euphrates valleys, and renounced all pretense of fealty to the son of Ashurbanipal. The Babylonian host was great indeed! The Medes, too, fought against Assyria. And some say the Lydian king is no great lover of Assyrian dominion, waiting but for the opportune time to throw in with the Chaldeans."

"And Egypt?" someone asked.

"Egypt..." Peleg rubbed his beard in thought. "Who knows for certain? To be sure, Pharaoh is eager for Assyria to be overthrown, for he has not forgotten the sacking of Thebes by Ashurbanipal. But neither is he anxious to exchange Assyrian clutches for Chaldean.

"The arm of Assyria," opined the old merchant, "has been shortened by the turmoil throughout the empire, and has been unable to reach toward the Nile for many years. The lord of Thebes is not greatly discomfited by events as they stand. I say he will come into the fray at his own time, when he judges it to his best advantage."

One of the old men spat. "That for Pharaoh! Since the time of the Lawgiver, Egypt has been a lion lying in wait for Judah! I hope the Babylonians feed him to his own hounds!" Some of the men murmured their agreement.

"What of the Babylonian lord?" asked Hilkiah. "What is said of him?"

"Babylon has never forgotten the days of Hammurabi, who ruled so long ago that his reign is almost legend," said Peleg. "But long time or no, empire is not a thing which, once known, can ever entirely die in the soul of a people. Nabopolassar has kindled again the lust to rule in the hearts of the Sumerians; but some say the real driving force is his son Nebuchadrezzar. He it is who forged the Medean alliance, it is said, and who now urges an attack on the Assyrian homeland itself. Some say he is a clever student of men; some say he is in league with demons."

The old men made the sign against evil spirits, as Hilkiah winced inwardly at such superstition. The trader went on:

"However it may be, Babylon has the Winged Bull staggering backward. The Assyrian forces still hold Nineveh and most of their northern cities. But Babylon, once she takes the bit in her teeth, will not be content to rule merely the lower valleys. I say the tide from the south is poised to wash away the last vestiges of Assyrian sovereignty."

The old men nodded solemnly, each looking at the ground and drawing his own conclusions about the traveler's tale. Hilkiah wondered how paying tribute to Babylon, if it ever came to that, would differ from paying tribute to Nineveh.

JEREMIAH LOCKED his eyes once more on the puzzling old passage:

"Hear the word of the Lord of Hosts: 'Behold, the days are coming, when all that is in your house, and that which your fathers have stored up till this day, shall be carried to Babylon;

nothing shall be left,' says the Lord. 'And some of your own sons, who are born to you, shall be taken away; and they shall be eunuchs in the palace of the king of Babylon.'"

He looked up from the yellowed scroll of Mahseiah which lay across his knees. As he ran Isaiah's words through his mind, his questions rose: In the days of Hezekiah, had not King Sennacherib of Assyria been the menace to Jerusalem? Indeed, for as long as anyone now living in Judah could remember, the rulers of Nineveh had been the oppressors, exacting their heavy tribute from the vassal state of Judah. Why then was Isaiah warning of peril arising from Babylon? And was not Babylon to the west of Zion? His vision had been of a foe from the north.

He pondered this for several moments. When his father returned from the marketplace, he decided, he would ask him what he knew of Babylon.

Jeremiah lowered his head and continued reading.

CONGRATULATING HIMSELF as a man of the moment, Hananiah the Gibeonite stopped and tilted back his head to take in the height of the city walls before him. He shaded his eyes and studied the fortifications around the Ephraim Gate, through which bustled traffic of all kinds.

So this was Jerusalem.

He had decided to come here as soon as King Josiah's proclamation concerning the restoration of the Passover celebration was read in Gibeon. The decision in itself was not unique. All over Judah whole families were busily making plans to go to the capital and take part in this historic reenactment of the greatest feast of their people, a feast not observed in Judah since before the days of David. The Passover of King Josiah was the resurrection of a rite from the mists of Hebrew legend. Excitement rippled like drumbeats across the land. No one wanted to be left out.

But Hananiah was not overly infatuated by the Passover celebration for its own sake. He had an eye for opportunity. He scented change in the air — and change, he reasoned, always presents opportunities to those clever enough to perceive them.

Interesting, he mused, how Josiah's restoration of the rites of Yahweh-worship coincided with Assyria's distractions at the hands of the Chaldeans. Well could the king afford to stoke the fires of Hebrew nationalism, now that Assyrian overlords were fighting for their lives against Babylon.

He paused just inside the Ephraim gate long enough to hear a wild-eyed, hide-clad streetcorner prophet bellowing on about the importance of the Passover. Hananiah covered a smirk with the back of his hand as he listened. Chances were, this same fellow during the reign of Manasseh would have waxed just as eloquent about the need to worship Ashtaroth. Hananiah noticed that the preacher's coin purse was nicely taut. Apparently the Passover message sold well these days.

Hananiah knew he possessed what most of the streetcorner itinerants did not: subtlety. This, he felt sure, combined with his sense of timing, would stand him in good stead in the interesting days ahead.

Yes, this was a time of opportunity, and Jerusalem was its focal point. This was where he needed to be.

HILKIAH LOOKED around his table in satisfaction. This would be an evening to remember. For the first time in thirteen generations, the house of Abiathar would keep the Passover according to the traditions of Moses. A twinge of jealousy teased at the corner of his mind when he thought that, had he been fortunate enough to be descended from Zadok rather than his rebellious cousin Abiathar, he himself might be presiding at the altar in the very Temple of Solomon. But it was good to be here nonetheless, to see his children and grandchildren gathered at the table, waiting for sunset and the beginning of Israel's most holy celebration.

All over Judah that day, houses had been swept and cleaned down to the tiniest corners. Priests and Levites, who in other times were avoided as pariahs, were on this day eagerly consulted as to the proper preparations, form, and order of the observance. This feast was an edict of Josiah, and no one wanted to be either disloyal to a well-loved and just king, or impious in their religion — two offenses which were one and the same in the minds of many in Judah.

It was time. Hilkiah stood and raised his cup. Closing his

eyes in reverence, he recited the opening words of the blessing which had not been heard within these walls for so long:

"Blessed art Thou, Eternal our God, King of the Universe, Creator of the fruit of the vine.

"Blessed art Thou, O Eternal our God, King of the Universe, who selected us from among the nations, and sanctified us with Thy commandments."

Hilkiah broke the *matzoh* loaf as the family recited the litany of God's deliverance from bondage in Egypt. The ceremonial plate was passed, and they ate the bitter herbs and the *charoseth*, a paste of fruit and nuts ground together. There was a long silence as all looked expectantly at little Othniel, Joash's youngest child. Seeing everyone staring at him, the boy stuck his finger in his mouth and would not look up. At last, Haggith leaned over and whispered in her son's ear. He shook his head, too embarrassed to say his lines. Finally, after much urging by those seated near him, the child, in halting speech and with frequent prompting, asked the questions expected of him:

"Why is this night different from all other nights?"

"Why do we eat unleavened bread?"

"Why do we eat the bitter herbs?"

"Why do we dip our food in the salt water?"

Jeremiah tried mightily to enter into the joyous spirit of the moment. But instead of his father's *haggadah*, the words running through his mind on an endless loop were those of the scroll he had read that afternoon: "These people come near to Me with their mouth," the Lord had said through Isaiah, "and honor Me with their lips, but their hearts are far from Me. Their worship of Me is made up only of rules taught by men...."

Jeremiah's spirit moved inside him in a way he had never felt, as though something within his breast struggled to be born. He sat with his brow furrowed, wanting to enter into the celebration, but helpless to still the writhing in his soul. His knuckles whitened as he gripped the edge of the table.

Across the table sat Lemuel, a sardonic smile scampering now and then across his face. The ceremony meant little enough to him, but if it distracted Father from berating him and his friends for a few moments, it was a small enough price to pay. And wait until he sprang his little surprise later. He could hardly wait to see Jeremiah's face then! *Look at him sitting there, affecting that pained, pious look,* thought Lemuel. *If he can't enjoy himself, he wants everyone else to know it. Well, just wait; soon he'll really have something to mope about!*

Libnah, at her end of the table, sensed with a mother's intuition the crosscurrents running between her two youngest sons. She saw the veiled, despising glances with which Lemuel speared Jeremiah, and the clouded perplexity of Jeremiah himself.

Hilkiah was blissfully unaware of anything other than the steady cadences of his recitation. He paused, handing the scroll to Joash, indicating that he should read a section of the narrative. The oldest son began to read.

The storm inside Jeremiah whirled faster. He felt it pressing its way into his throat, pricking his tongue with needle-sharp torrents of words, words of lightning and thunder.

Lemuel read next, in a flat, bored voice. Jeremiah clenched his jaw tighter.

Then the scroll was handed to him. He took a deep breath, glanced quickly around the table, and began to read:

"O Lord, our God, remember us this day for good, visit us with Thy blessing and save us to enjoy life..."

His voice tapered into silence; his chin dropped to his chest. The others looked at him in curiosity, then alarm, as his chest began to heave. Tears, like snail-paths, trickled down his cheeks.

"It is not enough," he said in a choked voice, so softly that he could barely be heard. "Not enough at all!"

Gradually his voice firmed. He looked up at them with eyes like an eagle's, as the Voice spoke from him with a power not heard in Judah since the days of Isaiah.

"'From the time I brought your forefathers up from Egypt until today,' says the Lord, 'I warned them again and again, saying "Obey me." But they did not listen or pay attention; instead, they followed the stubbornness of their evil hearts. So I brought on them all the curses of the covenant I commanded them to follow, but that they did not keep...*

"'They have returned to the sins of their forefathers, who refused to listen to My words. They have followed other gods to serve them.*

51

Both the house of Israel and the house of Judah have broken the covenant I made with their forefathers.'

"Therefore this is what the Lord says: 'I will bring on them a disaster they cannot escape...'"

"Jeremiah!" shouted Hilkiah, amid the gasps of his wife and daughter-in-law, "Be still! This is unseemly, in the middle of the Passover feast!"

But the vision was upon Jeremiah, and could not be suppressed.

"'Although they cry out to me, I will not listen to them. The towns of Judah and the people of Jerusalem will go and cry out to the gods to whom they burn incense, but they will not help them at all when disaster strikes!'"

"Those books you read have made you crazy!" shouted Lemuel, leaping to his feet and pointing a finger, dagger-like, at his brother's chest. He was angrier at Jeremiah for disturbing his timing than for anything the fool had actually said. It was always thus with this coddled brother of his; always stealing the show in some mad manner or other. "You speak treason; you ought to die for what you just said!"

Othniel began to whimper. Haggith leaned over, scooped him into her lap, then rose and walked quickly out of the room.

Hilkiah looked helplessly from Lemuel, whose face was a grimace of despite, to Jeremiah, who seemed not to have heard his brother — as though blinded and deafened by the zeal of his oracle.

Slowly the patriarch of the clan of Abiathar sank into his seat, dazed by the bewildering eruption of such passion in his house.

Lemuel came around the table to jut his face directly into that of his younger brother. "Let me tell you something, you mad fool," he snarled. "You don't deceive me, and you don't frighten me. You don't see any farther into the future than the end of your own nose. You're not a prophet — you're just a spoiled brat who can't abide not having everyone's attention. In fact, you are so blinded by yourself that you've let something quite good slip through your fingers. But I'm not as stupid as you. I have the good sense to see a chance when it comes my way. If you won't marry Hannah, then I will."

Jeremiah wavered from his stoic pose for the first time, glancing quickly at Lemuel in surprise.

"Ah, yes," Lemuel continued, gratified by the startled look on Jeremiah's face. "Yes! I will take Hannah as my wife. She will live in my house, not yours. She will bear my sons, not yours. And it is no one's fault but yours, O prophet of Anathoth." He snickered. "A woman needs a man who can make a decision, didn't you know that? How long did you think she would wait for you to make up your mind? But now it is too late for you, foolish one. Too late."

HANANIAH BIT DOWN on the tough horseradish root, feeling the pungent burning pass from his mouth into his eyes. He did not particularly care for this strange old ritual. But as he gazed around the table at the other celebrants, he didn't allow his feelings to show.

This new religious revival could be useful to him. He just needed time to calculate how it could best serve him.

7

A DISTANT ROOK croaked haughtily as a slight breeze wafted inside the campaign tent. Nebuchadrezzar walked out into the harsh sunlight and shaded his eyes against the sudden glare as he looked down toward the plain. Ashur, the ancient city, the birthplace of the Assyrian people, lay panting in her bend of the Tigris like a starved old woman. The host of the city would make their final sally today; they had no choice. For six months he had waited with the patience of death outside this city, had kept his fist tightened about its throat. His spies had done their work: He knew all the supplies inside the walls of Ashur were exhausted. Even the nobles in the citadel were suffering from hunger and disease.

They had to come out and fight. And they would be cut down like wheat.

He motioned to a courier, who hurried and prostrated himself before the prince of Babylon. "Go and tell Prince Irtu to make final preparations." The boy leaped to his feet and trotted off toward the camp of the Scythian mercenaries.

Nebuchadrezzar glanced at the sky. Even the birds sensed the smell of blood in the air; several carrion fowl wheeled in the clear blue dome above the Tigris valley. They would enjoy a feast today, along with the jackals and wild dogs. Once Ashur was destroyed, nothing else lay between his armies and Nineveh. They would press the attack on the capital until the kingdom of the north lay in rubble. Then, at his leisure, he could consolidate control over the lands to the south along the Great Sea — Samaria, Moab, Ammon, Judah…

A Scythian galloped up on one of the sturdy steppe ponies of his people. He dismounted and made reverence toward the Chaldean prince. "The warriors of Irtu are mounted and ready, honored patron," he announced in the guttural accent of his backward people. Nebuchadrezzar nodded and dismissed the messenger, who turned and mounted, trotting back to rejoin his commander. The Scythians had proven themselves quite useful. They had the fabled hardiness of their nomadic heritage. True, their customs were uncouth and their loyalty extended only as far as the guarantee of booty. But their lust for battle was un-questioned.

He instructed his servants to set up his pavilion on the crest of the rise overlooking the plain. From there he would have a better view of the victory.

THREE WEEKS had passed since the Passover feast. The sleep-ing village was awash in the light of the full moon. To Jeremiah, seated on the wall behind his house, the dark refuge of rest was denied. Every night Hannah's frightened face and Lemuel's smug one paraded before his eyes as he lay on his pallet. He came out here, hoping the breezes of the night would dispel the ghosts of what might have been, the specters whispering their silent taunts.

Choosing a night when he knew Jeremiah would be there, Lemuel had earlier brought Hannah to the house to formally meet his parents. With a grin of triumph he had led her into the room where Jeremiah sat. He looked up at once.

Their eyes met in a futile embrace. Her look was like that of a lamb caught in briers. She was in a trap not of her making, and she appealed to Jeremiah to save her, though she knew he could not.

He had said something inane and congratulatory, then left the room as quickly as possible before the words he wished to say could escape his clenched teeth.

Now, as he sat on the wall and looked out on moonlit Anathoth, he reflected on the change he had noticed in the people. They stared furtively at him, as at an idiot or some odd-ity from a caravan.

He could surmise the talk behind his back: "There he is; that strange son of Hilkiah. Imagine! Disrupting a family cele-bration with strange spoutings about war and disaster! He must be wrong in the head. And look at how he abandoned that lovely girl Hannah. Everyone knows she loved him, and he walked away from her as if he didn't care a fig."

In his own house he had become a stranger. Joash, never a man of many words, now positively avoided him. His father would not look directly at him anymore. Even his mother, who had loved him and doted on him as no other — even she now viewed him askance. She tried to hide her feelings behind a facade of forced cheerfulness, but he could feel her wondering glances on the back of his neck as he sat in his room reading. He could hear the whispers which stopped as he approached and began again when he had passed. He could hear the murmurs from his parents' chamber in the night when the rest of the household slept.

The night air was hot, as with the breath of summer. But it was not summer; only the month of Iyar, and there should have been cool winds and an occasional rain shower to nurture the barley and wheat fields. Indeed, the threat of famine hung over Judah like the burning talisman of a curse from heaven.

Jeremiah heard the slap of footsteps on a hard-packed dirt path. In the moonlight he saw two men, one carrying a bundle, walking a trail which led down into a network of ravines and gullies behind Anathoth. Jeremiah felt his heart begin pounding. He knew he must get up and follow these men; there was something he must see.

The trail led deeper and deeper into the rocky crevasses. Jeremiah, following silently at the distance of a stone's throw, watched as the men stepped now in black shadow, now in the silvery glow of the moonlight.

At last they reached their destination: a box canyon with a lone oak tree standing in its midst. Jeremiah hid in the rocks at the mouth of the canyon as the two men approached a small, quiet group gathered about the tree and the stone altar beneath it. In the clear, still night, their voices carried to his ears plainly.

"Brothers," one of them addressed the others, "it is now the night of the fullness of the moon, the time most sacred to our lord Chemosh. He is angry with us, for we have forsaken him because of the edict of King Josiah, and have neglected his proper worship. For this reason he has withheld the rains of heaven, and we are now threatened with hunger.

"Can anyone here doubt this?"

A low murmur of agreement waxed and waned.

"It is therefore time to return to the worship of Lord Chemosh, that perhaps we may avert his fierce wrath. The worship of Josiah's god has brought us near disaster, and the hour has come to rededicate ourselves to the true lord of power.

"Have you brought the sacrifice?" the speaker asked the two latest arrivals. The one carrying the bundle held it out to the speaker, who unwrapped it and held it aloft.

It was a child.

Jeremiah gasped in horror as the high priest laid the narcotized infant on the altar beneath the tree and brought out a shining blade. He lifted his hands and babbled for a moment in some ecstatic utterance, at which the others knelt and put their faces to the ground. Then, with a swift, brutal motion, he slashed the throat of the inert child. Above the gurgling sound of the baby's death he intoned, "Now receive this blood, O mighty Chemosh, as the sacrifice of your faithful people. No longer do we turn our faces from you to withhold anything from you. Now again favor us, and send to us the rain which saves us from the desolation of our land." The others moaned in assent, their faces still toward the ground.

When the child had ceased twitching, they kindled a fire on the altar. While the tiny corpse burned, the assembly chanted and shuffled in a dance around the altar until the last embers died away.

UNTIL DAWN Jeremiah sat in his hiding place, weeping in silent rage. As the sun rose higher above the box canyon's rim, the Voice was within him:

"Now you have seen what My people have come to. On every high hill and under every green tree they sprawl out like harlots, eagerly coupling with every god they meet — which are no gods, but things they have created themselves. And they slay their own children, devouring their own flesh to appease their abominations — a thing so horrible it could never even enter My mind.

"Now you know why I have turned my face from them. They do not honor Me except with their mouths. In their time of difficulty they go back to their false lovers, for they have forgotten My Name which I taught them when I brought them out of the house of bondage in Egypt.

"Now leave the house of your father. Go into all the land of Judah, and see. Watch the people, and learn. Then I will teach you what you must proclaim to them.

"For the day of My wrath is coming…"

Jeremiah wiped the tears from his face, rose from his perch among the rocks, and trod away, his chest like a stone.

Arriving home, he hoped he could gather a few things and leave without seeing anyone. But on his way out he had scarcely reached the courtyard gate when he met Joash, returning from the fields to fetch something he had forgotten that morning.

The eldest son of Hilkiah the priest regarded his youngest brother for several long moments as they stood face to face in the gateway. He saw written on Jeremiah's features a tale of some anguish, and, as always, the indefinable something which had made Jeremiah so strange, so enigmatic to him, almost since birth.

Joash cleared his throat. He looked away, over Jeremiah's head, and said, "You are leaving."

Jeremiah nodded, looking down at the ground.

"I do not understand the ways of kings," said the farmer haltingly, "or…or of prophets. It is enough for me to work the land, and I have never asked more from life. But for you…it is not so. It has always been different with you."

Jeremiah raised his eyes to those of his brother, who studied his face a moment, then looked away again.

"Lemuel is mean, twisted inside," began Joash again. "This, too, I do not understand. But I know it."

A silence passed, punctuated by the bleating of the flocks in the fields nearby.

"You go because you must," declaimed Joash finally. "I will not allow Lemuel to steal more from you than he already has."

Jeremiah eyed carefully his quiet, eldest brother, who at length turned to look him full in the face. Joash gripped him on the shoulder for a moment, then turned and went on.

Jeremiah tossed his pack over his shoulder, took one last

look at the home of his childhood, then turned and walked
down the road leading away from the house of Abiathar in
Anathoth.

PART II

The
Prophet

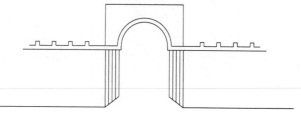

8

THE TOOTHLESS OLD WOMAN crouched against the stone wall, squatting in her own filth. Holding her grimy wooden bowl she barely moved her lips, lisping endlessly the litany of her misery: "Alms. Alms for a poor old widow. Alms..."

Jeremiah squatted beside her and dropped several coins into the bowl. She did not glance upward as they rattled to the bottom of the dish, but merely shifted her formula: "Blessings upon you." Pausing only slightly, she resumed: "Alms. Alms for a poor old widow..."

"Good mother," inquired Jeremiah quietly, "how long have you been sitting at this corner?"

Startled, she jerked her face around and stared at him with the vacancy of long madness. After a blank moment, she returned to her customary pose and patter.

"Alms. Alms for a poor widow..."

Jeremiah straightened and looked about him. Beneath the afternoon sun the people of Beersheba hurried past, few of them favoring the old beggar with so much as a glance. Now and then someone, without pausing in his gait, would carelessly drop a copper into her bowl as if disposing of a piece of trash. He would receive the hag's mindless blessing, but could not have heard, much less cared. From appearances, she had sat here for so long that she had become a part of the wall, a bit of scenery no one noticed any longer.

Jeremiah softly quoted to himself from the scroll of the Law he had borrowed from Mahseiah the scribe: "You shall open your hand to the poor, and give him sufficient to his need, whatever it may be...." Sadly he turned away, as the townspeople continued their benign persecution of the old woman.

"Alms. Alms for a poor widow..."

THE DUST OF THE LONG ROAD from the south clung to his throat as he made his way into Lachish. Reaching the well in the town's market square, Jeremiah quickly pulled on the flaxen cord which dangled into the cool darkness, hauling hand-over-hand from the depths a dripping gourd full of water. He drank greedily, spilling it down his chest in his haste.

Wiping his mouth on the sleeve of his robe, he paused and looked around him. It was the middle of the afternoon, and the merchants of Lachish were busily hawking their wares. Feeling hungry from his long, hot walk, he strolled over to a stall where a short, stout man was selling fruit.

"How much for the dates?" he inquired of the proprietor.

"Five coppers for the third part of an ephah," was the terse reply.

Jeremiah reached into his purse and stacked five coppers on the table in front of the vendor. The man placed a weight on one side of the well-worn balance, and put a small handful of dates on the other side. The scales balanced. But the portion of dates seemed impossibly small.

"Your weights cannot be correct," the hungry traveler said.

"And your coin is not good," retorted the merchant, sweeping the coppers into the dirt with a swipe of his hand, then looking past Jeremiah as if he no longer existed.

Jeremiah stared at the man for a moment in consternation. Deciding this churl would not have anything further to do with him, he moved to the next stall down the line. This one sold fruit as well.

"How much are your figs?" he asked the man squatting in the shade of his awning.

But the merchant would not answer, taking his cue from his colleague the date seller.

It was the same at every stall. The unspoken word went out: This dusty stranger — this troublemaker who interfered with the commerce of the merchants of Lachish — was not to be allowed to buy, nor even favored with so much as an acknowledgment of his presence.

Jeremiah went to sleep hungry that night, in the lee of an inn which refused him admittance. In the morning he went on his way.

THE SUN SANK in an explosion of orange and purple behind the hills of northern Judah. Jeremiah was bone-weary from his trek, and hoped desperately for a soft bed in Ajalon, which lay before him.

As he entered the city, a handsome, distinguished-looking woman touched him lightly on the arm. He stopped and looked at her.

"You have come a long way today, young stranger," she said, seeing quickly his dusty clothing and tired posture. "I have a room to let, and servants to draw a cooling bath for you. Will you not stay?"

"I will," he said, grateful for this apparent answer to his prayer. He followed her to a large, carefully manicured stone house in a well-to-do quarter of the town. As they entered the courtyard, he heard the splashing of a fountain. Inside the house, the smell of sandalwood and myrrh massaged his senses with soothing balm.

"Kirzah!" his hostess called as they came in. A young Cushite female slave trotted up. "Take this young man to the guest room," commanded the lady, "and see that he is made comfortable. By the way," she continued, laying a hand on Jeremiah's arm as they turned to leave, "my name is Orpah. You are a guest in my house. Please have Kirzah summon me if there is anything you lack."

"I am grateful for your hospitality, good Orpah," replied Jeremiah. "I have not always found such a welcome in the places I have sojourned."

"Indeed?" she smiled. "Well here you have but to ask."

That night, after a sumptuous supper of fresh lamb and almonds, Jeremiah lay on the softest of pallets. A cool breeze wafted in through the open windows of his room after softly rustling the leaves of the date palms outside.

He was at the point of dropping into a grateful slumber when his door creaked open.

He sat up in his bed, slightly put out by such an untimely interruption. In the doorway stood Orpah, his hostess, clad in a gauzy gown that made scarce concession to decency.

"I just realized, young stranger," she purred, "that I neglected to mention the price of my lodgings."

"I...I do not understand," he stammered.

"Oh, I'm sorry," she whispered, moving closer and seating herself slowly at the foot of his bed. "Let me explain more fully. My husband..."

"Your husband!" he shouted.

"Be calm, boy, be calm!" she laughed. "My husband, who, as you can see, is very rich, is also very absent. In fact, he is gone so much of the time that I can hardly remember what he looks like," she pouted. "So," she said, moving closer to him, "since this house is so very big, and I am so very lonely, it seems a shameful waste not to show kindness to handsome young strangers. Strangers such as yourself."

Her face was now very near his. He could smell the musky spices of her skin, and see the oil glistening on the curves of her shoulders. She was a comely woman. And he, too, was lonely — so lonely...

"And all I ask in return," she whispered as she laid a hand on the bed beside his thigh, "is a bit of comfort from the solitude of the night. A little enjoyment. A little..."

"I cannot! I must not do this thing," he said, pulling himself away from her narcotic eyes and standing on the opposite side of the bed. He took his cloak and began dressing.

"What are you doing?" she demanded petulantly.

"I am leaving. I cannot commit this sin and be a shame to your husband who alone may lie with you. It is wicked. It is adultery."

"Adultery!" she laughed. "I have not heard that word in ages! Where have you been, boy? The bodies of men and women were made for each other's enjoyment — has not the goddess Asherah so decreed through her prophetess? I desire you. No one need ever know of our little meeting. And you call it adultery!"

"Yes, for that is what Adonai Elohim, the Lord of Hosts, calls it. I belong to Him, as do you, whether you admit it or not. And if you do not repent and cease your wickedness, He will surely punish you."

"You begin to bore me, boy. Though it is a pity," she said, extending her hand to the place on the bed, still warm, where he had been lying. "Oh well," she sulked, "be on your miserable way, then. If you have not the good sense to take advantage of an opportunity, there are others who do."

"Yes," said Jeremiah, straightening his clothing. "So I have been told."

THE MAP SPREAD before him, Nebuchadrezzar sat with his chin in his hand, a thoughtful expression on his face. He beckoned a runner. "Go to the eastern quadrant, to Lord Cyaxeres. Find out how the Medean forces are progressing toward the walls of the central city. I am especially interested in knowing how much resistance they met near the main canal. Go!" The boy launched himself past the guards at the door in a dead run.

The prince of Babylon leaned closer over the map of Nineveh and its environs. After a moment's reflection, he made a series of small, careful marks at several points.

He had marched north from the sack of Ashur, up the valley of the Tigris, encountering little organized resistance. The few walled towns in their path were no serious challenge to the host of the south, and he reduced them, each in turn, to rubble. After the long siege of Ashur it was good for the men to enjoy some easy spoils.

They met their first serious challenge at Calah, where advance regiments of Assyrian cavalry, coming out and attacking the camp at night, sought to drive a wedge into Babylon's eastern flank. But the army of the south slept in its armor. The sally was beaten back, and the surprise onslaught blunted. After a month's fierce fighting, the city and its defenders were completely wiped out. Nebuchadrezzar pressed on to Nineveh.

For the past several days, the army had been bogged down in an annoyingly slow house-to-house campaign in the outskirts of the Assyrian capital. This was a great metropolis, and though the walls of the central city enclosed a profusion of towers, gardens, palaces and fields, the populated area outside the walls was actually greater than that inside. And the Assyrians were using this fact to their advantage, placing archers on strategic rooftops, blockading the main thoroughfares, using hit-and-run tactics to harry the advancing army from behind.

The situation demanded that Nebuchadrezzar spread his forces over a wider area than he liked. He deployed the

Medeans in the eastern part of the city, instructing them to take whatever steps necessary to eradicate resistance outside the walls. Judging from the smell of smoke in the air, Cyaxeres was leveling everything in his path to accomplish this objective.

Despite the delays, Nebuchadrezzar was as confident as ever of the ultimate outcome. In fact, he was expecting favorable news from the king of Lydia at any time. He felt confident Lydia would send at least an expeditionary force into the fray. The Lydians had no little to gain from the humbling of Nineveh, as he had pointed out to their emissaries on more than one occasion.

A runner dashed up to the door, was admitted by the guards, and rushed into the room. He prostrated himself full length on the floor before the prince. "Approach," said Nebuchadrezzar.

"My prince," the messenger panted, "Lord Nebel-Marduk sends word: He has destroyed a large force of Assyrian infantry in the southern quadrant, scarcely a stone's throw from the wall of the central city."

Nebuchadrezzar mused on this news for a moment, then dismissed the runner with a wag of his fingers. After the boy had gone, he permitted himself a tiny smile, leaned forward, and made another mark on his map.

AZZUR SAT near the well and observed the wanderer who came to drink. He was tall, well-knit. He wore clothing which, though faded and worn, showed the quality of its origins. His beard was still soft with the downiness of youth. He had a strong chin, and his eyes — there was *something* about his eyes.

The traveler slaked his thirst and straightened, looking about him at the famed city of Gibeon.

"Hello, young man! You look tired. From where have you come today?"

Jeremiah studied the friendly, open face. The man's prosperity was evident, both in his garments and in the fact that he had nothing more to do in the evening than sit by the well and speak to strangers. "From the country by Ajalon, to the west."

"Ah, but your clothing and manner speak of a far longer journey than that!"

"Well, that is true. I have been from Anathoth in Benjamin, all the way to Beersheba, to Lachish and Ajalon, and many other cities and towns besides, before coming here. I have walked the whole of Judah."

"No wonder you are weary! An ambitious journey, indeed! And what have your travels taught you, may I ask?"

Jeremiah looked carefully at Azzur. He took a deep breath, looked away, and said, "I have learned that men are not what they may appear, and that true wisdom is scarcer in Judah than dew in the sand of the Negev."

"Aha, I thought so! A philosopher! What is your name, young fellow?"

"Jeremiah, son of Hilkiah of Anathoth. And yours?"

"Azzur, son of Eliezer — of Gibeon. I noticed right away that you were an intelligent-looking young man. In fact, you remind me of my own son. I would count it an honor to offer you bread and a dry place to sleep. I would enjoy a chance to speak further with you about your pursuit of true wisdom. Will you accept my hospitality?"

Again Jeremiah studied the face of this friendly man. He scented nothing in Azzur's person or invitation which rang false. He decided to accept. "I will come with you."

"Good! Come along, then." Azzur turned and motioned to an old slave standing nearby, who in turn jerked the halter of the donkey he tended and brought it over to Azzur. The slave bent over and made a cup with his hands to help his master in mounting.

But Azzur silently protested, pulling the old slave by the hair until he looked up in confusion. By hand signs and exaggerated mouthings, Azzur made the deaf old man understand that he wished Jeremiah to ride, not himself. The misunderstanding solved, Jeremiah mounted, watchfully allowing the slave to lead the ass as they followed Azzur of Gibeon toward his home.

"How long has he been deaf?" inquired Jeremiah as they rode along.

"Old Samuel? Ever since I caught him spreading lies about me to the slave of my neighbor," replied Azzur matter-of-factly. "About ten years now, I should imagine."

"Ten years!" said Jeremiah, shuddering inwardly. "And how long did he serve you before...before he lost his hearing?"

"Oh, Samuel has been in my family since I was a pup. He wouldn't know what to do anywhere else — would you, old fool?" the master asked mockingly, tweaking the old man's ear as they walked along.

Jeremiah rode in silence, studying the face of the dried-up drudge beside him leading the donkey. Samuel's eyes never left the ground in front of his feet. His expression never changed. He was a human donkey, a piece of chattel. And judging from his profile, Jeremiah felt with a stomach-sinking certainty, that Samuel was a Hebrew.

9

CAREFULLY JEREMIAH phrased his next question. "Was it not once the custom — or, rather, the law — to free slaves of Hebrew blood after a certain period of time?"

"Oh, the old law of jubilee," chuckled Azzur. "You are quite a student of antiquity, aren't you, Jeremiah of Anathoth? My word, that old tradition hasn't been in use in these parts for...I can't imagine how long. What a thought!" he said, laughing again. "All the slaves freed! They'd starve to death within a month, if they didn't steal every last morsel from their masters' mouths.

"I was right about you," Azzur continued, turning toward Jeremiah with a broad grin. "You are quite learned! I most eagerly anticipate the discussions we shall have this evening! We are quite a historic people in these parts, you know. It was here in Gibeon that Solomon the great king prayed to the Lord for wisdom."

Azzur spoke on at great length about the salient facts and peculiarities of Gibeon. Jeremiah rode quietly on, still watching Samuel.

After supper that evening, Azzur engaged Jeremiah in discussing intricacies of the law of jubilee.

"I have thought about what you said earlier, on the way here," began Azzur, "and I have a proposition for you. This releasing of slaves every seven years was all well and good when the land was just being settled, and every family had its own little homestead and no more. In fact, it was an excellent arrangement — a man could work off his debts, and the homeowner could get his land established. When the seven years were finished, the man was debt-free and the homeowner had a productive piece of property."

He smiled at Jeremiah, appreciating the symmetry of his own logic. Jeremiah said nothing.

"But in these days," Azzur went on, "that system would be altogether impractical. I, myself," he said with demure pride, "own several very large tracts of land, acquired through the years by my family and myself. If I had to depend on chance and circumstance to get my laborers, I would lose my land." He fell silent, his expression challenging Jeremiah to refute the self-evident simplicity of his argument.

Jeremiah was hesitant to jeopardize the good will of his host. But finally he cleared his throat and said, "Good Azzur, I do not know how to direct you in the husbandry of your lands. But I do know this: The Lord of Hosts commands that Hebrew slaves be set free after seven years. He makes no concessions, as far as my studies indicate, to the convenience of those with large holdings." Resolutely he locked glances with the older man, who squinted at him for several moments, then smiled broadly.

"Ah, the idealism of youth! How simple life would be if everything were so easy to delineate." He chuckled to himself. "Hananiah had much the same set of mind when he was a boy, but early I taught him that solutions to problems in real life are not always so hard-edged as he might like. Oh, the arguments we had…"

As Azzur prated on, Jeremiah gazed into the heart of the fire on the hearth, wondering if his host had heard anything he had said.

The next morning, Azzur walked with Jeremiah out to the gate of his estate. "If you get to Jerusalem, you really must find my son. I feel sure you would greatly enjoy his company. I've met few young men of this day who can hold their own in debate with Hananiah, but you just might be one of them."

"It may be that I will meet him one day," Jeremiah said. "Perhaps I can return the kindness to him which you have shown me."

"Oh, think nothing of it!" laughed Azzur. "I have enjoyed having you. You have interesting ideas. I predict that within a few years you'll make quite a reputation for yourself, Jeremiah of Anathoth."

With a cheery wave, Azzur turned toward his house. Jeremiah watched him walk past Samuel, who sat by the door, staring at the dirt by his feet, awaiting his master's next command.

Jeremiah set his face south, toward Jerusalem.

JEHIEL SENSED the crowd growing more receptive by the moment. He had used all his tricks: He had raged like thunder, he had wept like a child. He had pounded his chest and leaped about like a monkey on a string. They were enjoying his performance. Now it was time to bring out his tried-and-true closing sequence.

He stared at them wildly, his face a mask of rabid zeal. Slowly, deliberately, he turned his back on them, fell to his knees on the Temple steps, and gaped upward at the entryway towering above them. He shouted at the top of his lungs: "Behold! The Temple of the Lord! The Temple of the Lord! The Temple of the Lord!" He bowed thrice in succession as he said it, then swiftly sprang to his feet and jerked around to face them again.

"This is the house of the living God! Upon this very place did the great King Solomon cause to be built the sanctuary of the Lord of Hosts! And of this very place," he screamed, jabbing his finger at the structure behind him, "the Lord Almighty, the Ruler of all creation did say, 'This is My house, which I will call by My Name, and My glory shall not depart from it!'"

He took a deep breath and went on. "Let the kings of the north rage! Let Babylon fight against the hosts of Assyria! Yes! And even Egypt, too! What is that to Jerusalem? This is the city of the Temple of the Lord! We are safe! We are safe!

"Zion shall not be moved!" he said in one last great shout, then fell on his face in a swoon.

When he judged the silence had lasted long enough, he roused himself, staggered to his feet, and motioned for his aide to come beside him. He gripped the boy's shoulder and leaned upon him as they made their way through the crowd. "Who will give an offering to the esteemed prophet Jehiel?" shouted the boy. "The Lord blesses those who look with kindness on His servants. Who will give?"

Jehiel, his eyes closed in affected exhaustion, heard the satisfying clink of coins dropping into the boy's purse. Yes, he had judged this crowd correctly. Never had his timing been better, his command of his public's emotions stronger. This day's take would be one of the best.

As the remainder of the crowd dispersed, the prophet and his helper found themselves facing a tall, thin young man who stood in their path. Nathan, the boy, tried to avoid the lone figure's discomfiting gaze. He altered their course, but the stranger stepped directly in front of them. This looked like trouble.

The stranger ignored Nathan, and stared directly at Jehiel, who still stood with a hand over his eyes.

"You don't know what you're talking about!" the stranger snapped.

No doubt about it, thought Nathan. *Trouble for certain.*

Jehiel didn't drop his pose. "Please, dear brother. I have been drained dry by the words the Lord has placed on my tongue. If you will excuse us, I must go and…"

"You lie!" hissed Jeremiah. "You stand up there and proclaim peace and invincibility, when nothing approaches but death and pestilence! You blind the eyes of these people with visions they're only too willing to believe, then tell them it is the word of the Lord. You are a fake and a liar!"

Jehiel dropped his hand and stared in cool judgment of his accuser. "If you have some burning message for the people," he said, gesturing nonchalantly toward the Temple steps, "why don't you speak? If you insist on preaching fire and disaster, please do so! No one hinders you!"

He leaned closer. "But first," he whispered, "permit me to open your eyes to some facts. Profits are up, boy! People are happy!"

Jehiel gave Jeremiah a condescending gaze, then walked away, his apprentice in tow.

Jeremiah smoldered in anger: *Why, Sovereign Lord? Why do You suffer such vermin to pour tainted honey into the ears of Your people?* He waited for some answer, some hint. But none came. The Voice was so silent within that it might never have been there at all.

His shoulders slumped in discouragement, he went down into the lower city to seek lodging. He found an inn — poor, disheveled, and not in the best quarter even by the standards of the lower city. But with the few pieces of silver remaining to him, it was the best Jeremiah could do. He stooped and went through the door into a low, dark room that smelled of stale cooking oil. When his eyes adjusted to the interior gloom, he noticed a short, bald man in a grimy apron banking a fire in a smoke-stained hearth in the far corner. Seeing no one else, Jeremiah approached him to inquire about a bed. He stood for several moments behind the fellow, waiting for his presence to be acknowledged. But the man worked steadily at the hearth.

Jeremiah could see a quarter of his face, enough to see an eye-patch and a frightful network of scars webbing the man's surly, closed countenance. Convinced he was being ignored, Jeremiah cleared his throat and said, "I would like a bed. What is your price?"

The fellow still made no reply, other than quickly jerking a thumb over his shoulder toward the corner of the room nearest the door. Thinking he had just been told no vacancies existed, Jeremiah turned to leave. Then he saw the room's other occupant, leaning on his elbows at a small table in the corner by the door, staring down into a clay cup half-filled with wine. The tired-looking man with wisps of gray in his beard looked up.

"I want a bed," repeated Jeremiah, "if indeed this is an inn, and not just a place where visitors to Jerusalem come to be ignored."

"All right, all right. Settle down. We don't get many people in here with manners, so don't take it personally if Squint and I don't speak as nicely as you like."

"Squint?"

The man pointed with his chin at his partner by the hearth, then looked down at his wine again.

"Is that his real name?"

"It suits him, and it suits me," replied the innkeeper before taking a long, deep drink.

Jeremiah eyed the room and its taciturn occupants a moment more, took a deep breath, and said, "Well, I need a bed, and from the looks of it I can afford yours. What is your price,

77

and what is your name?"

The man cocked an eye upward. "Two gerah the night, and Baruch. And I never give my name without receiving one in return." For the first time he gave Jeremiah the ghost of a smile.

"Jeremiah of Anathoth, and I accept." He grinned and took some coins out of his purse, leaning over to slap them onto the table. "This should cover my expense for two nights, and a bit of conversation besides. Apparently that, too, must be bought."

Now it was Baruch's turn to grin. He took the money. "Anathoth, eh? Interesting…"

"You know Anathoth?"

"No, my… I know someone who…" He shook his head. "Well, my generous young guest from the north, welcome to the house of Baruch. And if you need anything Squint or I can provide, you are surely in desperate straits."

He and Squint chuckled, and Jeremiah sat down at the table.

"AGAIN," commanded Shaphan sternly, handing the tablet back to Eliakim.

"Why?" whined the pouting boy, "I've done it three times already!"

"And still you have not copied it correctly," admonished the old scribe. "A prince of Judah must not make such careless mistakes — they can be deadly."

"Rubbish!" cursed the boy in a fit of pique. "How can any decision made in this backwater country be important to anyone? A prince of *Judah*! Hah! The palace eunuchs in Egypt have finer clothes than I!"

"Prince Eliakim!"

"It's true!" the boy shouted, stamping his foot. "In Egypt, they have beautiful horses, and the princes don't have to waste time with stupid old men and pointless lessons. They have slaves to do their lessons for them."

The boy turned and ran from the room. Shaphan watched him go, shaking his head helplessly. He turned to his one remaining pupil. Little Mattaniah sat big-eyed, looking from his teacher to the place where his older brother had been. Shaphan smiled kindly at him.

"Well, Prince Mattaniah, shall we go on?"

Just then a man entered the chamber. "Father! Father!" the child shouted. He jumped up and ran toward King Josiah, his arms outstretched in joy.

"Mattaniah," admonished the king after swinging his youngest son in the air, "you left your lessons without asking your teacher's permission." He set the child down and lowered his gaze, motioning for the boy to amend his error.

Dutifully Mattaniah retraced his steps to the low table at which Shaphan sat, hiding a smile behind the scroll he pretended to study. "Shaphan," the little fellow piped, "may I please be excused for a few moments to go and speak to my father?"

Shaphan lowered the scroll, the frown on his lips belied by the twinkle in his eye. "Yes, my lord prince. I give you leave."

Mattaniah pivoted and ran back to his father, who scooped him up once again. "There, that's better!" the king said. "Always best to do things in the proper fashion." He turned to Shaphan. "How did the lessons proceed today?"

"Not badly, my king...for the most part."

"Did Jehoahaz perform satisfactorily?"

"Yes, my lord, as always. He makes up in diligence what he lacks in originality. He finished early, and I dismissed him."

Josiah nodded. "And Eliakim? Did he also finish early?"

Shaphan shrugged, sadly. "Prince Eliakim is...prone to succumb to other interests. He left just before you came."

Josiah frowned. "I must have words with him again, I'm afraid. He must learn that there is more to being a prince of the house of David than doing as he likes, when he likes."

"Father," implored Mattaniah, "may we go to the stables today?"

"Again? What is this?"

"Yes, Father! I want to go for a ride! Please?"

"Well, perhaps..."

At that moment a herald entered, bowed to Josiah and Mattaniah, and held out a letter to the king. Josiah put Mattaniah down, and took the small scroll from the messenger's hand.

"This is sealed with the Egyptian royal signet!" he exclaimed to his mentor.

Shaphan did not reply, but merely returned the king's surprised look. Josiah dismissed the courier, broke the seal, and read the letter quickly. Then he handed it to Shaphan, watching the old man's face as he read.

"What will you do?" asked the scribe when he had finished reading.

"Receive him, of course," replied the king, pacing to and fro, his hands clasped behind his back. "But what will I reply when the question comes?"

"When you do not know the correct reply," advised Shaphan cryptically, "the best answer may be one which gives no answer."

Josiah stopped and stared thoughtfully at his teacher for a moment, then resumed pacing.

10

THE SUMMER SKY was overcast, and a cool, moist breeze from the north teased at the banners on the walls beside the Ephraim Gate. They carried the six-pointed star of the house of David, gold on a royal purple background. Amnon, the officer in command of the honor guard, looked up at the banners and shifted nervously. It seemed folly to boldly display the emblems of a bygone empire in the face of an adversary like Pharaoh's emissary. Still, the king had been quite specific. The entire corps of guards was to turn out in full dress regalia, in their finest spit-and-polished form. The emblems of David's dynasty were to be displayed at every turn, and Egypt's ambassador was to be received not as an equal in his own right, but as the servant of an equal. Amnon wondered whom Josiah was trying to convince: Pharaoh or himself.

As the Egyptian party crested the ridge at the western end of the Valley of the Sons of Hinnom, the gold of the ambassador's lacquered palanquin glittered dully in the diffuse light of the cloudy day. The litter swayed toward the entrance to Jerusalem like a majestic land barge, its curtains of richly embroidered silk swinging slowly with each step of its bearers. Eight massive Nubians carried it, their leopard-skin attire in sharp contrast to their ebony skin. A royal bodyguard, bristling with spears and gleaming swords, surrounded the party, matching its measured pace to the stately progress befitting Sakhri, plenipotentiary of the king of the sun.

Turning their glance neither right nor left, the Egyptians approached Amnon and his detail, who stood at rigid attention outside the city gate. Amnon felt himself sweating under his armor despite the coolness of the breeze.

The ambassador's vanguard reached them, and halted. The

curtains of the palanquin twitched aside, and the ambassador's secretary, a thin, hawkish man with straight black hair bobbed in the style of the Egyptian court, stepped lightly to the ground.

He looked about him in some confusion, expecting to see the king of this little country, who surely had the good sense to meet them at the gates of his rustic capital. But he had no time to voice indignation or anything else on behalf of the honorable Sakhri. Amnon immediately stepped forward and delivered the words prepared by Josiah:

"Most esteemed servants of Pharaoh, be welcomed to Jerusalem, and to the kingdom of the house of David. Josiah, who rules Judah in the name of the Lord Most High, eagerly awaits your attention in the Judgment Hall of Solomon. I am ordered to convey you there instantly. Please follow me."

With that signal, Amnon's men smoothly deployed themselves around the palanquin, inserting themselves between the emissary and his bodyguards. The secretary stood open-mouthed, even as the Hebrew honor guard began impelling the litter's bearers toward the gate. Hastily the secretary jumped inside, and a flurry of jumbled Egyptian voices erupted from within.

As the Egyptian body guard began belatedly to resist, they were stopped at spearpoint by a further contingent of Amnon's men coming forward from the gate. The two bands glared at each other for several tense seconds, but the Egyptians desisted. No words were exchanged.

When the honor guard had passed safely through the Ephraim Gate, Amnon breathed a silent sigh of relief. So far, Josiah's bluff was working.

They passed along the streets of Solomon's city, lined by the silent, curious, slightly apprehensive citizens of Jerusalem, as well as by troops of the guard.

As the litter passed by him, one of those standing in the crowd remembered the words of Isaiah: "Woe to them that go to Egypt for help, and rely on horses and trust in chariots, but do not consult the Lord...." As the passage came to him, Jeremiah saw a side curtain parted a finger's width, and an Egyptian eye looking out.

AT THE STEPS leading up the side of Mount Moriah to the Hall of Solomon, the Nubians made as if to carry the litter upward. But Amnon turned to face them, gesturing that they should halt and place the car on the ground. The eight huge black men looked at each other uncertainly, then back at the commander of the guard. With a firmness he did not feel, Amnon forcefully motioned for them to put the palanquin down. Slowly the Nubians eased the car down, until it thudded gently onto the pavement. They stepped away two measured paces. Again, Amnon silently mouthed a prayer of thanks to the God of Israel.

At length the curtains swished aside. Sakhri, personal ambassador of Neco, Pharaoh of Egypt, squinted at the unexpected tableau which greeted him. He was a corpulent man, in great contrast to his secretary. His eyes, deep-set in the pudgy folds of his face, quickly darted this way and that, taking in the situation which confronted him. Realizing he had few options, since all the weapons in the vicinity were wielded by Hebrews, he peered up the side of Moriah and winced at the apparently unavoidable prospect of climbing the steps himself.

Muttering under his breath at the unaccountable temerity of these crude Hebrews, he heaved his bulk from the couch and, puffing and sweating, climbed the steps of Moriah, grumbling the whole way. His secretary followed, a look of puzzled animosity on his face.

Atop the last excruciating step a guard admitted Sakhri and the secretary within the hall. As they passed through the ornate doorway to the throne room, the gold jewelry about Sakhri's neck and wrists jingled in a cheery counterpoint to his labored breathing.

King Josiah sat on the throne of David, his advisers and the nobles of his court ranged on either side of him. A simple gold circlet stood out boldly against his black, wavy hair, but his robes were of the richest purple silks and the finest white linens. On his chest blazed a golden *magen*, the shield of David. He set his gaze over the head of the Egyptians, not so much as glancing at Sakhri when he entered the room.

The emissary stood for a moment on the opposite side, waiting to be received by the Hebrew king. But after long minutes passed, he concluded no one at this court had the ability to speak. He impatiently motioned to the secretary, who addressed Josiah in Egyptian.

"Honored Josiah, ruler of Judah: The king of the sun, the mighty and exalted Neco, lord of the Nile and of the realms of heaven, Pharaoh of Egypt by right of divine descent, sends you greeting in the person of the most honorable Sakhri, ambassador of the royal court. He bids you peace and—"

"Upon what errand," interrupted Josiah in Hebrew, "does your master send you to us, Lord Sakhri?" The king was staring past the secretary, directly at the ambassador himself.

The secretary turned in consternation to his master. The two conferred in hushed, angry tones for several moments. They stared at each other until Sakhri gave a little shrug of resignation, and turned to address the king himself.

"O Josiah, son of Amon, worthy king of Judah," he began in his high-pitched yet powerful voice, speaking Hebrew with a flawless command, "Neco, Pharaoh of Egypt and protector of the lands of the south, bids me come and bring you comfort in these times of uncertainty." Sakhri paused, waiting for some bodily or facial clue from the sturdy-looking Hebrew on the throne.

Josiah sat still as a stone, his eyes never flickering from their steady grip on the Egyptian's. After an interval that seemed to last an hour, Sakhri cleared his throat and spoke again.

"No doubt the people of Judah are greatly discomfited by the events in the north — by the depredations practiced upon the upper Tigris and Euphrates valleys by the marauding Chaldeans of Babylon. Neco, too, looks with concern upon these things, and, though Babylon is surely not so foolish as to march against the kingdom of the Nile, the Pharaoh, in his infinite grace, knows the value of being certain of one's friends in times of change."

Again the ambassador paused, allowing the king to interject; to give some opening, some indication. Surely even a Hebrew could perceive the advantage of being under Egypt's wing if the Sumerian foe turned its attention south.

Josiah smirked inwardly at the self-serving hypocrisy sheathed in the flowing phrases of the fat man. Outwardly he gave no evidence of having heard Sakhri's remarks, for he did not move, scarcely blinked. When the silence again became uncomfortable, the Egyptian went on, his forehead beaded anew with sweat.

"Pharaoh Neco, the child of the sun, in his infinite grace, is willing to afford the people of Judah the protection of the glorious might of the kingdom of the Nile. He will extend his hand to you, and assure you of deliverance from the jaws of the Babylonian wolves—"

"And in exchange for his munificence," interrupted Josiah, "what does your master seek in return?" Josiah snapped out the words, which flew like daggers at the envoy.

Sakhri's stunned face was frozen. Meanwhile the secretary at his side darted his eyes back and forth from his master to Josiah, to the guards ranged all around the hall, and back to Sakhri. This interview was not going at all as they had envisioned it, and he silently pleaded with Sakhri to say the words to get them out of this hall, crackling with Hebrew hostility. This fool of a king might possibly be addled enough to kill them both if Sakhri's words displeased him.

The ambassador took a deep breath and turned again to face the impassive, granite gaze of this unpredictable king. "In return..." He paused, taking several more deep breaths. "In return, Pharaoh asks that Judah...asks that Judah pay a just and equitable tribute, in men-at-arms and commodities, to recompense the king of the sun for his expense in affording the protection of his eternal kingdom to the people of this land."

Josiah sat more still than before, if that were possible, and allowed the last resonance of Sakhri's speech to die into silence in the hall. So. The words he had expected had been spoken. But it was important that Sakhri uttered them in the way he had: as a merchant proposing a barter, rather than as a monarch demanding fealty.

The overt display of truculence had worked. He had gambled on Egypt's underestimation of Judah's resolve, and the die had fallen in his favor. Now he could consider a proper response to Neco's move.

He was well aware of the danger of sleeping in Pharaoh's bed, however well-couched and polite the invitation. Not for nothing had the feast of Passover reminded the people of their deliverance from bondage in the land of the Nile.

He allowed his eyes to disengage those of the envoy. He turned his head right to glance at the wrinkled, white-bearded face of Shaphan, who stood among the elders and counselors of the court. The aging scribe's eyes returned his look warmly, the tiniest of smiles fluttering at the corners of his lips. He was pleased with his pupil.

Josiah rose from his throne and paced deliberately to the nearest window, his hands clasped behind his back. His footsteps sounded loudly across the hushed hall. He was turned away from Sakhri, yet he could sense the presence of the Egyptian, could fairly hear his quickened breath and the dripping of his sweat on the flagstone floor. The king allowed the moment to stretch to the breaking point before pivoting to face the ambassador, carefully studying his face before speaking.

"Honorable Sakhri, you have well said that Judah is concerned about the changing tides of the nations. It is very true that we carefully watch the unfolding of events, with a cautious eye to the welfare of our nation.

"And you have also well said that it is prudent to be certain of one's friends in such a shifting and changeable world as ours. This we are most anxious to do.

"Return to your master," the king finished, "and thank him for his concern. He may be assured that we duly appreciate his solicitude for the welfare of the sovereign kingdom of Judah." He allowed his voice to pause significantly on the last four words. "Say also to him that we will pray to the Lord our God on his behalf, that his life may be long, and his vision keen in the unsure days ahead."

With that, Josiah, his hands still clasped behind his back, turned on his heel and marched resolutely out of the hall. Sakhri stared after him, open-mouthed. Was it possible? Was this madman actually presuming to be an equal among the great powers of the world? Dare he speak as if he ruled a mighty empire, instead of a tiny, half-eaten country perched precariously between the jaws of two mighty and ancient nations?

As the nobles of the court began conversing among themselves, ignoring him as though he did not exist, Sakhri realized fully, with a flash of hot embarrassment, that he had been dismissed. Dismissed! By the king of paltry Judah!

He snorted with indignation as the honor guard formed a resolute wall to escort him out of the palace.

11

JEREMIAH LEANED against the door of Baruch's inn and went inside. He collapsed on the nearest mat and leaned forward on the scarred, dirty table, his head on his crossed forearms.

For several moments he was the only one in the common room. Then a rear door banged open, and Baruch entered, his arms wrapped around a medium-sized earthen jar filled with wine. The innkeeper reached behind him with his toe and flipped the door closed again. Then his eyes fell upon the picture of dejection seated at the table near the door. He carried the jar to the storage rack along the wall by the hearth, setting it down with a grunt. He turned and approached Jeremiah, thoughtfully studying the form of his guest.

"Is it truly as bad as all that?" inquired Baruch softly. He was surprised when Jeremiah looked up: The young man's face was wet with tears.

"Friend Baruch," said Jeremiah, "my heart aches so badly I think I cannot live."

"Ah!" said Baruch, going to the wine jar and filling two cups. He came back to the table and clumped one cup down in front of Jeremiah. "Drink! This won't make your heart stop aching, but it may bring comfort while you unburden yourself. Now, then," the innkeeper continued as he settled himself down on the mat across the table from Jeremiah, "tell me what troubles you. Is it a woman?"

Jeremiah looked out the window, toward the north. Toward Anathoth. He gazed with pained perplexity for a moment, then turned back to Baruch, shaking his head. "No, my heart is not burdened by a woman. Would that it were so. Would to God it were so…" His voice trailed off with his eyes into an empty corner of the room.

Baruch's brow furrowed. He had seen many troubled men in here. He had shared cups with most of them. Sometimes wine loosened the tongue, sometimes it didn't. But he sensed something different, something deeper about the pain endured by this man from Anathoth. He was not sure he wanted to know more. This sadness reminded him of another time, a time he wished to forget — and almost had.

Just as he was about to get up and leave Jeremiah alone with his hurt, the younger man looked at him with eyes like shafts of brightness.

"Baruch," he said, "I received a word from the Lord today."

Baruch now knew for certain he wanted nothing more to do with this situation. But Jeremiah's eyes would not release him; he felt himself being drawn into the maelstrom at the center of the young man's soul.

"I was walking down the Street of Potters," said Jeremiah, "and I felt a sudden desire to go into one of the shops. I sat down, watching the men work. They would take a lump of clay, throw it onto their wheel, wet it, and begin the wheel spinning.

"Then they would shape the clay with their hands. I felt my heart soaring with pride as the clay rose up under the potters' hands, being modeled and shaped and made useful. The patient hands worked; the shape of the clay became more and more beautiful.

"Then something went wrong. A potter looked carefully at the clay he had been working. He took a string and cut it off from its base as the wheel slowed, picking it up to peer inside.

"What he saw didn't please him. And he took that gracefully shaped piece of clay — almost perfect it seemed — and because of some fatal flaw he alone saw, he smashed it down onto the wheel again, kneading it back into a shapeless lump as at the beginning.

"And I felt my heart being smashed along with the clay. I felt myself crushed and kneaded, my bones ground into nothingness. I wanted to weep, to cry aloud. I wanted to hide.

"That is when the word came."

Jeremiah leaned forward, gripping Baruch's tunic in the intensity of his vision. "We — *we* are the clay, Baruch! This land, this people! God has cast us upon His wheel, molding us for all these hundreds of generations to His purpose. He has pressed us with His fingers, crafting us to be the vessel of His will.

"But we are wrong!" It was almost a wail. "We do not take the proper shape for His purpose! We are a flawed lump of clay. And, Baruch..." The tears again ran down his face, unchecked. "...if Judah does not repent, if she does not heed the Potter's touch...she will be destroyed! Utterly destroyed! I have seen it! I know!" His last words came in a hoarse croak as his voice was bested by grief. Again his head dropped upon his arms as the recounting of the revelation drained the last of his strength.

Baruch sat stunned. He was silent while Jeremiah struggled to regain his breath.

The room grew quiet. Then Baruch spoke in a voice as distant as a dirge echoing inside a tomb.

"All these years — all my caution. And again I am found."

Jeremiah looked up questioningly.

"Found again. I cannot escape. He will have me, despite all I do."

"What are you talking about?"

Baruch's eyes snapped into sharp focus as he glared into Jeremiah's confused face. "You are a prophet!" It was not a question.

"My family has been cursed by prophets!" the innkeeper ranted. "Association with prophets caused my grandfather to be hunted like a beast, until he fled from his own home. Manasseh's soldiers came hunting through the night, like coursing hounds on a trail, trying to find him, all because he had dealings with prophets!

"And prophets caused the death of my father! As a child of ten I saw him cut down because he wouldn't tell them where my grandfather went! Gutted in front of his family like a slaughtered cow, and all because of a *prophet!*"

"Your grandfather was..."

"A scribe! Yes! Mahseiah son of Nahor, one of Judah's most educated men. A man who loved the Law! A man who studied the writings — at night with heavy linen over the windows to protect him from the prying eyes of Manasseh's baal-worshiping spies. A man who taught his family to revere the teachings of Moses and the prophets. And much good it did them!"

"But Josiah—"

"Josiah! What do I care for Josiah?" By now Baruch was fairly shouting. "I don't trust kings, no matter how righteous they may seem! Kings are worse than prophets if you get too close to them. And even if Josiah is a good man, how long can he live? And why should his son be any better than Manasseh, the wicked offspring of Hezekiah the Just? No, kings are just as false as any other promise. They turn in your hand like a broken-hilted dagger, and gash you. Kings, hah!" he spat. "Kings and prophets! I don't need either!"

Abruptly Baruch stood up. "Get out of my house!" he commanded Jeremiah. "Get out! I've had my fill of your kind! You and your words from the Lord — you'll get yourself killed, maybe, but you won't get Baruch bar-Neriah! You won't get me!" He shook his fist in Jeremiah's face. But his eyes were turned toward the sky as he shouted.

Jeremiah stood, his mind reeling from the words he had heard. He thought of old Mahseiah, sitting sadly in his pitiful little hut in Anathoth as he guarded the scrolls which had meant more to him than the peace of his own house.

Jeremiah moved to the door and opened it, with Baruch following. The prophet stepped outside, then he turned to face the innkeeper again. "Baruch," he said quietly, "a wise old man once told me something about the duty of a scribe. I think perhaps you know it too, though you seek to forget. Like your grandfather before you, your duty is to remember. You, too, are being shaped, Baruch son of Neriah."

The door slammed in Jeremiah's face.

12

AS HE WALKED through the gates of his father's estate, Jeremiah felt sprites of dread tugging at the corners of his mind. He had been gone three years. During his sojourn among the cities of Judah, what might have happened here? What changes might have occurred for which he was not prepared?

Wearily he knocked on the aged, water-stained front door and leaned against the wall of the portico awaiting a response.

The door opened, and his mother stood there, her eyes at first not recognizing her youngest son. Her face had aged greatly, and her hair was far whiter now than Jeremiah remembered. Then she discerned him, and joy burst across her visage like a sunrise.

"My son!" she shouted, grasping and pulling him to her.

He clung to his mother and wept. For three long years Jeremiah had not felt the touch of a loving hand.

Hilkiah, drawn to the commotion, arose from the place where he sat reading and limped toward the door, leaning more heavily than ever upon his crutch.

"What is this? Libnah, do we have visitors..." His voice faded as he encountered the scene at the entrance. Jeremiah raised his face from his mother's shoulder and regarded his father voicelessly.

Hilkiah's hands, hanging at his sides, twitched as if they might of themselves reach toward Jeremiah. The aged priest's mouth moved, but his tongue could not grip the words it sought, and no sound came from his lips. Was this really his son? This man looked much older, much more stooped with care than the boy who left three years ago. His eyes appeared to Hilkiah as dark doorways onto scenes of sorrow.

This familiar stranger now opened his mouth, and from his

lips came a voice Hilkiah remembered: "Father, I've missed you. Truly."

The three of them embraced, then went inside, the son with his arms around the shoulders of his parents. He remembered the warmth of this house during his childhood; how safe he had felt here! It was good to feel secure and loved again, so unlike what he had known wandering throughout Judah.

They entered the main room — and there she sat, upon a linen cushion, cleaning wool from a pile beside her. She glanced up at him.

Her eyes were not as he remembered. When they had been in love, her dark eyes had sparkled constantly with mischief or affection. And her lips had always seemed to turn up at the corners, as though a smile waited only for the proper moment to spread its glow across her face. Now her face was plain, drained of vitality. Her eyes appeared fatigued from holding in a remorse they concealed only poorly. Her mouth was a grim line of determination, a hard-set stamp of demarcation between the past she longed for and the future she was consigned to.

Hannah looked at him for perhaps ten heartbeats. Halfway through that span, Jeremiah suddenly detected a possible stirring in her languid countenance, a rising glimmer of something that had once been love before life thrashed it out of her. But the next second it was gone; she dropped her eyes again to her work, leaving him to go or stay as he wished; she did not seem to care.

THE DAY WAS CRISP, and the old men beneath the mulberry tree were bundled against the chilly breezes despite the bright sunshine and a sky so blue it made the eyes ache. The ancient tree was beginning to shed its leaves in the cold air of autumn.

The men greeted Hilkiah cheerily and nodded politely at Jeremiah as the two joined the circle of elders for the morning's discussion. Jeremiah was not entirely at ease in this setting. Yet his father had invited him to accompany him, and he did not have anything else with which to occupy his time.

"Well, Jeremiah bar-Hilkiah," began one of the graybeards good-naturedly, "tell us where you've been keeping yourself these years past. You're grown to a man since I saw you last."

The others nodded, smiling as they looked from Hilkiah to his son.

"I have been throughout the land of Judah," replied Jeremiah carefully, "from Beersheba to Gibeon. I have seen her people, her lands and cities." He refrained from saying more.

"Ah, yes," intoned another of the elders, "the land has changed much since the days of King Manasseh and Amon, his son." The other old men nodded.

"True enough," said another. "King Josiah, may he be blessed by the Eternal, has brought back the days of prosperity to Judah. Not for nothing did he call the people again to the worship of Adonai. See how we are blessed in these days!" An appreciative murmur washed over the group. Jeremiah stared fixedly at the ground, saying nothing.

"A proposition for your consideration," said one of the elders into the reflective silence. The others shifted, the better to hear the issue put forward.

"A man of poor sight wishes to make a sacrifice to the Lord. Now he is a pious man, a scrupulous follower of the Law. He culls a lamb from his flocks, a firstborn male, sound of limb. He carefully inspects the animal and concludes that it is fit to offer to the Lord. But because of his weak eyes, a small blemish escapes his attention. Nevertheless, he offers the lamb to the Lord, in all other ways according to the Law.

"Here is my question: Has the man committed blasphemy, by offering to the Lord a blemished sacrifice?"

The men's brows furrowed deeply as they studied the elements of the problem set before them. At length one of them spoke.

"I say he has not sinned. In all things he followed the Law as best he could, even to the inspection of the animal. His heart was pure in what he did. I say the Lord accepts the sacrifice."

"And yet," interjected another, "are we to believe this man did not know his eyes were weak? Are we to assume he could not call upon some other — his son perhaps — to inspect the beast? Perhaps this man's sin lies in failure to exercise due caution in light of his infirmity. I say he is, despite his good intentions, not righteous in his sacrifice."

The venerable assembly nodded in admiration of the logic

of this argument. But Jeremiah squirmed in his place. A fire was kindling in his chest, and he knew too well its source. He struggled with his feelings, trying to avoid making himself conspicuous among his father's friends. Clamping his teeth on the words erupting inside him, he remained silent, but his chest began to heave with the effort.

"Still," began another in a wheezy, gray voice, "was it not to the sons of Aaron and to the Levites that the Lord first give instruction concerning the offerings? Would not the priest who accepts such a blemished beast in the name of the Lord be culpable as well? And would it not be that priest's duty to warn the man of this impending sin against the Lord, so that he might repent, and make an acceptable offering?"

Smiles on the wrinkled and bearded faces showed their enjoyment of this intellectual exercise. Hilkiah opened his mouth to speak, but before he could begin, Jeremiah rose to his feet, his face contorted by holy wrath.

"Elders of Anathoth!" he began. "What are you discussing? Is there no sin in Judah, that you must weave theories to turn back and forth in your hands like a child's bauble? I have been through the land, and I have seen what these people do, who are called by the Lord's name.

"The people do not care for one another! They treat their poor brother or sister like a dog in the streets! Nor do they show compassion, as the Law commands. They defraud one another, and get rich by cheating their brethren. They commit adultery, and slaver over each other's mates like rutting beasts of the field. They oppress the poor, and deal with their Hebrew brother and sister like common chattel.

"And in the very Temple of the Lord, the house where His name dwells, the prophets lie to the people, saying 'Peace, peace!' when there is no peace! They defraud the people, who lap it up like eager dogs at the scrap heap. The liars gain wealth by feeding the people filth, and the people love to have it so!

"And in this very place," he thundered, "you suffer men to live who serve gods which are no gods. They worship a stone and call it 'Father!' They bow down to a tree and say 'You gave me birth!' And…they devour their own children," he stammered, tears stinging his eyes at the memory, "spilling the blood of innocent babies to slake the foul appetites of their abominations! These things God the Lord hates!"

Even the breeze seemed to halt at Jeremiah's words of fire and tumult. The old men sat as if stricken.

"Now, therefore, listen to what God, the Lord of Hosts, says about Judah: 'Have you seen what she did, that faithless one, Israel, how she whored after other lovers? And I thought when she had done these things, she would return to Me, but she did not. And her false sister Judah saw it, and went whoring also. She polluted the whole land with her sinful habits. She did not return to me with her whole heart, but in pretense,' says the Lord.

"There is disease gnawing at the heart of this nation. And the Lord will come in judgment and in anger if the people do not turn and seek Him with sincere hearts. There is no time for philosophy, only for repentance."

He stopped, panting with the exertion of his oracle. His eyes fell upon his father, who sat crumpled in shame at his feet. Jeremiah knew with the certainty of death that he had no comfort for his father. On this day, he had no comfort for anyone.

He turned away, leaving the old men where they sat withering within their cloaks beneath the dying leaves of the mulberry tree.

13

NEWS OF JEREMIAH'S dire speech to the village elders ran on a hundred tongues through Anathoth.

When he had gained the will to stand, Hilkiah left the mulberry tree and trudged home. There he closed himself in his room, winding himself tightly around the shame inflicted upon him by his son in front of his peers. Every whisper of the wind, every creak of the tree branches sounded to his ears like accusing voices. "There is old Hilkiah," they said, "the priest who raised a wicked son with a tongue like a jailer's scourge. He lacks even the respect due a father from his son."

The old priest began to decay from inside. He wanted to die for disgrace.

Libnah, for her part, felt torn between the opposing camps within her breast. She was wounded by the pain of her husband; Hilkiah was a good man who had always done his best. He did not deserve such dishonor in the days of his old age.

And yet — with a mother's certainty she knew Jeremiah would not say such terrible things solely for effect. His feelings always lay too close to the surface to let him gratuitously tread upon anyone, much less his own father. She felt anger at her husband's plight, but also fear that her son's oracle was true.

That night's dinner gathering was a desert of resentment, a sterile plain of closed glances and words left unspoken. Hilkiah concluded the benediction in a voice devoid of inflection or vitality. And so supper began: His family shared a room, yet was divided by barriers harder than stone, higher than the walls of Jerusalem.

Of all those gathered around the cheerless board, only Lemuel felt anything other than confused anger or distress. It was about time, he thought. About time that everyone else saw what a foolish, selfish, muddle-headed dreamer Jeremiah was. Lemuel's face wore a sardonic smirk as he saw with satisfaction the mess Jeremiah had managed to make of things.

Yes, it was about time.

He glanced at his wife. Hannah's face was indrawn. She wished deeply to retire from this field of battling wills, but could not decently do so.

She raised her eyes to look directly at Jeremiah, who brooded in his place, unaware. He appeared to be studying the table before him with great concentration.

In her puzzled sorrow, she lost her customary caution, forgetting to hide past and present feelings beneath a drab, dutiful exterior. In her gaze now was a ghost of the old look, mingled with a knit-browed confusion at the distress caused by one she knew to be tender-hearted and true in his deepest self, despite the hurt he had cost her.

A slap across her face from the back of Lemuel's hand sent her sprawling onto the floor, bloodying her lip.

"You whore!" shouted Lemuel, leaping to his feet in a frenzy. "You sit there making moon-eyes at this...this..." He pointed angrily at Jeremiah, stuttering in his wrath. "...this idiot?" Shocked out of their solitary grief, the family sat round-eyed and aghast as Lemuel stormed on.

"You've never forgotten him, have you? Despite all the hurt he caused you, despite the way he deserted you, knowing full well how you felt; despite all that, it is still him you love, and not me! Do you deny it, you ungrateful wench?"

Hannah sat silent, her eyes wide with fear, blood running down her chin.

"Is it he you think about in bed?" screamed Lemuel, his face purple in fury. "Do you lie with him in your mind, while I feed you and shelter you and clothe you? What is the charm of this wretch, that those on whom he inflicts the most harm willingly offer him sanctuary? By the names of all the gods, it shall not be so with you!" He started toward Hannah, raising his fist to strike her again.

Joash leaped from his place, grasping Lemuel's arm as it descended toward Hannah's unprotected face. The sinews bulged on his sun-darkened forearm as he squeezed Lemuel's wrist, forcing him away from the now-sobbing Hannah. Lemuel grimaced and strained, trying in vain to break his older brother's iron grip. At last he won free, and bounded from the room and out of the house with an animal cry of frustrated brutality.

Joash stood panting, looking after him for a moment. Then he turned to stare at Jeremiah in bewilderment and distrust.

"WHY, LORD?" Jeremiah prayed, sitting outside in the starry autumn evening, chilled by more than the cool air. "Why do I spread distress and woe at every turn? Why do my words fall like sword blows on those I love?"

The house was dark. The family had drifted away from the meal in a dazed, uncomfortable silence. No one spoke to him, no one looked at him. It seemed they wanted only to be out of his presence.

He was more lonely now than when he had walked the roads and byways of Judah. He felt turmoil inside like a storm cloud, whipping his heart in a cold swirl of doubt and anguish.

He slid off the rough stone wall and wandered into the night like a lost soul, absently pulling his cloak tighter. The breath of impending winter whispered about him, and winds of apprehension wafted treacherously through the open windows of his mind.

"I'M TELLING YOU he ought to die!"

Lemuel's face was livid as he brought his fist down on the table of the dimly lit room. His voice had by now risen far above the conspiratorial whispers in which the conversation had begun, and the four others in the room glanced nervously at the door and windows, hastily motioning their overwrought colleague to keep quiet.

"Lemuel!" one of them hissed, "he is your brother — your own flesh and blood!"

"Aye," murmured another, "and he preaches in the name of Yahweh. If Josiah's agents learn of our complicity in his death, we are dead men!"

"You are all old women!" sputtered Lemuel, getting louder again. "He is a disgrace! He has no support! He insults the elders of Anathoth, my father among them, and threatens the worship of Chemosh! Do you wish to stand idly by and allow this troublemaker to stir up more noise about what we are doing, we who have remained faithful to the gods of the earth and the sky?" Lemuel held their unwilling eyes with his dilated, angry look. "Why should this muddled wanderer, who goes off for years at a time, be allowed to upset our way of doing things? I say we take care of this misfit now, and I care not a fig whose brother he happens to be!"

"And I say there is more to your words than jealousy for the reverence toward Lord Chemosh," said another of the men. "Your ire burns hot toward your brother for something else — a woman, perhaps?"

"That is none of your concern!" shouted Lemuel, his fingers curling into claws at his side. "What matters is silencing this fool, and soon! Or do you wish to share the fate of the priests and worshipers of Ashtaroth at Nob, just up the road?"

The group fell silent as they remembered the chilling event: Josiah's guards had slain thirty men and women with the sword, then burned their bodies and scattered the charred bones on the ruined high places of the gods. Such a desecration was frightening to contemplate. Since then, devotees of the baals and asherim had been careful to conceal their religion from any not known to be sympathetic. The worship went on, but discreetly, amid hope for better days.

"Well," conceded one of them finally, "it may be that your counsel is sound, however flawed its motives. Very well — I will support this action. Who will stand with Lemuel and with me to slay the troublesome preacher?"

Slowly and quietly, all three of the others placed their hands atop those of the speaker and of Lemuel, who wore a hard, glittering grin of triumph.

Just outside the house where the plot was being laid, the wandering Jeremiah had stopped, hidden in the darkness. Hearing the incautious voices, he stood frozen in dismay. For as long as he could remember, Lemuel had despised him. Now, for the first time, he knew why: It was the night in the soul of his brother which hated the light of the Eternal in his own heart.

Each of the brothers was an instrument, a tool. And there could be nothing but enmity between them forever. Their hostility was born of the ancient war between the ruling forces of the two brothers' lives — one good, the other evil.

Jeremiah remembered the words of his calling: "I chose you while you were still in your mother's womb…" Could the dark architect of Lemuel's malevolence also make such a summons?

He did not return to his room that night, cloaking himself instead in the darkness among the ravines of the surrounding countryside, seeking some word, some counsel to aid in treading the ever narrower and more treacherous path he walked.

THE NEXT MORNING the house of Abiathar gathered for breakfast in apprehension, feeling in different ways the brittle tension in the air. Lemuel sat in his place, looking even more dour and disgruntled than usual. Hannah, her eyes red-rimmed and dark from lack of sleep, sat downcast, afraid to look up.

The door slammed open, and in strode Jeremiah, his clothing still wet with the dew of the autumn morning. Without a break in his step he paced directly up to Lemuel, whose slack, open-mouthed stare bespoke his surprise at the change in his younger brother. Jeremiah had none of the defeated, brooding demeanor of last night, but rather a hard, set look, a talisman of urgent purpose chiseled across his face. With his accusing finger pointed directly between his brother's wide eyes, his voice rang out:

"I know of the plotting in your heart. I know you have laid plans to take my life, because of the words the Lord bade me speak. I had no blood on my hands toward you, my own brother, but you have conspired with evil men to kill me, to blot out my memory from this place.

"Now, therefore, listen to what the Eternal, the Lord Most High, says about you and those with whom you devise your wicked schemes: 'I will punish you. Your offspring will die by the sword and by famine. Your memory will be completely erased from the land, and I will bring disaster upon you in the time when I judge this nation.'"

For a moment he held his pose, his finger aimed at Lemuel like a thunderbolt from the hand of God. Then he turned on his heel and walked out, slamming the door behind him.

He had gone perhaps twenty long paces from the house

when he first felt the fire in his veins begin to cool. His nostrils ceased flaring, his heart slowed its angry, racing gait. The pain of what he had said began to wrap his chest in dull, aching cords of regret. Another twenty paces, and he felt tears running down his face.

He had thought it would bring him fierce joy and a sense of vindication to pronounce the Lord's judgment on Lemuel and the men of Anathoth. But the scene burned into his mind was not the death of Lemuel, deserving though he was. Nor was it the punishment of the baby-slaying idolaters. Instead, the faces of Hannah and his mother wavered before his tear-veiled vision, and the faces of children and families caught in the winnowing fork of God's wrath. Prophesying judgment brought no satisfaction, nor did it lighten his burden. But he could do nothing else.

He walked into the broken country east of the village until the middle of the morning. Weak from his overnight fast and soul-weary from the questions in his mind, he crawled beneath the shelter of a heavy copse of scrub cedar and lay on his belly, his face in his arms.

"O Lord God," he moaned, "I am cut to the depths of my spirit by the pain I carry. Why must the wicked do as they like, despite Your warnings and Your displeasure? Why, instead, do the righteous suffer at the hands of sinners?

"I am pinned beneath Your will; I feel it crushing me between You and my enemies.

"I cannot ignore the fire You have kindled within me — it blazes, and no matter how I try to hold it in, I cannot. But when I speak, my enemies gather round like wild dogs. I am a lost lamb surrounded by a hungry pack whose only wish is to tear and rend. Hear my cry, O Lord! Deliver me from the teeth of those who oppose me! Fulfill Your promise, which You made when You called me, saying, 'I will make you like a bronze wall against your enemies.'"

His words spent, he lay silent, overcome with grief, and with longing for — he knew not what.

The wind, sighing through the pungent green cedar branches, slowed and stopped. Even the sparrows in the brush ceased their busy chatter. And the Voice was within him.

"Jeremiah."

One word. His name. Never before had the Voice spoken his name. And in those few syllables, resounding repeatedly through the hallways of his soul, he heard his entire being described, known, spun out like a thread of flax in the hands of a master weaver — seen through and through.

Jeremiah. Yahweh knew his name — and everything else. The Lord God knew his hurt, his anguish; knew the pain of pronouncing death on those he loved; knew the sorrow of being alone; knew the lash of unjustified hatred; knew the piercing misery of being abandoned by those closest to him.

And He knew more. He knew Jeremiah's pride, his self-will. He knew the dark, secret places where Jeremiah imagined himself a lofty figure on Judah's landscape — a seer, a tower; perhaps even a Moses. The Lord God Almighty knew the traces of contempt that sometimes peeked from the corners of his vision as he beheld the sin of the people. He knew the unholy, blood-red lust for revenge that sometimes made his thoughts crawl like snakes in a vat of excrement.

Yahweh knew. He knew. And Jeremiah cried out in silence with a wail beyond weeping. He flung his arms over his head as if to hide from God's face. He was unworthy — wholly unworthy. Yet again the Voice was within him.

"If you have raced with men on foot and they have worn you out, how will you compete with horses? If you stumble in the plain, how will you manage in the thickets by the Jordan?"

Jeremiah's inner cry was cut off now, abruptly hushed by the power of the knowing One.

"My beloved will be given into the hands of her enemies. My inheritance has become like a wild beast — therefore I despise her. I will bring others to spoil My vineyard. My beautiful fields will become like a wasteland, because no one cares.

"So bear your shame, Jeremiah. My anger will cause this bitter harvest. But know that after the time of tearing down will surely come a time of building up. After I uproot Judah, I will again have compassion on her. If she will turn and renew her love for Me, I will bring her again to her own land, each family to its own home. In this hope, you may find your hope."

His senses numbed, Jeremiah fell into the deep sleep of

utter exhaustion. When he awoke, feeling hungry, the sun was dragging its gold-and-purple train down the western sky. He slowly sat up and looked below the colors, back toward Anathoth. He could think of but one place there where he might find shelter and comfort.

He crawled out from under the cedars, and set out for the hut of Mahseiah the scribe.

14

NEBUCHADREZZAR WAS ANGRY. He had kept his generals in attendance for the better part of the morning, standing in nervous rigidity as he sat wordlessly behind the gold-inlaid, lacquered table in the throne room of the just-conquered palace in Nineveh.

He stared at them now with a look more dangerous than the lances of the Assyrian guards who once stood sentinel here. In a placid voice dripping with quiet contempt, he spoke.

"What you have done is nothing more nor less than allow them to slip through your fingers. Does anyone wish to dispute this?"

The vast hall was silent as death.

"You had their necks in the noose, and in the night you allowed them to slip away." He allowed the faint echoes of his voice to dissipate completely. Then with a motion as swift as a serpent's strike, he smote the table a resounding blow with the flat of his hand. Almost involuntarily, the generals dropped to their knees and made obeisance.

He stood, stepped from behind the table, and paced around their crouching figures. He continued his tirade with a voice still as soft as the hiss of an asp.

"The entire court of Nineveh...every commander, every person of royal blood, every officer of the court — escaped. Flown like a mother bird who has decoyed the fox from her nest. While you lie drunk in your bivouac, toasting your certain victory, the prize slips from between your very teeth and scurries like a band of thieves into the night — along with a goodly portion of the royal guards and several infantry regiments." He gently turned on his heel and paced slowly back the other direction.

His tone remained calm: "How can I place further confidence in such as you? I left you in absolute control of the city. I hastened to the bedside of my ill father — your king — believing the word I brought to him of the conquest of Nineveh was the truth. And you have made me a *LIAR!*" Only the last word was a shout.

When the reverberations died away an eternity later, one of the prostrate commanders muttered, his lips against the floor: "But...my master the prince must surely know that his host will smash this small band of holdouts as soon as we run them to ground. The mighty Prince of Babylon has taken the invincible Nineveh — can a retreating rabble have any hope to stand before him?"

Nebuchadrezzar paused, turning to study the undignified form of the speaker. He stepped slowly toward him, then squatted beside him. "That, however, is hardly the point, is it? My charge to you upon leaving was to take the citadel, capture the king and nobles of the court, and hold them here until my return. And the fact is, it did not happen. Is that not so?" He paused, waiting.

The general scooted his head up and back, attempting a nod without lifting his face from the flagstone floor. The back of his neck tingled in anticipation of the sword stroke.

Nebuchadrezzar stood and walked slowly back to the table, seating himself behind it once again.

"*Rise!*" he snapped, his voice a whiplash.

The commanders scrambled to their feet, hastily straightening their tunics and righting their tilted helmets.

"What intelligence have we of the Assyrians' escape route?"

The response was quick: "My lord, they have retreated to Haran, about six days' march to the west, in the plain between the rivers."

"How many days hence are they?"

"Your worship, they — they left two nights ago."

"Very well." The prince rose and began walking toward the doorway, framed by two huge winged bulls carved from cedar. "We will engage them at Haran," he barked over his shoulder. "Inform the army to prepare for the march. We'll leave as soon as the remaining spoils are ready for shipment to Babylon."

"My lord—" began one of the commanders, just as Nebuchadrezzar reached the doorway. The prince paused, turning his head slightly to indicate his attention.

"Will it be your desire to leave a garrison here at Nineveh?"

The prince turned again, thoughtfully contemplating this rich hall in the capital of a fallen empire. He beheld its tapestries of gold and silver thread, its warmly gleaming furnishings of rare woods, its gold-leafed statuary, its murals of brilliant hues.

He looked back at his men. "Burn it," he said.

THE MESSENGER HURRIED up the steps of the colonnaded pavilion, sweating in the heat of the Egyptian sun. He threw himself to the floor, awaiting Pharaoh's summons.

Neco lounged impassively on his cushion of leopard and zebra skins, gazing out over the sun-washed Nile rolling sluggishly past in the wavering heat. Without turning his head, he signaled to a nearby slave to cease strumming the kithara, and motioned the messenger forward. The courier crawled forward on his belly until he reached Pharaoh's feet, which he kissed. Then he rose to his hands and knees, delivering his news without so much as raising his face.

"O son of heaven," he began, "tidings have arrived from the king and nobles of Assyria. The king desires that your strong arm might stretch out to his aid, for he is sorely beset in the north by the hosts of the Chaldeans of Babylon."

Neco shifted slightly on his pallet, still looking out over the river, but now with a more thoughtful expression.

"The king of Assyria is at Haran," the courier continued, "expecting imminent attack from the prince of Babylon. He desires most earnestly that you, the glorious child of the gods, come swiftly to his aid and array your strength with that of Assyria, that together you might yet defeat the armies of this odious enemy."

"What is the best route to Haran?" asked Neco, his eyes remaining on the far shoreline.

An adviser hurried near the royal presence and answered, "O most gracious lord, your armies might easily march up the coast of the Great Sea, along the Plain of Sharon in Philistia, and so on up to—"

"Send in Sakhri," interrupted Neco. A eunuch scurried away.

Presently the obese ambassador plodded into the pavilion from a nearby chamber. With great effort he made obeisance and levered himself again to his feet, awaiting with bowed head the pleasure of his monarch.

Pharaoh's eyes turned for the first time to rest on one of those present. He looked intently at his senior counselor. "Sakhri," he droned, "the Assyrians wish to see Egyptian might striking the armies of Babylon at Haran. The shortest route there, along the coastal plain of the Great Sea, could bring my armies bumping into Judah's king. What say you?"

"My lord Pharaoh," began Sakhri, lifting his head to answer, "the whole world knows your might is sufficient to crush into dust the puny armies of this petty monarch. That is beyond question. However, you go out to engage a more worthy foe in the Babylonians. I do not think it advisable to distract your loyal and valorous hosts even by so much as a skirmish with the Hebrews.

"It is therefore my counsel that you take your armies north by sea and put in at Accho, far beyond tiny Judah. In this way, you may proceed up the Plain of Megiddo, and come to Haran without wasting time on the posturing king of Judah."

"And why," asked Neco, "should we be concerned with the fate of the Assyrians, who made war against this very city not so many years ago?" His hooded gaze challenged Sakhri to give answer.

"My lord," the counselor responded smoothly, "Assyria already is gored to the heart. And after you have crushed the armies of Babylon, you may give proper and leisurely consideration to the best and most fitting manner of bringing all the lands along the Great Sea into your undisputed and beneficent dominion. Indeed, this turn of events may create opportunities not yet foreseen." The ambassador crossed his hands on his breast and bowed as he concluded his remarks.

Neco again looked out over the Nile. Several moments passed as he contemplated the majestic stream which for millennia had given life to the kingdom of the sun. In a date palm nearby, a mynah bird squawked its coarse cry.

"Send word to the harbormaster at Tanis," commanded the Pharaoh finally. "The armies shall embark ten days hence. Let preparations be made."

THE COUNCIL was hushed, the faces grave. Oil lamps flickered, casting large, wavering shadows on the stone walls as King Josiah and his privy counselors huddled around a map of the coastline.

"Father," said Jehoahaz earnestly, "if they come ashore at Joppa, they will pose a fearful threat to Jerusalem." The prince's eyes were round with worry.

"I do not believe this is their intention, Prince Jehoahaz," said old Shaphan, his gnarled, misshapen hands gripping his cane as he leaned over the chart. "If it were so, why would they bother taking ship? Why not simply march over land, through the Negev, or up the coast along the Plain of Sharon? No, I believe they mean to circumvent Judah entirely, and land to the north of our territory — at Tyre." He turned to a younger counselor at his side. "Or perhaps Accho?"

"Yes, Father," intoned Ahikam, "Accho would be logical. If they intend to take the field against Babylon, they would cross the Jezreel Plain at Megiddo, and pass to the south of the Sea of Chinnereth, which would take them into Syria and north to Haran." The son of Shaphan rubbed his chin thoughtfully as he traced the route with his finger.

The door to the chamber slammed open, and in stalked Eliakim. "Oh, I'm sorry!" he began sarcastically, "I didn't realize there was a council taking place. You see, the king's oldest son wasn't invited." He scowled at Jehoahaz, two years his junior.

"Eliakim, you're not needed here," grated Josiah, stepping forward, his hands on his hips.

"I quite gather that, my lord," sneered the prince, biting each word like a piece of bitter fruit. "I haven't been needed for anything, other than standing idly by as my dull younger brother usurps the place that should be mine."

"Eliakim, that decision is not yours—"

"Nothing is mine!" shouted Eliakim, his face contorted in fury. "I have only that which you grant, my king, and that is nothing!" He pointed angrily at his father as he continued. "But it shall not always be thus! Not always!" He turned and left, slamming the door behind him.

Josiah glared at the door for a moment. His shoulders slumped in resignation, and he shook his head.

Then he turned back to the group at the table. "How many men can we raise and arm in the next ten days?" he asked.

All eyes looked at him intently. Shaphan voiced the thought on all their minds. "Do you intend to oppose Neco in the field?"

"Either we oppose him now or oppose him later. Why do you think he undertakes this gambit against Babylon? Hasn't Egypt's intention been clear to you all this time? Neco would like nothing better than to watch Babylon and Assyria devour each other, then to stroll out and pick up any pieces that might be left. Since Assyria fails to blunt Babylon's advance, Egypt will attempt to halt — or at least impede — the rapid consolidation of Nebuchadrezzar's ambitions. Then Pharaoh will use the hiatus to assert control on all the lands between the Nile and Syria. We are in the middle — as we have been for so many ages.

"But," he continued, "if we deny Egypt entry into the fray in the north, may we not retain some measure of independence? May we not at least win some small merit in the eyes of the Chaldeans, who appear to be the next overlords? One thing is certain: If we sit passively by and wait for events to come to us, we shall have less control over our fate than if we act."

The heir of David was by now striding back and forth, his face flushed with the image of the endeavor, his hands clasped tightly behind him. He stopped and looked at Shaphan, his life-long teacher.

"Shaphan, your eyes say something, but I cannot read them. What are your thoughts?"

After a moment's perusal of his student's face, the stooped old man shrugged and looked at the far wall. "I am no king. It is yours to command, not mine."

"But...?" prompted Josiah, after a long pause.

"But," sighed the scribe, "your words sound like those of a man whose mind has been made up for some time. And I wonder," he continued, shifting his eyes to lock with those of the king, "how much time you have given to seeking the will of Adonai in this matter."

The king looked away, trying to hide his exasperation. "But the prophecy—"

"Yes, the prophecy," agreed Shaphan, nodding his head slowly: "You shall go to your grave in peace, and your eyes shall not see the evil which I will bring on this place...." The scribe squinted his eyes at the king's back. "Recall, too, the blessing pronounced upon the great King Solomon by the Lord Himself. Yet the ending of Solomon's life was not as at the beginning."

Josiah whirled as if to interrupt, but Shaphan continued: "When the Lord's word is spoken, He is not bound by what our shallow, shaking hearts may make of it. He is the Lord! And if men He has blessed do not walk in paths that please Him, He is able to grant other visions, and bring to pass other prophecies."

The king sighed, shaking his head impatiently. "And what would you have me do, Shaphan? Sit idly and wait for Nebuchadrezzar or Neco to come in force to the gates of the city? What would your counsel be then?"

Again the old man shrugged. "You are king. You must give the accounting for your stewardship of the land. I watch and advise." Shaphan turned his face toward the far wall. He would say no more.

15

JEREMIAH PLODDED toward the door, his back stiff and sore from the burden he had carried on foot from Anathoth. Easing it to the ground and wincing as his sinews popped and twanged from the shifting of the load, he knocked softly on the weatherbeaten door.

Cautiously he looked about him. Though it was the second watch of the night and he had scarcely seen anyone on the road or in the city, he could not help feeling his back exposed at every step. He had not forgotten the venom in Lemuel's voice as he plotted with his cronies.

The door creaked open a crack, sufficient to show Jeremiah a scarred, surly visage.

"Squint, it is I; Jeremiah of Anathoth."

Promptly the door thumped closed.

He knocked louder. "Squint, open to me! I have something I must give to your master. Squint!"

Again the door opened, a bit wider. Now it was Baruch's face which met him. "Why are you pounding on my door," he asked, "when all honest men are asleep?"

"Baruch — I bring you greeting…from your grandfather."

"I wish no tidings of my grandfather from you." The door began to shut.

"Wait!" Jeremiah blocked the door with his hand, earnestly pleading with the innkeeper. "You must hear me! I bring you a message from your grandfather — perhaps his last message. You cannot refuse to listen to such a word!

"And he sent something else." Jeremiah turned, taking hold of the leather thongs by which he had carried the earthen pot. He dragged it forward. "This is his life's most carefully guarded treasure, which he asked me to bring to you. You must listen to me, out of respect for your grandfather." He probed Baruch's countenance intensely, begging silently for the slightest cleft in the stone wall of the innkeeper's bearing.

Grudgingly Baruch opened the door barely enough to let Jeremiah enter, dragging the clay pot by its leather thongs. Jeremiah remembered, many years before, his difficulty in first entering Mahseiah's hut in Anathoth. Despite the discomfort of his present situation, he smiled at the recollection.

"What are you smiling about?" demanded Baruch gruffly.

"I was remembering...oh, never mind." He straightened as Baruch secured the door. The innkeeper turned back to Jeremiah, his arms crossed in front of him.

"Well, what is it you wish to say?" In the weak glow from the coals on the hearth, Jeremiah could see that Baruch's face was cast iron.

"May I sit down?" asked the prophet. "I have walked uphill since the first watch of the night, carrying this pot." Without waiting for a reply he eased himself down, leaning his back against the wall with a deep sigh. Baruch remained standing, glaring at him.

Jeremiah looked up. "Your grandfather is very ill. I cared for him several days until he bade me leave, for a number of reasons — among them, to bring you this." He pointed with his toe at the pot. "Mahseiah told me to say this to you: 'Son of my son, soon I shall die. If this sickness does not do the job, another will. And when I die my heart will be comforted knowing that a son of my blood still lives, and still remembers.'" At this last word Baruch's eyes widened, his facade wavering for the first time. Jeremiah held his eyes for a moment, then went on.

"He gave his life to the work of remembering, Baruch, for this is a scribe's duty: to record the words correctly, to make a true and proper record. He considered himself a warden of the Lord's gift of words. He felt keenly the responsibility to pass on a record to those who might come after.

"It grieved Mahseiah that he was not able to pass his blessing on to your father. But he now seeks to pass it on to you. Baruch is your name, and blessed you shall be, if you listen to your heart. But if you turn your face away from the heritage which is yours..."

Baruch's eyes were drawn irresistibly toward the clay pot. When Jeremiah's voice lapsed into silence, Mahseiah's grandson slowly knelt down, placing his fingers gingerly on the straps which secured the lid in its place, as if afraid to touch them. He untied the bindings, and after another hesitation carefully lifted the lid.

Inside were the scrolls.

He looked up helplessly at Jeremiah, a question traced in fear upon his features. Now that he had seen, had listened, had heard again the call of his heritage, he could no longer ignore responsibility for what might follow. Jeremiah gave him a tiny smile of reassurance.

Baruch looked again at the scrolls, and sighed deeply.

"Squint!" he called. "Bring a lamp."

16

THE MORNING was clear and bright, the sky breathtakingly blue as Josiah led his army out of Jerusalem. Brave pennants fluttered in the breeze as the eager crowds cheered the martial display. The king was resplendent in his armor, standing like a statue in his war chariot drawn by three spirited chargers, their nostrils flaring red. Rank after rank of the royal guard marched by in strict discipline, their polished gear flashing gallantly as they strode confidently out the Ephraim Gate, following their king to their destiny.

Jerusalem's favorite prophets were in full cry, calling down curses upon the heads of the Pharaoh and his host, and assuring the cheering mobs of the self-evident blessing of Yahweh on the king's brave enterprise. The trumpets blared their harsh benediction, the tabors and drums rattled and thumped an insistent, hypnotic, warlike pulse, as the son of David went out to war at the head of his army.

The column turned north, toward Megiddo in Esdraelon — toward the Plain of Jezreel, battlefield of the ages.

From his chamber in the palace, Shaphan looked on as the last ranks filed through the gate. Then he turned away, his eyes closed in prayer.

THE PORT OF ACCHO was a scene of pandemonium. Horses whinnied, charioteers cursed, dockmen carried load after load of gear onto the quays. The sky was overcast, and the restless water of the harbor was a steely gray.

Four hundred long, flat wooden ships lay at anchor, their square sails furled, their steering oars shipped. So many were the vessels in which Pharaoh had brought his army north that the line of them seemed to stretch to infinity, up and down the bay. They bobbed in the choppy swells, moored together like great sea-beasts brought to tether.

Two hundred thousand troops massed in and around Accho, preparing for the march northeast to Haran. The might of Egypt was an awesome sight, as she spread her bivouac for miles around the bay.

IN MEGIDDO, some fifteen leagues to the south, Josiah and his commanders gathered in a citadel built many generations before by Solomon.

"Their numbers are so much superior to ours," the king was saying as he looked at the map. "We must meet them here." His finger rested on the narrow throat of the Jezreel Plain, where the Kishon flowed past the eastern flanks of Mount Carmel. The pass was bounded by Carmel on the southwest, and the foothills of Mount Tabor on the northeast. "From the elevations on either side, our archers can rain arrows upon their heads, and the pass narrows the flank on which our chariots and infantry must confront them." The generals nodded in agreement.

It was a time of brave words and taut bellies. "Father," said Jehoahaz, "allow me to lead the charge upon the enemy's front lines."

"No, my son," smiled the king, placing a hand on the prince's shoulder. "You must not be so eager to win glory — doubtless you will have many other opportunities." The older men smiled. "It is my wish, Jehoahaz," he continued earnestly, "that you command the archers stationed on Mount Carmel. Your duty will be to weaken the Egyptian column as much as possible, to give the greater success to our infantrymen and charioteers as they drive Pharaoh back into the sea."

The unspoken thought on everyone's mind was that Jehoahaz could more easily return to Jerusalem from the flanks of Carmel than from a frontal assault on the host of Egypt.

That night, Josiah wandered the quiet camp. Sleep had eluded him the past several nights. As he walked quietly about, he reviewed again and again the crucial facts of the imminent encounter with Neco's forces: two hundred thousand Egyptian warriors; less than half that many Hebrews. Neco could deploy four thousand chariots to his five hundred. Why had he come here? Why did he lead brave, loyal men into the maw of such superior numbers?

The moon was rising over the plain, silvery clouds scudding past it in the cool north wind. As he looked west, he could see the faint reflections of the numberless campfires of the Egyptian army. He could feel the battle looming up inside him. His fingers tensed, gripping an imaginary sword. He was afraid with the fear known only by kings and generals. What if he was wrong? How many sons and husbands would not return to Judah? Was Shaphan right? Did he rush before the Lord, forcing his own will upon events?

"O Lord God," he prayed, "if there is sin in this undertaking, lay it not to the charge of my people. Upon me alone be the blood-guilt of this fight.

"O God," he continued, feeling emotion push his heart into his throat, "grant us victory over the hosts which oppose us. Give us deliverance, and freedom to celebrate Your goodness. Show mercy toward this people on whom You have placed Your name." He groped to express the chaos in his soul, but the words would not come.

AS NECO LOOKED OUT the doorway of his tent, each summer-wearied leaf on the trees seemed plainly defined. The morning was sunny, the air crisp and cool with the exuberant clarity of autumn. The Pharaoh held his arms out to allow his dressers to put on him his polished bronze breastplate. Not that he expected to need his armor. At the leisurely pace he intended to set, it would take them at least a month to reach the vicinity of Haran by the old caravan route. By that time the Assyrians should be vanquished — and, he hoped, the Babylonians sufficiently weakened that his fresh troops could make short work of them before winter set in. He felt little danger, surrounded as he was by his vast horde, but it was not bad policy to be cautious. After all, they traveled through uncertain country.

By midmorning, with a great bellowing of long brass trumpets and a smothering swirl of dust, the mighty host of Egypt was under way. Pharaoh Neco rode in his ceremonial chariot, its hubs and spokes of gold-sheathed bronze flashing brilliantly in the sunlight, drawn by a team of four quick-blooded white horses. Beaten gold was spread liberally throughout the team's linkage, and each horse was covered with a blanket of yellow-and-white silk, crowned with a plume of yellow-dyed egret feathers — all to represent their master, the son of the sun. Four Nubian slaves paced beside the chariot, holding poles which supported a shade of white linen, that Pharaoh, the child of heaven, might travel in comfort. The royal bodyguard surrounded him, three hundred elite troops who looked neither right nor left as they marched.

The army spread along the road beside the Kishon River, moving in lazy grandeur toward its appointment with destiny. The sun was just past its zenith when outriders of the vanguard came pounding breathlessly back to the rear of the column where Pharaoh's troupe marched.

The commander of the vanguard leaped from his chariot and threw himself face-down in front of Neco's horses. The Pharaoh, his brow wrinkled in puzzlement, lifted a finger, signaling a halt to his driver. The horses pulled up, snorting and tossing their heads. Neco motioned for the messenger to approach.

"O son of heaven," began the commander, "it is with great regret that I inform you of an obstruction in the way to your glorious victory over your enemies."

"What is the nature of this obstruction?" inquired the Pharaoh, his eyes roaming the landscape ahead of him.

"My god and my king, in the pass leading to the Plain of Jezreel, a host of Hebrews awaits, and their countenance is warlike."

Pharaoh's brow furrowed deeper, and he looked sharply at his commander. "How many? How are they armed?"

"Radiant master, your humble servant estimates their number at some seventy thousand. Two infantry companies there are, and at least one of chariotry."

It was a sizable host, as well as unexpected. Neco fumed with impatience. He did not wish to be forced into pitched battle, especially in terrain which presented no ready advantage to his superior numbers.

Why was the Hebrew king doing this? This territory was leagues north of his borders! Neco had presented no threat to him, for the timing had not been proper. He was severely nettled by the obstinate truculence of this bumpkin. Yet he was not ready to commit his troops unnecessarily, if it could be avoided.

"Send to their ruler, and say this to him: 'What do I have to do with you, king of Judah? I am not coming against you, but against the enemies to whom heaven has impelled me. Stand aside, lest you be destroyed.'"

The commander rose, trotted to his chariot, and vaulted inside. His team wheeled and drove away in a cloud of dust and a clanking of trace chains.

FROM HIS VANTAGE POINT on the edge of the foothills Josiah watched as the small party separated from the front lines of the Egyptian infantry, walking out onto the plain under the banner of truce. He signalled three of his men to meet them midway between the two armies. In the brilliant autumn sun the two parties met, standing tensely between armies. At last they separated, pacing rigidly back to their respective ranks. Josiah's men returned to their master.

"Well?" he demanded.

"They demand that you allow them to pass, my King. They claim their fight is not with you, but with Chaldea."

Josiah looked past his men at the plain below. He felt himself at that moment to be the fulcrum of his nation's fate. He could stand aside, allowing Neco through. Perhaps Egypt would be mangled in the jaws of Babylon, perhaps not. If not, he knew with certainty that he would again see this host — but encamped in the Vale of Kidron and at the feet of Moriah.

The hot blood of the sons of David pounded in his temples. He would fight this battle at the time and place of his choosing.

He wheeled about fiercely and commanded, "Bring my chariot! Tell the host to gird for battle, and send word to the archers to remember the signals."

CONCEALED on the craggy flanks of Mount Carmel, Jehoahaz watched the opposite side of the valley as his father's chariot raced from the command post toward the front ranks of cavalry in the center of the plain. Its wheels raised two thin trails of dust as it whirled toward the troops. His heart was pounding raggedly in his chest, his knuckles whitening as he clutched the grip of his bow. A messenger raced up behind him, panting.

"Lord prince, your father commands the archers to take their positions and mind the signals." The messenger's eyes were wide with tension, as Jehoahaz felt his own must be. He nodded at the boy, waved his lieutenants into position, and turned back to observe the events unfolding on the plain.

Jezreel waited, with the patience of long custom. The silence before the battle dropped over the field like a net of dread. Many armies had clashed on her level expanses through the centuries. Rivers of blood had nourished her grasses, and the bones of countless warriors lay moldering in her soil. The weapons changed, as did the scarcely remembered names of the kings and would-be conquerors, but Jezreel remained, and finally conquered all. For ages past she had lain here remembering. And she would be here still for the final conflict of time, at the dawning of eternity.

She waited — she who was known as Jezreel, Megiddo, and Armageddon. Her arms were ready to welcome the fallen into her cheerless bosom.

A clear shout carried in the silence from the throat of Judah's king, echoing from Carmel's rocky slope across the valley to the foothills of Tabor: "For Adonai and for Jerusalem!"

The war cry of Zion roared outward from the myriad throats of her host. Chariots surged forward, Josiah's foremost among them. The Judean cavalry bore down on the front ranks of Egyptian infantry, who presented their heavy bullhide shields and braced their lances in the ground behind them, awaiting the crushing onslaught of this unlooked-for adversary.

An instant before the armies clashed, Jehoahaz turned to his lieutenants and shouted, "Now!" The archers above the plain unleashed a sibilant flood of arrows onto the heads of the Egyptians' southern flank. Likewise the contingent stationed in the hills across the valley fired their bolts, and the Egyptian army was caught in a three-way pincer: Josiah's cavalry drove a deep wedge into the ranks of their infantry, and the northern and southern flanks were smitten by the rain of death from above. Racing behind the cavalry charge, the Judean infantry waded into the fray, stabbing and thrusting.

AT HIS COMMAND POST in the rear, Neco sat listening to the crash and tumult of combat, waiting impatiently for his couriers to bring him word. Finally, messages began flooding in.

"The Hebrews have concealed archers in the heights above the plain, and they are decimating our infantry..."

"The Hebrew chariotry has plowed deep into the ranks at the front; we cannot deploy our own chariots because of the narrowness of the way and the crossfire from their archers..."

"Our infantry is falling back, unable to withstand the combined cavalry and infantry confronting them..."

Neco jumped to his feet in alarm. Something must be done, and quickly. He summoned a captain of the bodyguard.

"Take a party of your men and a company of infantry. Find the positions of the Hebrew archers in the hills to the north, and destroy them. We must give some relief to our infantrymen and find a way to outflank the enemy." The captain saluted and left.

JOSIAH, his arms and hands spattered with drying Egyptian blood, surveyed the swaying battle line in exhilaration. The enemy was thoroughly confounded by the deadly hail from the heights; in fact, the king some time ago had stopped looking up and wondering about the effectiveness of their placement.

Meanwhile, the infantry and cavalry below continued advancing into the enemy's weakened front lines. Judah was able to pull back regiments and allow more rested troops to replace them. In this way they continually pressed the narrow front back upon the desperate Egyptians, who tripped over themselves and the dead bodies of the archers' victims. Their numbers actually worked against them. Josiah was wildly hopeful they could gain sufficient advantage that Neco would at least sue for respite.

Suddenly a bloodied messenger staggered near, the broken shaft of an Egyptian arrow protruding from his shoulder. Josiah turned to see him, and was chilled to realize this man was Eliaab, a captain of the archers on the northern heights.

Eliaab gasped for breath, and held onto the side of the king's chariot as the air rattled in and out of his ravaged chest.

"My lord, they... The Egyptians have found us... They have slain us all..."

His knees buckled, and he fell dead at the feet of his king.

At that moment another torrent of arrows poured down from the northern hills, but they were directed not at the Egyptian host. Instead they sliced with deadly effect into the northern flank of the advancing Hebrew infantry. The side ranks buckled as man after man fell, an arrow lodged in his chest or neck.

Simultaneously a fresh company of enemy infantry counterattacked along the weakened northern front, pressing the Hebrews back over ground they had won scant moments before. The line of Judah weakened, threatened to break and allow the army of the Nile to outflank the smaller Hebrew force.

Josiah saw with alarm the sudden shift in the battle's momentum. He shouted to his trumpeter to sound the charge, throwing the reserve battalions back into the fight to sustain the integrity of the battle line. The weary warriors answered their king's call, surging forward against the new onslaught.

But now more Egyptian infantry were arriving, charging under the covering fire of their archers. A wedge was opening between the edge of the plain and the heights, and Josiah could see the Egyptian cavalry, waiting with bloodthirsty impatience behind the dusty, gory hand-to-hand combat of the infantries. Their chariots were armed with cruel axle-blades, and their archers were eagerly notching arrows to the string.

Just then he felt a hammer blow to his chest, followed by a searing pain. Looking down he saw the feathered tip of a shaft protruding from the edge of his breastplate. Attempting a breath, he felt his lung aflame. He tasted the hot, salty tang of his own blood arising in his throat.

He looked in frightened confusion at his driver, who without a word wheeled the horses and raced away from the front. Josiah slumped down, his vision going black.

ON THE SIDE of Mount Carmel, Jehoahaz watched in rising panic as the Egyptians pressed harder on Judah's northern flank. He was about to stand and command his men to charge down the slopes and engage the enemy hand-to-hand, when a hand gripped his shoulder. He turned, startled, to see the weathered, bloodied face of Elnathan, a noble of his father's court.

"I have come from your father, the king," Elnathan was saying. "He sent me to you, commanding that you should immediately return to Jerusalem."

"But the army, the battle..." stammered the prince.

"...is going poorly," finished the older man urgently. "Your father is wounded..."

"The king!" gasped Jehoahaz.

"You must return," continued Elnathan urgently. "It is his command, and there must be a son of David to take the throne in Zion if..." He did not need to finish the sentence.

17

THE SOMBER CROWD in the Temple court listened as the priests recited the *qaddish* for the slain king. The entire city had ground to a halt, aghast at the fate which had befallen the honorable and righteous Josiah. The future, which had seemed so bright and certain only weeks ago as the armies marched north, now seemed foreboding, threatening. The nation stared helplessly at its dead king, seeing the fact of its own mortality displayed with unmistakable clarity on the bier of Josiah — and on the fearful face of his son and successor, Jehoahaz.

Appearing extremely uncomfortable in the royal raiment of the house of David, Jehoahaz led the procession to the Tombs of the Kings, as was his duty. Shrill keening and loud moans accompanied the chants of the priests as Josiah was laid in the silent halls of his fathers.

They returned to the palace, walking the narrow, twisting streets leading out of the old City of David where the sepulchers were located. Ahikam paced slowly beside the king. Jehoahaz turned to him, his voice murky with emotion. "I am not ready to be a king, Ahikam."

"No man is ever ready, my lord," replied the scribe, "and those who think they are may be least so. Necessity creates leaders. It is your destiny. You can do nothing else than face it." For a moment as they walked, he held the king's eyes with kind intensity.

"Why was it prophesied that my father would die in peace?" demanded the younger man after a moment's silence. "Surely this was a false word!"

Ahikam made no answer, but remembered vividly the words of his father Shaphan in the council chamber: "Adonai can grant other visions, other prophecies..."

Slowly they continued their walk back toward the house of the king.

As they passed the Ophel Tower, a strong, clear voice sounded from a place near the wall where a large crowd gathered. The king was irresistibly drawn to the firm cadences of the speaker, and halted his party, stopping to listen.

The fellow was unlike most prophets. He made no loud shrieks, performed no gyrations to keep the attention of the listeners. He stood on a low wall before the tower and spoke in a clear, steady voice which carried like a hymn to every listener. He was tall, somewhat slender, and his hair and beard were just beginning to show traces of gray. And his eyes — they were dark points of eternity, peering with a disturbing intensity into the eyes of the people as he spoke:

"'I remember the devotion of your youth,' says the Lord, 'how as a bride you loved Me and followed Me through the desert, through a land wild and unsown. Israel was holy to the Lord, the firstfruits of His harvest.'

"This is what the Lord says: 'What fault did your fathers find in Me that they strayed so far from Me? They followed worthless idols and became worthless themselves...'"

The crowd nodded, murmuring agreement with the preacher's assessment of the people's sins under the evil kings of Israel and Judah.

He continued: "'My people have committed two sins,' says the Lord. 'They have forsaken Me, the spring of living water, and have dug their own cisterns, which are broken and cannot hold water...'"

Again there were nods of assent to the sins of the past.

"The men of Memphis and Tahpanhes have broken the crown of your head, O Judah..."

Now louder came the expressions of sympathy from the hearers, who expected next a eulogy for King Josiah, customary in speeches of this type. Perhaps the speaker would present a recitation of the righteousness of Josiah's reign, a history of his restoration of the true religion of Yahweh...

"Have you not brought this on yourselves, O people of Judah?" said the prophet instead. The crowd, stunned by the unexpected words, stood silent as he continued, his voice rising.

"Did you not cause this by forsaking the leading of the Lord God? Now some of you will go to Egypt to drink the waters of the Nile. Others will go to Assyria to drink from the Euphrates. Your gods come from far and wide, O Judah! 'Consider how evil it is when you have no awe of Me,' says the Lord.'"

A low mutter of dissatisfaction began at the rear of the audience as the preacher continued.

"'On every high hill and under every green tree you lay down like a whore. I planted you like a choice vine, like a carefully tended sprout. How then have you become a corrupt, wild vine? You have as many gods as you have cities!

"'Although you wash yourself with soda and use lavish amounts of soap, the stain of your guilt is still before me...

"'Why do you go about so much, changing your ways? You will be disappointed by Egypt just as you were with Assyria...

"'In spite of all this, you say, "I have not sinned! He is not angry with me!" But I will pass judgment on you, because you say "I have not sinned..."'"

A man near the front raised a hand, his thumb extended. "Away with this fellow!" he shouted. A loud chorus of agreement confirmed the group's shift in mood toward this bearer of tidings both ill and ill-timed.

The crowd's murmurs grew angrier. The preacher stood defiantly in his place as if to say more, but a short, bald fellow with an eye patch stepped up beside him and pulled him down into the street, escorting him away. Royal officers restrained those who would follow the preacher, and eventually the throng began to disperse.

Ahikam and King Jehoahaz went on their way. The son of Shaphan turned to the king. "You asked how the prophecy of your father's peaceful end could be true. I say this to you, my king: Better to die cleanly on the field of battle than to live in times such as those prophesied by that man."

It was Jehoahaz' turn to be silent.

THE PRINCE OF BABYLON popped another almond into his mouth, and rubbed his hands over the brazier. The evening was chilly. He looked up at the roof of his pavilion, at the flickering shadows cast by the small flame.

After a moment of reflection, he pulled his robes tighter about his shoulders, and turned to his general seated on the floor before him.

"So the fat old lion of Egypt has finally rolled off his couch, eh? Interesting. Doubtless Neco means to make some sort of league with what is left of Assyria.

"And what's this of Judah?" he continued. "Their king took the field against Neco, you say?"

General Nebuzaradan nodded. "Yes, my prince. And apparently put up quite a fight before the Pharaoh's superior numbers made themselves felt. It is said he was wounded in the encounter; I have no word how severely."

"Judah, Judah..." mused Nebuchadrezzar. "Do you wish to hear something interesting, Lord Zaradan?" The general raised his eyebrows as his master continued. "A legend of the Hebrews traces their ancestry back to a man known as Avram, who, they say, left Chaldea hundreds of generations ago, in the days of Hammurabi, to come to the land where they live today. Indeed, it is said he sojourned here in Haran for a time."

"Why would anyone leave so pleasant a homeland to go to a dusty place such as Judah?" queried the general.

"They claim their god led Avram away and commanded him to go there."

"Poor choice on the part of the god," opined Zaradan.

"Perhaps," agreed Nebuchadrezzar, "and yet, at one time the Hebrews commanded the wealth of the entire world. Every trading vessel called at Israel's ports, every caravan passed through her gates. The land is ideally situated as a trading crossroads, you know."

A few moments of silence passed, as the brazier crackled. Nebuchadrezzar picked up another handful of almonds and studied them as he mused. "And during the days of Assyrian overlordship, at the very height of Sennacherib's power, the capital of Judah — what is it called? Jerusalem, yes, that's it — Jerusalem was never occupied. She paid tribute, but she was never occupied. Do you not find that interesting, Lord Zaradan?"

The general shrugged. "Perhaps. And yet the same could be said of Nineveh, before you came."

Nebuchadrezzar chuckled. "Yes, Zaradan. Indeed."

SAKHRI STOOD AGAIN in the Hall of Solomon, this time in circumstances more to his liking. No belligerent guard challenged the troop of fully armed and battle-hardened infantry which escorted him into Jerusalem. No bellicose bluffing on the part of the king of Judah — now a young, frightened monarch, scarcely more than a boy.

The ambassador was having his revenge in full measure. He had relished this day since the Hebrew blunder on the Jezreel plain. He reclined on his couch in the palanquin, which sat squarely in the center of the throne room — an overt and deliberate insult. His secretary delivered Pharaoh's terms to the Jehoahaz and his court — another calculated snub, designed to display the vast gulf separating the prince of heaven and his kingdom from this rude little monarchy in the midst of nowhere.

"In his kindness and grace, the son of heaven deigns not to punish the people of Judah beyond the evils they have brought upon themselves by the unprovoked attack upon the ruler of the Nile and his invincible host..." The secretary delivered his speech in Egyptian, and an adviser to Jehoahaz translated it in a whisper.

"...However, in the interest of future peace and equanimity between our nations, His most royal majesty Neco, emperor of the eternal realms, requests the honor of having Jehoahaz, lately king of Judah, as his permanent guest at court, to await the pleasure of the son of heaven and to function in all ways as his loyal and honored friend..."

The face of Jehoahaz turned ashen. At the same time, on cue, Eliakim stepped casually into the hall, smirking knowingly as he looked from Sakhri to the throne.

"And it is the further wish of His most beneficent majesty that Eliakim, hereafter to be known as Jehoiakim, sit henceforth upon the throne of Judah, to reign in every respect as king, and as the loyal and trusted ally of the son of heaven."

Eliakim strode casually to the throne, stood before his brother, and said unceremoniously, "Get up." He grinned, daring Jehoahaz to do something foolish.

Not a breath of air stirred in the hall. Jehoahaz was like a trapped bird, struggling to escape a room but finding all the ways shut. His eyes reached frantically for those of Shaphan, Ahikam, Elnathan, others. But each in turn looked sadly down, unable to aid, helpless to comfort. At last, rising like a crippled old man, Jehoahaz stepped aside from Solomon's throne.

His brother eagerly took his place, and at once called out in a gloating voice: "Nobles and people of Jerusalem and Judah, it is good that you have heard the new name by which you shall know me. *Jehoiakim* I shall be to you, for truly God has set me in this place.

He leaned back, and continued. "My father erred in launching an ill-advised and unprovoked assault upon the great and powerful Pharaoh, and for this stupidity he paid with his life..." A gasp arose from the assembled nobles at hearing such defamation of a beloved king barely in his tomb — and from his own son!

"...It is my intention that such mistakes not be repeated," finished Jehoiakim, inclining his head slightly toward Sakhri, receiving a barely-discernible nod in return.

Shaphan, sickened, turned and hobbled from the chamber. *Let them kill me,* he thought — he felt too old to live in such times.

"The king of Judah has spoken wisely," intoned the secretary in his nasal, reedy voice. "And the great and merciful Pharaoh recognizes the fairness of Jehoiakim and his willingness to recognize the provocation by the late king, his father. In consideration whereof, his serene and righteous excellency, the child of the gods agrees to accept a talent of gold and a hundred talents of silver..."

Now a louder gasp came from the court of Judah. Even Jehoiakim peered in open-mouthed surprise at Sakhri. This was not his understanding of their bargain.

The ambassador's face gave no evidence that he had seen or heard anything in the room. He lay on his couch, gazing out a window in feigned boredom.

18

JEREMIAH'S EYES HURT, his neck ached, and the fingers of his right hand seemed permanently cramped in a writing grip. It had taken all of three days to copy the deeds wanted by the old linen merchant and his sons, but the coin he had gained by doing the task would buy him bread and a few more days' lodging at Baruch's inn.

Lately Baruch had been offering him free board, but Jeremiah was determined not to accept the innkeeper's bread without payment unless dire necessity dictated. It was enough that Baruch sheltered an increasingly unpopular resident; he should not have to feed and house him for nothing.

He leaned on the scarred door and went inside. He slumped down close to the hearth. The winter month of Shevat had descended upon Jerusalem with its drizzly chill. Jeremiah spread his cloak by the fire to let it dry.

Squint came in, tossed a stick or two on the flames, nodded curtly to Jeremiah, and left. Jeremiah often wondered what thoughts scrambled about beneath that bald, blunt dome. No use asking directly, he knew; Squint used no words when gestures or stares would serve.

Presently Baruch entered, blowing on his hands. He glanced at the hearth, and fetched an urn of wine and two drinking-bowls from a rack on the wall. He walked over to where Jeremiah sat, placed the bowls on the low table, and poured for them both.

"Have you heard the latest news?" inquired the grandson of Mahseiah.

"No, I suppose not," said Jeremiah, picking up his cup.

"You remember Uriah, the old man who used to preach by the Temple?"

"Ah, yes! The only preacher I've heard in Jerusalem who does not fit his message to the purses of his listeners."

"Yes...well...he tweaked the wrong ears, it seems."

"How so?"

"Jehoiakim did not appreciate Uriah's pointed references to current forbearance toward the baals and asherim."

"Well might he not! That usurping king spits in the face of his father each time he winks at the idolatry creeping back into Jerusalem. Only last night, on my way home, I saw a family on the roof of their house pouring out drink offerings to the star-gods of the Chaldeans! If matters are so bad in Jerusalem, I can only imagine the apostasy rampant in the outlying districts. Uriah did well to condemn such—"

"The point is," interrupted Baruch, "Uriah will speak no more on this or any other subject. He is dead."

Jeremiah's expression begged silently for explanation.

"Jehoiakim sent his father-in-law Elnathan to Egypt, where Uriah had fled from the king's anger. I think Jehoiakim must surely have given Elnathan some false pretense, for the son of Achbor would never have willingly agreed to such an unjust act. At any rate, Elnathan brought Uriah back to Jerusalem, and Jehoiakim had the old man slain."

Jeremiah stared into Baruch's unwavering eyes for long moments, then turned his gaze to the flames in the hearth. He knew what Baruch's next words would be.

"Don't you think it would be wise to—"

"No! I will not leave Jerusalem! I...I cannot. The words — they burn in me, they eat my insides. No, I must stay, and I must speak."

Baruch studied Jeremiah's profile, silhouetted in flickering light and shadow by the fire. The man from Anathoth stared into the flames with the resignation of one who has added the columns of his fate countless times, and always reached the identical sum. His jaw clenched in and out as he sat unmoved and unmoving.

With a sigh, the innkeeper rose and went to another corner of the room. He returned, carrying a strip of parchment, an ink-block, and a stylus.

He grunted as he sat down, cross-legged. He spat on the

block, rubbed the stylus on it, and held it poised above the parchment. "Very well," he said, looking expectantly at Jeremiah. "What did He tell you today?"

JEREMIAH LAY TOSSING on his bed that night. He craved sleep, but something teased at the corner of his mind, a persistent itch in his brain that would not let him rest. Thoughts were forming, a message.

Then the Voice was within him:

"You must stand in the Temple court, Jeremiah, and speak the words I give you."

"What words, Master?"

He lay in the darkness, listening to the silent thunder inside his mind, breathing the fire from the mouth of the Lord, an unquenchable flame that he must spew from his lips in the court of the Temple.

"Ah, Lord God!" he begged at last. "Do not make me say this thing! My words will be like thorns driven in the eyes of the people! Will You not have mercy on Jerusalem? Will You not give me a little more time to speak to them, perhaps to turn them from their sin, to avoid Your burning wrath?"

"Do not pray for this people!" the Voice admonished sternly. "Do not offer any petition for them. Do not plead with Me for them, for I will not listen to you. Haven't I shown you what they do in the towns and streets of Judah? The parents send the children to gather wood, the mothers bake votive cakes, and the fathers kindle the fire to sacrifice to Ishtar, the abomination of Nineveh!

"No, do not pray to Me for this people. I have suffered long with them, calling to them as a husband calls to a wife who has gone whoring with other lovers. I will have no more patience with them. I will pour out My wrath upon them, and they shall be destroyed — every man, every beast, every tree, and every stalk of grain. They will burn, and not be quenched."

Jeremiah lay whimpering under the hot deluge of God's anger, sobbing in his bed until the morning.

The next day Baruch watched with trepidation as his guest move slowly toward the door, a grim mask of duty on the haggard face. Baruch nodded silently to Squint, who arose, tossed a robe around his shoulders, and quietly followed Jeremiah outside.

Under a weak sun piercing infrequently through the gray clouds, Jeremiah stood in the outer court of the Temple, beside the entrance nearest the Bronze Basin. He watched as worshipers brought their sacrifices to the Levites, and saw them surreptitiously fingering the baal-totems they carried on strings about their necks. Best not to ignore any of the gods, they seemed to be thinking. Yahweh gets his due, and Baal-Molech gets his, all in the proper manner and the proper place — here in the Temple of the Lord.

Jeremiah remembered the corruption he had seen across Judah, the stench he had smelled...

He remembered the genteel facade worn by Orpah of Ajalon, concealing her lustful desires...

He remembered Samuel, the degraded, worn-out slave of Azzur the Gibeonite....

He remembered the beggar woman of Beersheba, endlessly repeating to callous crowds the formula of her hopelessness...

And he felt anger, the very anger of Yahweh rising in his throat as he strode forward to stand between the bronze pillars of the Temple, on the steps leading to the Holy Place. He stretched his arms wide, closed his eyes, and spoke in a voice that filled the courtyard like wine in the cup of God's wrath.

"Hear the word of the Lord, all you people of Judah who come through these gates to worship Him! This is what the Lord Almighty, the God of Israel, says:

"'Reform your ways and your actions, and I will let you live in this place! Do not place your trust in lying words, saying "The Temple of the Lord! The Temple of the Lord! The Temple of the Lord!"

"'If you really change your ways and your actions and deal with each other justly, if you cease oppressing the alien, the fatherless, and the widows among you, and if you cease shedding innocent blood in this city'"—Jeremiah remembered the news of Uriah, and shuddered—"'and if you stop following other gods to your own harm, then I will let you continue to live in this place, this land which I gave your fathers as a permanent inheritance.

"'But look, and see! You are trusting in lies, worthless lies!'"

The hearers in the courtyard, mostly priests and Levites, stared at Jeremiah as if he were speaking gibberish.

"'Do you not murder? Do you not steal? Do you not commit adultery and burn incense to the baals, and then come into this place — upon which I have placed My Name — and say "Aha! We are safe!" Safe? To do these detestable things? Is My house — which is called by My Name — a den for thieves, that you make such claims?

"'But I have been watching you,' declares the Lord."

Scowls were replacing the puzzled looks on the faces of his hearers. But Jeremiah was firmly in the oracle's grip. He forged ahead, his eyes wide with urgency. He had so captured the attention of everyone nearby that no one noticed Squint edging around the courtyard, trying to reach the prophet before the muttering crowd turned upon him.

"The Lord says this: 'Go look at Shiloh, where I first made a dwelling for my Name, and see what I did to it because of the wickedness of Israel. In the midst of your evil, I called to you again and again, but you would not listen. I spoke to you time after time, but you would not answer. Therefore, as I did to Shiloh, I will do the same to this city — to this place which bears My Name, this place you trust in, this place I gave to you and to your fathers. I will evict you from My presence, just as I did to Ephraim, in the days of the evil kings of Israel.'"

No sooner had he finished than Jeremiah was surrounded by a mob of fist-shaking, white-eyed, grimacing priests and Levites. Squint, prevented by the throng from reaching the beleaguered preacher, faded into the background to await more fortuitous timing.

"You speak blasphemy!" one fellow shouted, spitting in Jeremiah's face. Another hissed, "This is the Temple, not some backcountry outhouse, you raving fool!" The noise began to attract others; the mob grew rapidly, trapping Jeremiah.

In a corner of the courtyard, at the edge of the swirling eddies of the self-righteously indignant and the merely curious, stood Hananiah, son of Azzur of Gibeon. He had witnessed the fiery speech of the tall, slender preacher, and its aftermath. He stood, studying the mob, thoughtfully stroking his beard.

The palace guard, alerted by the nearby commotion, was summoned into the Temple courtyard. They shouted above the din, striking here and there with the butts of their spears, gradually bringing the rowdy swarm under grudging control. They pulled the crowd back, layer after layer, until at last they reached a battered and bleeding Jeremiah at the center.

"Who accuses this man?" sternly queried the commander of the detail.

"I do!" chorused from twenty throats at once, as priests and Levites eagerly jockeyed to gain the commander's eye. Finally he beckoned three senior priests to accompany him to the palace compound. As the group left, Squint stepped alongside to support the dazed Jeremiah.

A council of nobles was hastily assembled. The captain of the guards bowed to the princes of Judah, seated in a semicircle in the courtyard joining the palace to the Temple court. "This man was preaching in the Temple, your excellencies, when—"

"Not 'preaching'!" shouted the tallest of the three priests, trembling with anger. "He was blaspheming!" The speaker was Pashhur, son of Immer. He was the Temple's chief priest, and wielded no little influence both in and outside the sanctuary.

Pashhur stared apoplectically at Jeremiah, pointed a quivering finger at the panting, bleeding figure, and added, "He prophesied against the Temple of the Lord!"

"Aye," chimed in another. "He said the Temple would be as desolate as the hill of Shiloh. He speaks treason against Zion and the Temple!"

A confused babble broke out as each of the three priests tried to condemn Jeremiah at once. "He deserves death!" shouted one. "This traitor must die!"

When the guard was able to silence them, he turned to Jeremiah. "You have heard your accusers," he admonished. "What say you?"

Slowly Jeremiah gained control of his breath. He raised his head and probed the face of each prince in the semicircle. When he had taken their measure, he said, "I am sent by Adonai Elohim to speak against this house and against this city, and I do not deny the account given by my accusers. If it is treasonous to announce the wrath of God against His chosen, the people of

His Name — then so be it. But the people must repent! You must reform your ways and your actions and learn to obey the Lord your God!"

His fierce stare swept the semicircle — and was unchallenged.

"If you turn, and obey the Lord, He will relent and not bring the disaster He has pronounced against you.

"As for me...do whatever you wish with me. But know this—" Again his eyes, like an eagle's, issued their scintillant warning. "—that if you put me to death, the guilt of innocent blood will be on you and on this city and all who live in it, for I speak to you the words the Eternal has given me, to warn you of what is to come to pass."

Elnathan, son of Achbor, seated with the nobles, lowered his head in shame.

Ahikam, chief scribe of the court, stood and said, "This man does not deserve death! He speaks in the name of the Lord!"

The sound of a cane rapping on stone was heard, and the attention of everyone shifted toward a nearby doorway where Shaphan stood, his figure bent nearly double with age. Painfully he made his way toward the tribunal. Ahikam hurried to his father's side to aid him. When they reached the middle of the semicircle, the old scribe stared balefully at them all and spoke in a weak, raspy voice.

"In the days of King Hezekiah the just, a prophet arose from Moresheth, in the country of the Shephelah. Micah was his name, and he said this to the people of Judah, in the name of the Almighty:

> 'Zion will be plowed like a field,
> Jerusalem will become a heap of rubble,
> and the hill of the Temple a mound overgrown
> with thickets...'

"Did Hezekiah, who feared the Lord all the days of his life — or anyone else for that matter — put Micah to death? Rather, did not God relent, because of the righteousness of Hezekiah, and hold back the disaster He had foretold by the mouth of Micah?

Shaphan's expression precluded any reply. He stared at his son, then about him at all the others, and said slowly, "Doom is coming upon us all."

He turned and shuffled back toward the doorway from which he had come, still aided by Ahikam.

One by one the others drifted away, for there was nothing to add. Even the priests wandered back to the Temple, refusing even to glance at the man of Anathoth as they passed.

Soon, only Jeremiah, Squint, and the captain of the guards were left in the courtyard. The officer looked about him.

"Your accusers are gone."

Jeremiah nodded once, then said quietly, as if asking himself, "For how long?"

IT WAS CLOSE to sundown, and Jeremiah wandered through the twisting byways of the Old City. He had started this way because the route carried him past the tombs of the kings, and the children who taunted him in the streets avoided this place in superstitious fear.

The quiet was welcome. He wished for quietness of spirit, but that blessing usually eluded him these days. Word of the near-riot in the Temple courts had spread like wildfire through Jerusalem. Jeremiah's reputation, which before consisted mainly of hazy rumors, had now crystallized into that of a raving heretic, a maniac who wanted to destroy the Temple — a picture which the priests and Levites lost no opportunity to paint.

The prophets, too, found little to appreciate in the preaching of this upstart outsider. There was first their professional jealousy toward this fellow who had no need to gesticulate and perform acrobatics to get attention. He had but to speak. Further, it hardly aided their trade to have the people hear such words of despair for Jerusalem, when the prophets' main focus in these times was fomenting hatred toward Egypt. Neco maintained his stranglehold on the nation, squeezing from Judah gold and silver to finance his campaign in the north against Babylon. Thus Pharaoh was a popular target for prophetical theatrics, and the performers did their part to discredit Jeremiah's contrary influence.

In more thoughtful quarters, however, the preacher from

Anathoth had his supporters. Elnathan, Ahikam and others felt the insistent tug in their spirits when the earnest man with the blazing eyes spoke his oracles. But they had to be careful, for their lord Jehoiakim would not tolerate much talk of Yahweh's displeasure. Of more concern to him was the burden of governing a kingdom being slowly but steadily bled away by Neco. The prophet from Anathoth was merely a nuisance to him, to be removed if possible.

Jeremiah stopped his stroll to look at the royal sepulchers around him. The sinking sun cast long shadows of the city walls upon these white and silent structures. Jeremiah felt a sudden wish to be with the kings of his people, embraced in the forgetfulness of death. Melancholy rushed over him in a heavy purple tide. He stepped forward and leaned his face against a tomb.

"Adonai Elohim, Lord of Hosts," he prayed, tears starting down his face, "why is my pain unceasing, my wound beyond healing? I...I have eaten Your words, I have taken them in like the richest banquet, and they have become the desire of my heart. But, Lord God, I'm given no place with the joyful. I am not allowed to rejoice. Instead I sit alone, because of Your hand, which is upon me.

"O God, I regret the day I was born! I wish my mother's body had become my tomb." He sobbed aloud, thinking of his mother's face. Libnah, faithful wife and mother in Anathoth, who had taken such pride in her son — where was she now? Did she hear the shameful talk about the son of her bosom? Did she hear that name which she had called softly, as a blessing, now used coarsely in the mouths of the vulgar? Even the children chanted in the streets of Jerusalem, "Jeremiah, 'God-is-high,' hates the Temple, he must die."

As the sun dropped behind the southwest ridge of the city, he wandered down by the Pool of Siloah and out the Gate of Potsherds, overlooking the Valley of the Sons of Hinnom. He sat down on a stone, feeling as desolate as the filth-strewn valley. He watched as darkness took the land.

As he sat in the last glow of twilight, a faint sound whispered to him from the wind. He strained his ears and looked about in the near-darkness, trying to see the source of the sound

— a remote wail which lay just at the threshold of his hearing. With a start, he realized he was hearing an echo, a reverberation from the past.

Then he knew: He was hearing the death-screams of babies and young children thrown live into the furnaces of Baal-Molech — here, in this valley, with the blessing and even the participation of King Manasseh of Judah.

His tortured vision saw them, shrieking and struggling vainly in the merciless grasps of the priests, pouring out their lungs in terror, pleading for mercy. All the while the worshipers chanted their obscene liturgy and watched in approval as the children were tossed to the god's consuming embrace.

And in the horror of his vision, the Voice was within him:

"The repugnance you feel, Jeremiah, is as nothing when compared with Mine at seeing such abominations committed by My people, to whom I gave My Name. For this cause I have brought you to this place, that you might feel a portion of My anguish, and hurt as I hurt for the sins of this people. But I have spared you, for if I allowed you to feel the full measure of My agony, your heart would burst and your life would cease.

"Now, therefore, this is what you must do..."

A CROWD OF ELDERS, standing about in twos and threes, fell silent as they saw the dour figure enter the Temple courtyard. Jeremiah did not deign to look at any of them, but strode decisively to the Temple steps. In his hand he carried a flask of earthenware, an expensive *baqbuq* of the finest quality. Its neck was long and slender, tapered with exquisite craftsmanship. He carried it by the neck, as one might carry a plucked fowl.

When he stood between the brass pillars called Boaz and Jachin at the sanctuary entrance, he turned and announced in full voice: "Come to the Potsherd Gate, and hear the word of the Lord."

He glared at them a moment, then stalked out of the courtyard. After a silent exchange of glances, every elder there moved as one to follow.

As the odd procession wound through the midmorning streets, it lured the curious, the idle. By the time they reached the Old City, quite a crowd was proceeding in Jeremiah's wake.

But he did not see or hear them. His entire being was focused, as on a diamond's glitter, upon the message which sat like a live coal on his tongue.

He strode through the city gate. The sloping landscape beyond was littered with remains of the city's cast-asides: broken shards of spoiled pottery, wornout clothing, fragments of moldering food already picked over by beasts and beggars.

Some twenty paces down the side of the valley, he whirled around. Still holding the flask by its slender neck, he pointed it, like a king's scepter, at the crowd.

"This is what the Lord Almighty says, princes of Judah and people of Jerusalem. Listen!

"'I bring disaster on this place, such that will sting the very ears of those who hear it! And why? Because My people have forsaken Me, and made this place a haven for foreign gods.

"'They have sacrificed to gods neither they nor their fathers knew, and they have filled this place with the blood of the innocent! They built shrines to Baal-Molech and burned their own children in the fire as offerings — something I never commanded, nor would such vileness enter My mind!

"'So take warning,' says the Lord, 'for the day will come when people will no longer call this place Topheth, *altar*. Nor will they call it after the Sons of Hinnom. They will call it the Valley of Slaughter.

"'Judah and Jerusalem will be ruined, and the plans of her kings and rulers will come to nothing! They will fall by the sword of their enemies, and their carcasses will feed the birds and the creeping beasts.

"'And this place will become a curse for the whole earth. People will gasp when they see what I have done to Jerusalem! Indeed, the people of this city will again devour the flesh of their children, but not to offer them to Molech! No, they will eat their own children and the flesh of their neighbors, because their enemies will besiege them, and starvation will be as a sword in their bellies!'"

Now the prophet shifted his weight on the angled ground, raised the skillfully wrought flask above his head — and smashed it to the ground. It shattered into countless fragments, mingling indiscriminately with the rest of the rubbish about his feet. "'In this way will I smash this nation' says the Lord, 'so that it cannot be repaired. The dead will be buried in Topheth until there is no more room. Indeed, the houses of the kings and people will be defiled, just as this place is defiled.'"

He returned up the hillside, through the astonished crowd. He possessed one utterance more today, but he must make in another place.

Sensing his purpose, the crowd followed him back into the gate, back through the still-crowded streets of Jerusalem, and back to the Temple courtyard. He strode to the center, stretched out his arms and shouted, "Listen, people of Jerusalem! The Lord God is bringing disaster on this place, because His people are stiff-necked, and will not serve Him, nor will they listen to His words—"

Suddenly he was seized from behind by several Levites. They bound him painfully with leather thongs and tied a wad of linen in his mouth, silencing the powerful voice.

They shoved him into a side chamber where Pashhur waited. Seeing him again, Jeremiah's eyes went wide. The chief priest merely sneered. "Ahikam and his crippled father cannot hear you now, blasphemer."

He turned to the Levites and snapped, "Beat him with rods and put him in the stocks. Perhaps a night in their embrace will teach this meddler to mind his tongue."

They dragged Jeremiah away.

19

THE STOCKS clamped his legs at a wide, excruciating angle, and chafed raw, bleeding rings around his ankles. He could not sit up, but was forced to lie on this gravel yard just outside the Benjamin Gate. The pebbles dug into his back.

The night was cloudy and starless, as if even the heavens had turned away from him. Alone, cold, and miserable, it was not long before helpless tears of rage and humiliation began to burn the corners of his eyes. The anger spewed from between his clenched teeth, to blister his tormentors.

"Listen, O Lord! Hear what my accusers say. See what they do! Do not forget that I stood before You and spoke in their behalf, to turn Your wrath from them. Should such good be repaid with evil?

"Yet they have dug a pit for me. They have beaten me with sticks like a dog, and have bound me here like a wild beast — all because I did not hold back the words You gave me to speak!

"May their children starve in the streets of this city! May they die by the sword of the infidel, and may their wives become childless and widows by the arm of their enemies! May they all die, the young men and the old, for they have made a snare for my feet and laid a trap for the servant of the Lord.

"Do not forgive their crimes, O God! Let their sin remain before Your face, and let them all be cast down. Deal with them, Holy One, in anger and in fierce wrath!"

As he vented the flood, Jeremiah felt voided, like a disease-filled bladder emptied into outer darkness. A wave of nausea washed over him, followed by a hollow feeling of bottomless despair. Great, shuddering sobs racked his body.

"O Lord," he groaned, "You...You have deceived me!" As the horrible words left his tongue, he sensed the stench of desecration rising in his wounded, whimpering soul. Yet he could not halt it.

"You deceived me, and I was well and truly deceived. You have overpowered me, and You stand above me as victor. I am ridiculed all day long; even the children mock me. When I speak I cry out 'Violence! Destruction!' — yet the people laugh and insult me from the rising of the sun to its setting.

"And yet, Lord," he sobbed raggedly, "if I tell myself, 'I will not mention Him or speak anymore in His name,' Your word burns in my heart like a fire. Like a flame it devours my bones and I cannot hold it in!

"Why have You abandoned me? You, who caused Elijah to triumph at Mount Carmel, sending fire from heaven, and who made the birds of the air bring meat to him by the brook — why have You forsaken me, and given me over into the hands of my opponents to do with as they have done? Where is Your strength? Have You, like the brook Cherith, dried up in the middle of the season? Shall I drink no more from Your fountain?"

Overwhelmed by helplessness, Jeremiah lay in the dark courtyard moaning like a lost child, until numb exhaustion dropped its merciful cloak over his consciousness.

And in the silence of sleep's cocoon came the Voice.

"Be silent now, and listen. I am with you, to deliver you. I have promised that you shall be as a bronze wall to your enemies and Mine, and so you shall be. I am able to redeem you from the grasp of those who oppose you.

"But you must repent! You must turn back to Me, and speak true and worthy words, not worthless jabbering and cursing. These people will continue to fight against you, but they will not overcome you. I am with you, to rescue you and save you."

Jeremiah's breathing deepened, and his brow smoothed. He slept.

WITH DAWN, the birds of the city began their first chirping. Jeremiah blinked and awoke just as Pashhur entered the gravel yard with a party of priests and Levites. The chief priest came and stood above Jeremiah, his arms akimbo as he looked down.

"Release the mighty prophet," he sneered, and two of the

Levites began unlocking the stocks. They lifted the heavy wooden yoke from his ankles, and yanked his feet from the slots which held them. Jeremiah cried aloud as the sinews and tendons of his groin and inner thighs stabbed him repeatedly with searing shafts of pain.

The priests and Levites laughed as the prophet crawled on hands and knees to the wall, leaning against it as he raised himself to his feet in exquisite torture. Finally he was standing, his brow shining with the sweat of the unbearable effort.

He raised his eyes to Pashhur's amused face, and said between panting breaths, "Today your name is Pashhur, and you are free to practice such cruelty upon the servant of the Lord."

The party grew silent, their smiles wavering uncertainly on their faces as they awaited Jeremiah's further words.

"But the Lord has a different name for you, son of Immer," said the prophet, his voice gathering strength. "Adonai calls you 'Magor-missabib,' 'Terror-on-Every-Side,' and this is why: The Lord says, 'I will make you a terror to yourself and to your friends; with your own eyes you will see them slain by the sword. I will hand all the people of Judah over to the king of Babylon, who will take them away to his city. And you, too, Pashhur, shall go to Babylon, where you will die and be buried, because you have allowed My people to trust in lies!'"

"Babylon!" scoffed the priest, after a tense pause. "Don't you think you should be more concerned with Egypt just now? After all, it is Neco who steals the bread from our tables, not Nebuchadrezzar.

"Babylon!" he said again, attempting a laugh and looking at his cronies for support.

Jeremiah's eyes never wavered from Pashhur's face. "You have heard," he intoned when they finished their nervous chuckling. "Upon your head will be your fate, if you ignore the word of the Lord."

"Get out!" hissed the priest, his composure pierced at last. "Leave this place at once, before I repent of my mercy and slap you in the stocks for another day and night!"

Jeremiah gripped Pashhur moments longer with his stare. Then he turned and limped slowly through the Benjamin Gate, into the early morning streets of Jerusalem.

20

NECO SAT THOUGHTFULLY in his silk-draped chamber in the citadel of Carchemish, commandeered for his personal dwelling. For the past several months his patrols had encountered fewer and fewer outriders of the Chaldeans — none, in fact, since the warmer breath of spring had greened the hillsides. For weeks now he had pondered the scarcity of evidence of enemy troops.

Their supply line, he reasoned, was far longer than his own, and the nomadic raiders of the steppes posed a constant threat. Could hostile forces have severed it, forcing Nebuchadrezzar to divert his attention to repairing the rift in his rear lines? Rumor had it that Nabopolassar, Babylon's aging and infirm king, was breathing his last. Could a palace dispute have arisen, drawing the prince back from the field to press his claim to the throne?

Coming to a decision, Neco summoned a runner. "Go to the generals. Tell them to prepare the armies for a march. We leave in three days." The page crawled backwards from the presence of the Pharaoh, who rose and paced pensively to a window which overlooked the featureless plain east of the city, across the Euphrates. *Where are you, Nebuchadrezzar?* he wondered. It was time to find out.

ON EGYPT'S second day out of Carchemish, Nebuchadrezzar sprang the trap. The Egyptian host's line of march took it through a low defile in the plain, created by a seasonal wadi's erosion of a large plateau. When the bulk of the army of the Nile entered the long, shallow gap, the Chaldean and Medean infantry, concealed on either side of the ridges bounding the depression, launched a fierce assault. Simultaneously, the Chaldean and Scythian cavalry roared around the end of the northern ridge, ripping into the vanguard of Neco's forces with the savage shock of an avalanche.

This was no Megiddo, where Pharaoh's numerical superiority dictated the eventual outcome. Neco faced a force every bit as large as his own, and superior in fighting spirit and experience of conquest. It required all his wile and determination to avoid having his line of retreat cut off. In two days, by dint of savage fighting and clever maneuver, he managed to regain the safety of Carchemish with perhaps a third of the large, confident force that had marched through its gates four days earlier. Three days after that, Pharaoh sued for safe conduct back to Egypt, in return for which he agreed to be bound forever by the Wadi-el-Arish, the southwestern border of the Negev.

The challenge was ended; Babylon had won. A new world order had emerged.

WHEN HE SAW the white-clad runners enter his pavilion, their faces freshly caked with dirt and their cheeks ceremonially gashed in grief, Nebuchadrezzar felt a thrill of emotion surge through his sinews. Before a word was spoken, he knew what tidings they brought.

"Oh, great Nebuchadrezzar, conqueror of Assyria and despoiler of Nineveh! Dire the word we bring you this day," began one of the men in the singsong tone of the professional mourner.

The prince of Babylon kept his face a stoic, emotionless mask as he awaited the rest of the message.

"Your sire, the king of the great city of Babylon and master of the lands between the rivers — Nabopolassar, emperor of the realm of the eternal ones — has gone to the embrace of the great god Marduk."

Slowly, decorously, Nebuchadrezzar rose from his seat and bent to his knees, slightly inclining his head as the rest of the attendants within hearing fell to their faces and began a low moaning.

"My grief knows no bounds," intoned the prince in a flat, inflectionless voice. "Babylon shall never again know the like of the king, my father, Nabopolassar the Great."

His mind's eye pictured the throne of Babylon, and himself

seated on it: Nebuchadrezzar, emperor of Babylon. At last his destiny was realized. The heavens had spoken.

THE ARMIES OF BABYLON raced pell-mell through Syria, toppling Damascus almost as an afterthought. They tore down the coastal plain, rampaging through Philistia as if in violent catharsis of the pent-up energies imposed by the long standoff with Egypt.

When the proud column arrived at the Ephraim Gate, there was no question of resistance. Word of the rape of Ekron, Ashdod, and Gath had spread like the smell of smoke on the wind, and Jehoiakim had no stomach for a hopeless cause. Any hopes he might have had of Egyptian intervention were dashed at Carchemish. Quickly he sent word to Nebuzaradan, commander of the contingent, that the king of Judah declared himself a loyal vassal of Nebuchadrezzar, king of Babylon, and wished to pursue terms of peace with the illustrious lord of the Tigris and Euphrates.

The prophets in the streets of Jerusalem were unstinting in their praise of the glorious Chaldean army, the self-evident blessing of the Lord on Nebuchadrezzar and his reign. In the Temple, offerings were solicitously made for the blessing of Adonai upon the newly ordained master of the world, and for Nebuchadrezzar's continued kindness toward Jerusalem, the city of the Name of God.

And on the rooftops, as the starry host was unveiled each evening by the fading of the day, countless votive flames could be seen as more and more people in the city of Yahweh courted the favor of the gods of the Chaldeans, their new masters.

"BY COMMAND of Nebuchadrezzar, supreme master of the lands from the Rivers to the Great Sea," read the herald, his voice echoing in the Hall of Solomon, "you shall assemble before Ashpenaz, chief eunuch of the house of the emperor, all the male youths of noble and royal blood of the houses of Judah, that he may choose from among them those who will await the pleasure of the emperor in the palace of Babylon."

The court buzzed with apprehension. What was the import of this summons? What did the emperor intend for those chosen by this Ashpenaz? Would their sons become eunuchs in the court of Nebuchadrezzar? Would their parents ever again see the faces of their offspring?

Despite the heavy cloud of misgiving, Judah was in no position to deny her new lord. Accordingly, at the appointed time a tense assembly of young men, the flowering of Judah's best houses, gathered in nervous anticipation in a chamber just off the Hall of Solomon.

Inside, Ashpenaz, flanked by an escort of bodyguards from the emperor's household militia, raised a pudgy, jewel-encrusted finger to the doorkeeper of the court. "Bid the youths enter," he commanded in his falsetto voice, "and form a line about the chamber, that I may see their faces and deportment." The doorkeeper nodded, and swung the heavy door open, motioning the chief eunuch's instructions to those waiting.

The boys, dressed in their finest clothes, padded quietly into the hall. On any other day, the exuberance of youth might have glinted through the gravity of the royal court in ill-concealed horseplay, the occasional harmless mischief which is the natural province of high-spirited boys. But on this day no one had the stomach for such. The boys' eyes were big with anxiety, their glances edgy, their movements awkward. They assembled in a shuffling line, their eyes downcast, their breath quick with barely bridled dread.

Ashpenaz strolled down from the dais where he had observed their entry and made his way carefully along the line. Now and again he would stop, gripping the chin of one or another of the lads, raising the reluctant face to his own, turning it this way and that, then passing on. At no time did any youth's eyes meet the eunuch's.

After an endless few moments, the eunuch walked to the center of the hall. "You. You. You and you..." He pointed at some twenty boys, beckoned them forward from the line of their peers. Twenty youths, young princes of the house of Judah, stumbled forward on trembling legs to kneel. Twenty fathers felt their hearts drop into their bellies as they saw their sons chosen for service in the far-off palace of Nebuchadrezzar.

"Jonathan." "Zechariah." "Daniel." "Mishael." "Azariah..." In dead voices the boys gave their names to the scribe who recorded each in the wedge-shaped script of the Chaldean court. When he completed his task, he took the parchment to the chief eunuch, bowing as he offered it to Ashpenaz. The eunuch inspected the scroll for a moment, then turned and addressed the court in his high, yet powerful voice.

"These youths are most fortunate," he began. "They will attend the emperor of the world, his majesty Nebuchadrezzar. They will eat at his table, and learn the wisdom of the ages which is gathered together in one place in the magnificent city of Babylon. They will be educated in the speech, customs, and sciences of the great sages of Chaldea.

"They will be given new names, for their lives have changed this day. Their abilities shall be channeled to serve Emperor Nebuchadrezzar. Just as this land of Judah now depends upon the strong arm of the emperor, and owes him the best that is within it, so these boys, the sons of your noble houses, shall learn to serve him with the best that is in them.

"So has the emperor decreed. So let it be done!"

THE LOW CONVERSATIONS halted instantly when Ahikam entered. The patrons of Baruch's inn, several of whom were gathered there for drink this early summer evening, had little occasion to mingle with the noble houses of Judah, and the presence of the chief scribe and his son in this quarter of the city was scarcely less jarring than seeing a leper in the Temple. Ahikam and Gedaliah, glancing about them self-consciously in the hushed inn, made their way to a corner by the hearth where Jeremiah waited.

"Let us step outside," the prophet said, motioning toward the rear entrance of the low, smoky room.

"Indeed," said Ahikam, grateful for Jeremiah's suggestion. Feeling every eye on his back, he and his son followed the preacher as they threaded their way to the door.

Once outside, the prophet turned to the scribe and asked anxiously, "What is this urgent message that brings you so far from the houses of the nobles?"

Ahikam peered intently into the worry-creased face of Jeremiah. "The king grows impatient with the condemnation you heap upon him."

"The words about his new dwelling goaded him particularly hard," added Gedaliah.

Jeremiah nodded and looked away. Jehoiakim had commissioned a new house, unwilling to live in the residence of his father. He had hired workmen, artisans, and carpenters to build a grand palace, richly furnished in cedar and inlaid with exquisite carvings in ebony, ivory, and mahogany. Many loud and impressive speeches were made on the day of its dedication.

The prophet Hananiah, especially, had overwhelmed the people with the eloquence of his address, comparing the foundations of the king's new house with the strong foundations of the kingdom of Judah. He managed to so ingratiate himself on the occasion that he now enjoyed special favor with the king, and had thus acquired no little influence in the affairs of the court and Temple.

But Jeremiah had spoken differently of Jehoiakim's house. Weeks went by, and the workmen received no wage for their toil. Grumbling comparisons were made of penurious Jehoiakim and his just father, King Josiah. And so, when Jeremiah delivered a scathing attack on the king for trying to surpass his father's memory with the superficial splendor of his new dwelling, he touched a raw nerve that jolted the king and secretly delighted many of the common people of the city.

"You should leave Jerusalem for a while," continued Ahikam. "Allow the sting of your words to fade. Let other matters distract the king from his displeasure. A few weeks, a few months..." Ahikam shrugged.

"I will seek the will of the Lord in this," replied the prophet finally. "Perhaps He wishes me to go, perhaps to stay. But I thank you for your aid in this matter," said Jeremiah earnestly, gripping the arms of Ahikam and his son. "May Adonai bless you for thinking of me."

"May He bless the nation," replied the chief scribe. "May He protect and preserve us."

Jeremiah looked at them both for a moment, dropped his eyes to the ground, and went back into the inn.

"GO AND BUY a linen belt and put it around your waist," the Voice said as he lay on his pallet, his eyes wide as the words echoed in vast silence within his mind. "Do not let it touch water. Then go to the Euphrates and hide it there in a crevice in the rocks."

To the Euphrates. To Babylon — the same destination as the convoy leaving Jerusalem tomorrow, taking the nobles' sons to the court of Nebuchadrezzar. Was this the Lord's way of telling him to leave Jerusalem? Had El Shaddai sent Ahikam and Gedaliah to him this evening to prepare him for the journey He now commanded?

After a long, silent interval of careful thought, he arose and began gathering his belongings.

21

THE CAMPFIRE splashed a warm circle of orange against the dark Syrian night. Though the day had been warm, the night was cool in the highlands of the Lebanon range.

Jeremiah had walked two days on the outer fringes of the convoy as it traveled north along the old caravan route. On the second day, as they approached Megiddo and the Jezreel plain, an outrider had spotted him, and galloped up and challenged him. He was hailed before the military commander of the expedition, a hard-bitten Sumerian named Sarduz.

"Who are you?" demanded the commander, as Jeremiah knelt before him.

"I am Jeremiah of Anathoth, a servant of the Most High God."

"Why are you trailing this convoy?"

"The Most High has commanded me to go to the Euphrates, to see the land of the masters of Judah. It is He who has given the kingdom of Judah into the hand of your king, Nebuchadrezzar."

"Hah! A fine way for a god to treat his people! And why does this 'Most High' of yours wish you to see the land of Chaldea?"

"I... I do not know."

"Well! By the beard of Marduk!" laughed Sarduz. "An honest priest! Never before have I heard one admit ignorance of the motives of the gods." The commander chuckled a moment more to himself, then said to the guards, "This one seems harmless enough. Permit him to travel with the convoy. Perhaps the Hebrew boys would enjoy an elder of their countrymen to converse with."

"TELL US ANOTHER STORY of David," said Daniel now, as they sat in a ring about the dying fire. Jeremiah looked around the circle. Their young eyes, lit by the flickering light, glittered at him expectantly. Since joining the march, he had become a surrogate father and elder brother to these apprehensive youths who journeyed forward into the unknown. He smiled, stared into the glowing coals for a moment, scratching his beard thoughtfully.

"Very well," he announced, looking up at them. "I shall tell the tale of 'A Drink for the King.'"

The boys settled closer, warming to Jeremiah's voice as much as to the fire.

"This came to pass in the waning days of Saul, when the discontented and distressed of the land were coming to David at his stronghold in the caves of Adullam. In those times, the Philistines ravaged the land of Judah, coming and going almost as they pleased. The Lord had ceased to be with Saul, and he was hard pressed.

"But the Lord blessed David and protected him. And one day, as David sat in the cave, he sighed and said, 'Oh, how I wish I had a drink of the pure, sweet water from the well at the gate of Bethlehem, the place of my birth!' He said it as a random fancy, nothing more. But Shammah the Hararite, one of the Three Mighty Men of David, overheard his master and reported it to the other two."

The boys' eyes sparkled with delight at the mention of the three great folk heroes. Involuntarily they leaned closer.

"The Three Mighty Men departed that very night and journeyed from Adullam to Bethlehem, in the hills south of Jebus, as Jerusalem was known in those days. They arrived in the darkness before dawn, and what should they find but a garrison of Philistines, armed to the teeth, with watchmen pacing the perimeter!"

Jeremiah dropped his voice to a stealthy whisper. "Silently they crept past the guards until they reached the well, and drew a draught of the sweet, cool water, pouring it in a skin to carry it back to their master. All was going well until a Philistine warrior, unable to sleep, came yawning to the well for a drink.

"The Philistine stopped in mid-yawn, staring at the Three

as if at an apparition. Then he shouted, 'Attack! We are attacked by the host of David!'"

Jeremiah's voice rang through the night as he parodied the frightened Philistine. The boys giggled.

"At the mention of David's name, the entire garrison was instantly in an uproar, for the Philistines feared David and his strong and crafty host much more than they feared Saul. Of course, the hapless one who shouted was dead in his tracks, but his alarm had been heeded.

"Such a melee it was for the Three, as they escaped from Bethlehem! It was still dark, you see, and the Philistines ran here and there, tripping over each other and lashing out at one another — such was the panic David's name held for them. And the Three ran to and fro, dodging and slaying and laughing with valiant joy all the while. By the time the Hebrews left the garrison, the Philistines thought they were set upon by two hundred fierce fighting men!

"Well of course, the Three won through into the open country, and so back to Adullam on the evening of the day after they had left. And they presented to David their master the skin of water from the well of his birthplace — such was the love and loyalty they held for him. And what do you suppose the great David did when offered such a hard-won gift?"

He paused, looking significantly around the ring of wide-eyed, forward-leaning faces.

"David, the Lord's anointed, would not drink the water. He said, 'How can I drink this water, O my God? For these good men went at the risk of their lives because of a careless wish uttered from my lips.' And David poured out the sweet, cool water as a drink offering before the Lord, because of the love he had for his Three Mighty Men."

The rapture of the tale was broken by the soft sobbing of one of the boys. Quickly Jeremiah went to him. Daniel, who had emerged as the informal leader of the group, looked up at the older man, the tears on his face reflecting the firelight. "How long will it be, Jeremiah?" he asked, his voice catching on the sharp edges of his sorrow. "How long before we again drink the water of Judah? How long will we be in the land of this foreign king?" His eyes pleaded with Jeremiah for an answer —

but more, for comfort. The prophet sighed, gazing around the circle, as Daniel's question echoed mutely in the faces looking back at him.

"The Lord has not yet told me, Daniel," muttered the prophet, his words clouded with regret. Bitterly he sought within himself the reassurance he did not have, as their heads dropped between their shoulders. "It is His, and His alone, to say when the time of your exile must end.

"But know this," he continued, his voice stronger. The boys looked up at him again. "In the heart and soul of each of you," he said, as one by one he met their eyes around the circle, "there is a tiny portion of Judah. The hills of Zion are part of you, regardless of where you sojourn. As long as you hold fast to the love of Adonai, and do not forsake Him, He will comfort you and strengthen you, just as He did David, who languished for years in the wilderness before he came into his kingdom.

"Do not forget that you are sons of Israel, the people of the Name of God!" he went on, his words flashing like swords in the firelight. "The same God who delivered the giant Goliath into the hand of a shepherd boy from Bethlehem can deliver you from the evils of Babylon! And who knows? Perhaps one day He will restore the fortunes of Israel. Perhaps one day you or your sons or your grandsons will return from this strange land to which you are going, and again take up your dwelling in the land promised to our fathers."

Daniel dabbed at his eyes with his fingers. He looked at Jeremiah and bravely tried to smile, but could not quite manage. He stood and hurried into the darkness, seeking his bed, to be alone with his sadness.

One by one the boys followed. At last only Jeremiah was left, gazing into the last embers of the fire as the Syrian night closed down around the camp.

JEREMIAH STOOD on the bank of the Euphrates River. The convoy had taken two-and-a-half-score days to make the journey north to Carchemish and then down the Euphrates to the outskirts of Babylon. From where Jeremiah stood he could see the gleaming ziggurats rising above the massive walls of the metropolis. A steady traffic of barges and cargo boats floated lazily by on the broad brown current of the river. They were bound for Babylon, the heart of the world.

Jeremiah turned and climbed up the bank until he found a fissure in the flinty slope adequate for his purpose. He untied the white linen belt, still almost as clean as the day he bought it, folded it carefully, and wedged it firmly in the crevice. Then he sealed the opening with rocks, closing it so tightly that no casual passer-by would notice the place where the girdle was concealed. Rising and dusting his hands, he turned and gazed another moment at the gates of Babylon, then slowly began making his way toward the city.

Amid hurried throngs he wandered along the network of canals which ran throughout the city. He was awed by the dazzling, casual displays of wealth. Surely not even in the days of Solomon, when all the world had brought her tribute to Jerusalem, had Judah seen such profligate displays of bounty!

He heard the cries of strange birds, imported from the jungles of the southern Nile and from even more distant lands to the south and east of Medea. He walked past piles of exotic spices exuding their dark, mystic fragrance into the air. He saw people of all hues; ebony-skinned Ethiopians and Nubians, fair-haired wanderers from beyond the mountains of the far north, dusky bedouins from the sandy deserts of the Arabah. A thousand voices, a thousand tongues clamored at once all about him — all hawking some ware, plying some trade in this confusion of riches, this dense riot of sound and color which was Babylon.

Night fell over the city, and still the clamor of commerce went on under the sputtering glow of oil lamps and torches. Small barges and wicker-and-pitch *gufa* plied up and down the canals. Jeremiah walked through the Borsip Gate, bustling with porters and merchants, and across the stone bridge to the west bank of the Euphrates. He ambled through the quieter streets of Borsip, just a village by the standards of the great city across the river, though as populous as any city of Judah save Jerusalem.

Passing through the suburb he continued upon the gradually sloping plain to the west, until the noise and hubbub of the masses in the city faded into the solitude of the Sumerian night, the silence broken only by the yipping of wild dogs and the cries of night birds. As Jeremiah turned to look back, the moon rose, round and orange, appearing to float upward from Babylon like a great glowing ball bubbling upward from a pond of twinkling lights.

He sat down atop a small ridge, hugging his knees to his chest as he observed the city by the Euphrates. He struggled to understand this place, its essence. What was Babylon, that the Almighty chose her over Jerusalem, the city of His Name? Was this to be the new dwelling place of His people? Did He now take a new nation to be His own — this maze of canals and commerce and strange voices and even stranger gods?

The moon rose higher in the sky, casting black shadows on the silvery gray of the plain. Babylon's walls rose like eternity from their place by the river; her ziggurats stabbed the starry sky like lances of a proud army. On the myriad lips of her sons and daughters was her hymn of praise: "Babylon the Great! Babylon the Opulent! Babylon the Queen, the Everlasting!"

"O Lord God," prayed the prophet, "who is this nation, this king whom You have placed over Your people? Will You forget Jacob, and disinherit the sons of Abraham for the sake of this vain city by the river?"

As his anguished eyes watched, a cloud darkened the silver orb of the moon. A breeze from the north picked up a tiny handful of dust and swirled it past his feet. He looked in the direction of the breeze, and saw a huge, billowing cloud of dust rolling toward the twinkling lights of Babylon, like a gigantic storm breaker on the Great Sea. As Jeremiah watched, the roiling turbulence enveloped Babylon in a swirling mass of chaos. Her towers broke in pieces with a sound like the snapping of live bones. Her walls crumbled into dust. The lights along her thoroughfares and waterways were smothered, as a child puffs out the feeble flame of a guttering tallow candle.

The cloud passed on, and Babylon was no more. Her glory was less than a memory, and jackals made their dens in the crumbled walls of the king's palace. The winds of the desert drifted dust into the dry ditches where the canals had been.

"And what of Your people, O God?" asked Jeremiah, his heart pounding with the enormity of the vision. "Will they, too, lie beneath the dust and be forgotten, as this place is forgotten?"

"In that day and time," said the Voice, "the people of Israel and Judah shall join together, weeping. They shall seek Me, and shall ask the way to Zion. They will turn their faces homeward, and will say to one another, 'Let us join with the Lord in an everlasting covenant which will not be forgotten.'

"I will punish Babylon, as I now punish Judah. But I will restore Israel to his pasture, to the slopes of Carmel and the hills of Ephraim. I will give pardon to the remnant of My people, which I shall bring from this place."

"How long, Sovereign Lord? How long until the restoration of Jacob?"

"For seventy years Judah will sojourn in this land..."

With a start, Jeremiah looked about him. The landscape was as before, except that the shadows cast by the moon were shorter; the moon was almost overhead by now. Babylon sat by the Euphrates, the lights fewer now, as more and more of her denizens sought a place to rest for the night. But her walls rose as strong as ever, her towers as proud.

He rose to walk back toward the sleeping houses of Borsip, drinking deeply from the revelation on the moonlit plain. Seventy years. A long time, but not forever. Babylon, thrown down — forgotten. How was it possible? And yet the Lord had shown him...

For the first time since his vision beneath the acacia tree, now ages ago in another life, Jeremiah felt a faint tendril of something other than the certainty of judgment. He had no less surety of that, but the doom of judgment might now be tempered with the quiet blooming of hope. His step quickened. A smile fluttered shyly upon his lips.

THE MARKS on the bank of the Euphrates showed how high the rain-swollen river had risen. Well below the line of the flood was the crevice where Jeremiah's linen belt lay hidden. He pried the rocks out of the opening and reached inside. He pulled out the remains of the belt, moldy and useless now that the Euphrates had invaded its hiding place. And the Voice was within him.

"Thus it shall be with the people of Jerusalem. The waters of the Euphrates shall overpower them, and their pride shall be spoiled. I bound them to Me, tied them about My waist as a prized adornment, but they would not stop following other gods. I desired them to be a clean, pure garment, but they would not listen."

Jeremiah dropped the rotting strip of linen into the brown, smooth water of the river and watched it slowly vanish beneath the surface.

22

JEREMIAH RETURNED to Jerusalem just as the first cold winds of Heshvan came whistling in from the north. He huddled by the hearth in the inn, rubbing his hands as Baruch brought him a bowl of hot spiced wine. Squint stood in the corner like a scarred, eye-patched statue.

"What has passed in Judah during my absence?" Jeremiah asked, first blowing on the wine, then carefully sipping a tiny swallow. He gratefully felt it warming his insides, driving the chill of the road from of his flesh.

"Nothing good, that is certain," replied Baruch. "The crops were bad this year, and the rains of winter have not yet come. People of the land come crowding before Jehoiakim, to plead for assistance. A half-ephah of barley now costs a full day's wage."

Jeremiah frowned. "What does Jehoiakim do to relieve the people?"

Baruch gave a sardonic little snort. "Do? Precious little. At first he gave out a little grain from the city's storage cribs. But now he pulls a woeful face and sends them back to their villages to pray for the mercy of the gods."

Jeremiah's eyes flashed. "Only One God's name avails, and He has little cause to show mercy."

Baruch looked at Jeremiah for a moment, then dropped his eyes. "Yes... I suppose you're right," he mumbled.

"I must go to the Temple!" said Jeremiah decisively. "Perhaps now, with starvation staring them in the face, I can get them to listen..."

"No!" said Baruch. "You can't do that!"

"Why?" puzzled Jeremiah.

"Because after you left — and you left just in time, I might add — Jehoiakim made a proclamation at the urging of Pashhur and some of the other priests. He forbade you to set foot in the Temple courtyard, upon pain of death. If you go there you will be slain."

Jeremiah stared at Baruch. "What then am I to do? How can I...?"

He turned his eyes to the fire, and sat silent for a moment. Then he said, "I am weary from today's travel. I must go and rest. Perhaps...perhaps then I will see..." The prophet rose, and wandered toward the sleeping chamber, drifting like a boat lost at sea.

Baruch glanced at Squint, who gave a barely visible nod. Their crazy vision-merchant was back.

THE NEXT MORNING, Jeremiah found Baruch outside in the yard of the inn, bringing water from the well. "Baruch, I know what must be done! The Lord showed me in a dream during the night!"

Baruch looked warily up at the prophet as he continued stepping toward the door, each hand carrying a bucket full of water. "And what did you see?"

"Come inside!" said Jeremiah eagerly.

"Excellent suggestion," commented Baruch wryly, as Jeremiah held the door open for him.

When he had poured the icy-cold water in the wash basin by the wall opposite the hearth, he turned to Jeremiah. "What will you do?"

"Baruch, you must get your writing utensils. The Lord has commanded me to dictate to you a scroll."

KING JEHOIAKIM proclaimed a day of fasting for the land. Delegations from all the cities of Judah were to be in Jerusalem on the ninth day of Kislev, and intercession was to be made for the rains to return. A large assembly was planned in the Temple courtyard. The priests busily groomed themselves for the auspicious day.

In the inn, Jeremiah and Baruch were finishing their transcription. All the words of prophecy given to Jeremiah since his first call were painstakingly documented in the scroll. It had taken many days of diligent labor to copy out the entire history of Jeremiah's burden of faith — but at last it was done.

"On the fast day," announced Jeremiah matter-of-factly, "this must be read to the entire assembly."

Baruch responded quickly. "How will you do that, may I ask? Have you so soon forgotten? You are debarred from showing so much as your face in the Temple..."

"Yes, yes. I have not forgotten." Jeremiah looked long and carefully at the innkeeper, grandson of Mahseiah the scribe. Baruch's eyes stared back, puzzled at first, then suddenly growing wide with incredulity.

"You expect me to — You think I shall — No! No! It is impossible!" the innkeeper stammered.

"Baruch, Baruch! These are the words of God! He commands that the people must hear! I would be struck down before finishing so much as the first page. Surely you can see—"

"I can see that you are asking me to stick my head in the mouth of the beast which devoured my father!" shouted the innkeeper, vaulting to his feet. "I knew this day would come! I knew deep in my soul that one day I would regret sheltering a troublesome prophet under my roof!" Baruch ranted on, pacing angrily back and forth.

Squint came in the back way and stopped in the doorway, watching with one-eyed suspicion the scene which greeted him.

"Baruch," Jeremiah pleaded, "it is not I who asks you. Don't you see? Don't you feel the pull within your heart? This thing must be done, and *you* are chosen for the task. He does not choose lightly, Baruch. And if you reject His anointing, you will find that there are worse adversaries than priests and kings."

Baruch still paced, fuming.

"The Lord is tearing down the very house He built, my friend," said Jeremiah. "He is plucking up the vineyard He planted with His own hand. It is not a time for seeking ease and prosperity for yourself. The tides of God's wrath will sweep across this nation, and many who seek to save their lives will lose them. But if you seek His will, He will preserve you. He has shown me this."

Baruch stopped pacing, and glared at the prophet. "Am I, too, a figure in your visions?" he challenged.

Slowly, deliberately, Jeremiah nodded, the intensity of his expression precluding any doubt about the sincerity of his assertion. Baruch felt himself hemmed in by the ferocity of Jeremiah's faith, dazed by the adamant brilliance of his vision. He stood still, his eyes averted, loath to take up the mission being offered, but feeling his will to refuse ebbing away in the glow of the prophet's will.

"Baruch," called the prophet softly, "it is time for you to fulfill your heritage. Time for you to remember."

The innkeeper sat down heavily on a table, burying his face in his hands. Jeremiah looked on anxiously. Squint shook his head in consternation, turned, and went back outside.

THE PEOPLE STOOD shoulder-to-shoulder in the Temple courtyard. Only the stern-faced guards kept them from spilling through the gate of the palace grounds. For half a morning they had stood there, listening to the mellifluous speeches of the priests, who urged greater piety, more frequent prayers, stricter attention to the traditions of the elders.

The day was sunny, with no promise of the rain so urgently needed, yet it was cool. Most of the men had rubbed dirt on their faces as a badge of their fasting. Delegates from all parts of the land were in attendance. It was a fine, dramatic outpouring of concern. That such an impressive demonstration could go unnoticed by Yahweh never entered the minds of these concerned citizens of Judah.

Baruch, sweating profusely despite the crisp air, walked up to the proctor, standing with arms crossed at the street door of the house of the proctor Gemariah, brother of Ahikam. The proctor scowled at him, not recognizing this furtive-looking one who donned the scribe's traditional garb as if it were a costume worn for the first time.

"Let me enter. I... I have a message to read to the people," stuttered Baruch nervously.

"Who are you?" demanded Gemariah. "I haven't seen you in the Temple before. You're not a scribe!" he accused.

Baruch dropped his head, wanting to slink away in disgrace. Drawing several deep breaths, he again faced the skeptical proctor.

"I am Baruch, son of Neriah the scribe, and grandson of Mahseiah the scribe. I have a message from Adonai Elohim to read to the people. Now let me pass." Zeal, competing with fear, burned in Baruch's eyes as he stared at the proctor, daring to be turned away again.

Reluctantly the proctor opened the door. "You may pass," he said. Baruch entered, and Gemariah closed the door behind him, shrugging doubtfully.

Baruch climbed the stairs to the upper story. The speakers addressed the crowd from a window which opened onto the courtyard. The priest at the window looked quizzically at Baruch. Seeing the scroll clutched to his chest like a talisman, the priest motioned him to the window.

As he stepped to the window, the sea of upturned faces in the courtyard struck him like a silent, massive fist. His eyes bulged, his mouth turned to fleece — he could not swallow. With fingers of stone he undid the binding of the scroll and fumbled it open. His ears were sharpened to the keenness of a hound's: He heard every shuffling of feet, every nervous cough, every rustle of clothing.

After several false starts, he managed to make his voice audible.

"This... This is what the Lord says:

'When men fall down, do they not get up?
When a man turns away, does he not return?
Why then have these people turned away?
Why, indeed, does Jerusalem always turn away...?'"

The people began to look at each other in confusion. This message bore little resemblance to the others they had heard thus far.

"'How can you say, "We are wise, for we have the law of the Lord," when actually the lying pen of the scribes has handled it falsely? The wise will be put to shame; they will be dismayed and trapped.

"'From the least to the greatest'"—Baruch could not help glancing to his left, at the walls of the palace courtyard—"'all are greedy for gain, prophets and priests alike. All practice deceit. They dress the wound of My people as if it were not serious. "Peace, peace," they say, when there is no peace.'"

Not a figure moved, not a voice whispered in the courtyard. Some faces were contorted in anger, some wrinkled in confusion. A few were furrowed with the beginnings of contrition. But a special grace was granted Baruch, son of Neriah, on this day of fasting. He felt a power not of himself thrumming upward from an unsuspected source, ringing in his throat like the call of battle trumpets. Gradually he forgot to look at the scroll — the phrases sprang directly from the papyrus to his mind as he pronounced the words of stone and thunder copied by his own hand from the lips of God's prophet. The son of Neriah and Mahseiah was remembering.

"'I will take away their harvest,' declares the Lord. 'There will be no grapes on the vine, no figs on the tree — their leaves will wither. What I have given them, I will take away...'

"We hoped for peace, but no good has come; for a time of healing, but there was only terror. The snorting of horses is heard from Dan; at the neighing of their stallions, the whole land trembles. They have come to devour the land and everything in it, the city and all who live there...

"The harvest is past, the summer is ended — and we are not saved!"

Micaiah, the son of the proctor Gemariah, was seated in the room behind Baruch. He felt drawn to Baruch's words like a beast led by a halter, transfixed by the power, the pungent conviction with which the son of Neriah bludgeoned the ears of Judah. This man was right. Their fast was a mockery. Their ceremonies were meaningless. The people's piety extended no farther than the next rainfall.

Afraid to hear more, yet unable to leave, he listened on, helplessly.

"...The Lord says this: 'I have heard what the prophets say who prophesy lies in My name. They say, "I had a dream! A dream!" How long will this continue in the hearts of these lying prophets, who prophesy the delusions of their own minds? They think the dreams they tell each other will make the people forget My name, just as their fathers forgot My name at the orgies of Baal.

"'Therefore,' declares the Lord, 'I am against the prophets who steal from one another words they attribute to Me. I am against these who wag their own tongues and say, "The Lord says..." They lead My people with lies, yet I did not send them, nor did I appoint them. They are useless to My people,' says the Lord."

Hananiah felt a wave of rage singe him as he stood a few paces behind Baruch's right shoulder. This fellow was a bit too free with his accusations. In fact, his words sounded suspiciously like someone else's.

"...Thus says the Lord: 'I gave Israel a certificate of divorce and sent her away to Nineveh because of her harlotry with other gods. She polluted the land with her adulteries — selling herself to stone and wood.

"'Yet her unfaithful sister Judah saw all this, and still had no fear. She, too, was unfaithful to Me.

"'Judah has not returned to Me with will all her heart, but only in pretense!'"

For two hours, the son of Neriah rained words of fire upon their heads. When he finished, he felt as empty as a drained wine cup. Quietly he turned, bound up the scroll, trod down the steps and out into the street, and went home.

After closing the inn's door behind him, he leaned against it tiredly. Jeremiah, who had waited anxiously for his return, rushed up to him, nervously studying the face of his friend for an indication of the message's reception. "Well?" he asked. "What was it like?"

Baruch sighed and looked into the prophet's eyes. "I felt... Him."

Jeremiah's eyes widened in wonder and awe. The silence between them was too large for words, too deep for explanation.

Suddenly Squint came hurrying into the room from the stairs leading from the roof. Jeremiah and Baruch looked up at him with puzzled expressions. In answer he pointed out the window. Through the gate came a man wearing the clothing of a noble family. His face was contorted in fatigue; he panted as though he had been running. He glanced around him as if to verify his location, then strode rapidly to the door and pounded upon it with his fist.

Baruch looked at Jeremiah, his nostrils flaring in a sudden rush of fear. His heart clanging in his chest, he called out, "Who is there?"

"Jehudi, son of Nethaniah! Open to me! I come from the council of the princes of Judah!"

Again Baruch and Jeremiah exchanged a long stare. "Whom do you seek?" asked the innkeeper at last.

"He who read the scroll in the Temple! The nobles of Judah are assembled in the chamber of Ahikam, the chief scribe. They wish to hear the scroll read again!"

"What do I do?" whispered the frightened innkeeper urgently. "To go so near the house of the king, and to read such words..." The fierce rapture of the Temple courtyard was swept away in the rush of panic now engulfing the son of Neriah. He looked to Jeremiah for mooring against the waves of trepidation beating against his heart.

"Baruch," said Jeremiah finally, gripping him by the shoulder, "this is a summons. Who can say for whose ears Adonai intends this message? Go and speak. Again you are called."

Baruch's eyes probed deeply into Jeremiah's, for ten panting breaths. Then the innkeeper turned and looked at the door of his house as if he had never seen one before. For so long he had pulled this inn about him like a cloak. He had sheltered here from the dangerous call of his heritage. Now the time of hiding was ended. Long and intently he studied the scarred, water-stained planking of the door which, once opened, could never again be closed.

Glancing back once more at Jeremiah, he picked up the scroll from where it lay on the floor, put his hand slowly to the latch, and opened the door.

"Very well," he announced to Jehudi. "Let's be on our way."

Jeremiah stared after them for long time. Then, sighing, he softly closed the door.

He turned to Squint and shrugged. "Now we wait." A tiny half-smile died in birth on the prophet's lips. Squint grunted and left by the back door.

23

IN THE CHAMBER of the court official Elishama, in a wing of the winter palace of Jehoiakim, the shuddering glow of the flames in the bronze brazier cast in stark relief the somber countenances of those circled around it. They were gathered in a silent wake for the dying soul of the land they loved.

The convocation in the nearby Temple courtyard still ground on, each speaker trying to outdo the last in professions of love for Judah, her king, and her people. The convicting words of Baruch were soon dissipated in a flurry of rousing speeches urging the people to be strong, firm in their hope, and most of all loyal to Judah.

But it was not so here in the chamber. Ahikam was present, and his brother, the proctor Gemariah. Beside them was Gemariah's son Micaiah, who had brought them the news of the words read by Baruch, and Elnathan, grizzled and old but still strong and alert. Delaiah, Elishama, and many other officers and nobles of the court were there, each submerged in misgivings and fears about the unfolding destiny of Judah.

Jehudi entered, turned, and motioned hastily to a nervous Baruch. The scribe shuffled in, looking behind and about him as if he feared ambush. He clutched the scroll to his chest as he had when he entered the room above the Temple courtyard.

Ahikam looked questioningly at Micaiah, receiving a confirming nod. This was the fellow.

"Baruch," called Ahikam. "Don't be afraid. We have sent for you because Micaiah, my nephew, has told us of a powerful message you brought to the Temple today."

Baruch glanced skittishly at them, then nodded hesitantly.

"Well then, friend Baruch. Sit down near the light, and read to us." Ahikam motioned gently toward the brazier. Elishama signaled to a young aide to bring an oil lamp near. When all was arranged, Baruch moved cautiously into the light, unrolled the papyrus scroll, darted a final glimpse around the circle of half-lit faces, cleared his throat — and began.

The honed spearpoint of the oracle pierced them almost immediately, despite the halting speech of the restive scribe and innkeeper. The faces of the nobles and officers in the chamber, though concerned before, now took on the bleakest aspect of anguish. Again and again their souls were lanced by the keen, unerring aim of the prophecy.

Judah was a vessel on a potter's wheel, found unfit and smashed into a shapeless lump...

She was an expensive and carefully chosen vase, shattered and cast among the litter of a defiled place...

Adonai was pouring out woe upon them from the north; like a swollen river of blood it would rush over them. The dead would be so many that burial would be impossible...

Judah was a wild she-camel in heat, sniffing the wind to find a mate for her lust. Though God called her again and again, she would not listen. She searched diligently for opportunities to do evil...

She was like a white, unspoiled linen girdle which would be overwhelmed by the influence of the Euphrates, becoming good for nothing, rotted, filthy.

Despite the zeal of Josiah, despite all his insistence on restoring the true forms and traditions of the Law, the men gathered here knew deep within themselves that the hearts of the people had not changed. As soon as the people had opportunity, they eagerly went back to their old ways: worshiping tree and stone, star and moon — worshiping themselves. Adultery and dishonesty were their sacraments and the blood of the innocent and helpless their drink offering. With relentless accuracy the words of Baruch's scroll penetrated this pretense and hypocrisy, laid open the flesh of the nation and exposed the maggots gnawing at the vitals of Judah.

The nobles felt in the words of the scroll the blunt agony of truth: Judah was doomed. By the time Baruch's voice finally fell silent, each of them, in his own way, had been drenched in the dark fear that precedes the death of a beloved.

Elnathan tore the hem of his garment as he wept softly. Micaiah held his face in his hands. Elishama stared with the eyes of a dead man into the dying fire.

Ahikam raised his tear-streaked face to Baruch. "Did you write all these words at his bidding?" No one in the room needed the name of the person to whom Ahikam referred. The fiery, tenacious cadences of Jeremiah's voice had quivered in the chamber, summoned by the reading of the scroll.

Baruch nodded. "He spoke the words, and I copied them."

A silence as long as grief darkened the room.

"The king must hear," said Gemariah finally. "If he would only listen, perhaps..." The phrase died a conspicuous death.

"Baruch, you must go back to Jeremiah," said Ahikam grimly. "You both must hide, because Jehoiakim will be fiercely angry when the words of this prophecy are read to him. But hear them he must."

Baruch rose to leave, still holding the scroll.

"Leave it — will you?" said Micaiah. Baruch paused, looking from the scroll to the tortured, resigned face of the son of Gemariah. Slowly he placed the papyrus roll in Micaiah's hand, then walked to the door. Jehudi, waiting by the entrance, gripped his shoulder in a gesture of complicity and gratitude. Then Baruch was gone.

JEHOIAKIM, SON OF JOSIAH, eleventh ruler in Jerusalem since David, sat peevishly in an inner chamber of the winter palace, huddled within his clothing beside a fire. His face wore its perpetual scowl as he pried apart the shell of an almond and popped the meat into his mouth. Absently picking another nut from the silver bowl at his side and carefully inserting the tip of a knife blade into the crease of the shell, he asked, "What is it, Jehudi ben-Nethaniah, that you disturb me on this solemn day of fasting?"

The king's wit prompted a chuckle from his attendants, including his son, Prince Jerahmeel, who stood at his side.

"My king," Jehudi began. Kneeling behind him were Elnathan, Gemariah, and Delaiah. "My king, a scroll has...has been found."

"Really?" drawled Jehoiakim, never glancing toward Jehudi. "A scroll. How interesting." He chewed noisily for a moment. "And what does it say, this scroll?" At last Jehoiakim's hooded eyes lazily regarded Jehudi as the younger man stood uncomfortably before him, holding the scroll under his arm.

"My king... I think it best that you listen to the words of this scroll and decide its message for yourself."

Jehoiakim stopped chewing for a moment. A brief glimmer of increased interest showed in his eyes. He inserted the penknife in another almond shell. "Indeed. Very well, then, Jehudi. Get on with it."

Jehudi unrolled the scroll. Clearing his throat several times, he began to read.

As the words came tumbling forth, the air in the chamber began to swell with hostile silence. Jehoiakim's face went from an expression of boredom to one of slit-eyed menace. His knuckles whitened on the hilt of the knife.

And still the words came: "'...A horrible and shocking thing has happened in the land,'" read Jehudi. "'The prophets prophesy lies, the priests rule by their own authority, and My people love to have it this way! But what will you do in the end?'"

"Stop!" ordered Jehoiakim. He motioned to Jehudi. "Bring this scroll to me."

With halting steps, Jehudi came to the king and offered him the scroll. Jehoiakim examined the document. "Hmm," he mused, "I seem to remember reports of a madman using words like these." He scratched his beard with the blade of the knife.

"Show me the place where you were reading," he snapped. Jehudi indicated the column he had just finished.

Carefully the king spread the scroll on the table beside his chair. Delicately, as though making an incision in live flesh, he sliced the papyrus, severing from the rest of the text the portion Jehudi had just pointed out. Picking up the excised portion between his thumb and forefinger like dead vermin, he placed it in the brazier, watching as the flames licked at it eagerly.

"There," the king announced, when the papyrus was reduced to a crumbling piece of gray ash. "I did not care much for that bit of the scroll, Jehudi. Please continue. Perhaps it gets better from here." Smirking, he handed the roll back as his henchmen chortled behind their hands. Jehudi resumed reading.

"Stop!" commanded the king when Jehudi had read several more columns. Again he called for the scroll; again he contemptuously destroyed the damning lines.

Elnathan, from his place behind Jehudi, could no longer restrain himself. He rose and stepped forward, a hand raised in plea. "My king! No! You must not—"

"I do not recall acknowledging you, old man," snarled Jehoiakim. "Was there something you wished to say to your king?"

"My lord... This prophecy—"

"Ah!" interrupted Jehoiakim, "so this drivel is granted the dignity of such a lofty title as 'prophecy!' We know how to deal with prophets, don't we, Elnathan?" The king's eyes glittered in mockery, as the old man's jaws trembled. At last Elnathan dropped his face in shame and kneeled again, Jehoiakim's oily sneer burning in his ears.

"Continue, Jehudi. Let's hear what else this 'prophet' has to say."

With heightened pain Jehudi read once more, only to be stopped again. For hours Jehoikam relentlessly pursued the same slow process of ravaging the scroll, until the whole of it was reduced to a pile of feathery gray ash.

"Is that all, then, Jehudi?" The courtier bowed his head, giving no response.

"Very well," snapped the king. "You may leave, and take your older friends with you."

When they exited, the king turned to his son. "Jerahmeel, you were in the Temple courtyard earlier today, were you not?"

"Yes, Father," answered the young man.

"And did you see the one who read this?" asked Jehoiakim.

"Yes, my father, I did."

"Good. Take a guard detail with you and find this fellow. Find also that wretched Jeremiah. The words were his.

"Bring them both to me at once," he said, reaching with his knife into the brazier, and beating the feathery remnants of the scroll into a fine gray dust.

THE ARMED MEN strode into the inn yard. Jerahmeel, reaching the door, pounded on it with the hilt of his sword.

"Open in the name of the king!" he demanded.

There was no answer.

Again, and louder, he beat on the door. "Open, I say! Open at once!"

One of the guards went over to a slitted window set at chin height in the stone wall, and peered into the dark hole. "I see nothing," he reported.

Jerahmeel turned to the others. "Break it down!" he commanded.

A rough-hewn wooden bench sat beside the low wall, just inside the gate of the yard. Four of the men hoisted it, hauled it back to the door, and dashed it against the latch. Once, twice, three times the old door shuddered under the crashing weight. On the fourth assault the wooden latch splintered with a loud ripping noise, and the door swung open upon a dark and empty room.

"Search all the chambers," Jerahmeel ordered. The guards spread throughout the place, ransacking as they went. Jars and tables were overturned, lamps and clay bowls smashed on the floor, mats and cushions ripped and thrown into corners.

"Shelemiah! Seraiah!" the prince called. "Go and look in the stable. Perhaps the cowards are hiding in a pile of dung."

At that moment Squint appeared in the back doorway with a load of wood in his arms. His face was a mask of fear and astonishment at the violence done to the premises. He dropped the wood noisily to the floor as Jerahmeel shouted, "You!" The prince sprang across the room and grasped Squint by the front of his robe.

"Where are they? Where are Baruch and Jeremiah? Answer me, you miserable vermin!" Viciously he shook the scar-faced man, who seemed unable to free the tongue in his head.

At last Squint began frantically signing with his fingers, yammering in an inarticulate yowl. He tugged again and again at his ears, vigorously shaking his head. After a few puzzled moments the prince shoved him away in disgust. "I might have known," he sneered. "A deaf-mute!"

Squint cowered beside the hearth while the prince brandished his sword. "One false move from you," he said, "and I'll split you like an overripe melon!"

The destructive quest continued, but failed to produce its quarry. The guards all returned to the common room, reporting no success.

Jerahmeel picked up a still-intact wine bowl and hurled it against the wall above Squint's head, showering him with fragments. Squint covered his head with his arms and blabbered incoherently.

The prince strode to him, knocked aside the man's arms and shook a fist in his face. "I will find your masters," he swore, "and I will bring them to the king! And if I ever have reason to believe you've led me astray, I will come back here and tear out your liver, you stoneheaded wretch!"

He slapped the top of the man's bald pate before spinning on his heel and stalking out of the ruined inn. "Come on!" he snapped to the others. "This Jeremiah was from Anathoth. Perhaps he seeks refuge there."

Squint covered his head again with his arms, peeking out from under the bend of his elbow. He watched carefully as the detail strode across the yard and out the gate. Then he rose slowly, dusting the shards of the broken wine bowl from his shoulders and lap.

Edging to the broken door, he craned his neck to watch the soldiers and their prince swaggering down the narrow street and out of sight.

He turned toward the back door, stepping over debris as he crossed the room. Looking once more toward the front, he opened the back entry and walked out. Still watching in every direction, he stepped near the wood piled against the back wall of the inn. In a guttural voice he said one word: "Clear."

The wood began to slide and tumble this way and that as Jeremiah and Baruch clambered from beneath the sticks. They walked inside the back door and surveyed the damage.

"Well," announced Baruch after a long, silent look, "I believe it's time to change to a different line of work.

"Do you suppose," he asked, looking at Jeremiah, "there is any scribe work to be done hereabout?"

174

24

SAKHRI LISTENED, his eyes shifting in calculation, as the messenger announced the man who waited outside the chamber. So Judah wished to treat with Egypt, did she? Perhaps the Babylonian collar began to chafe.

Sakhri signaled his servant to show the envoy into his quarters. Perhaps some use could be made of this circumstance — some advantage gained by the Pharaoh.

The aging ambassador swung his feet down from the couch, wincing when his gout-wracked feet struck the floor. He sat as erect as he could and arranged his robes.

The emissary from Judah entered. It was Mattaniah, the younger brother of King Jehoiakim. Sakhri curtly returned the greeting of the sturdy Hebrew. He studied the young man through slightly squinted eyes; evaluating, calculating. This fellow was unpleasantly reminiscent of his sire, the troublesome Josiah. He had his father's build, his jaw. But his eyes... Perhaps a trace of weakness there — perhaps a shade less imagination.

Nonetheless, Sakhri thought, best not to judge too hastily. He decided to speak first.

"Prince Mattaniah," he began in less than his best Hebrew, "may all those in the Undying Realms smile upon your ways. What happy errand brings you to my humble house?"

THE WICK GUTTERED, and Jeremiah rose to fetch more oil for the lamp. "Wait," said Baruch. "I believe it's enough to let me finish."

The scribe copied the last few words onto the parchment strip, looked once again to make certain of the draft, and put down the stylus. He sighed as he opened and closed his cramped fingers.

"Why did you insist on using parchment this time?" asked Jeremiah, standing in the darkness just beyond the wavering circle of light cast by the dying lamp. His back was to Baruch.

"Because parchment lasts longer and is more durable," replied Baruch, rolling the strip from one side, then carefully binding the scroll and slipping a lambskin cover over it.

"Parchment burns too, does it not?" reflected the prophet .

"Yes," replied Baruch. "But this scroll will not share the fate of its predecessor."

Jeremiah turned and watched quizzically as Baruch went to a corner of the small, windowless, upstairs room and removed the lid from the clay pot containing the scrolls of his grandfather. He made a place for the folio he had just finished, carefully inserted it, and replaced the lid.

Baruch stood and faced Jeremiah. "This scroll is not meant for the fire," he said. "It is meant to be preserved — that others might remember."

The gazes of prophet and scribe clenched in the sputtering light of the lamp. And then it was dark.

SPRING CAME TO JUDAH, then summer. And with the passing of spring passed the deadline for Judah's tribute to start for Babylon, via guarded caravan. The tardiness did not go unnoticed, but by artful contrivance, the client king managed to be missing whenever an emissary of Nebuchadrezzar appeared. His aides and attendants made excuse after excuse to explain Jehoiakim's absence to the increasingly impatient messengers.

Uncertainty was in the wind, and disquiet spread like a disease in Jerusalem.

NEBUCHADREZZAR STRODE the uppermost terrace of his newly constructed garden tower. He had it built as a wedding gift for his newest wife. She took little enough notice of it, but he found himself enjoying the place more and more as the days passed. He walked to the edge of the terrace and looked out over his city.

Babylon's canals stretched like strands of a silvery net spread upon the city. From thousands of cooking fires arose a haze of smoke, lying like a low, wispy blanket over the blocky single-story houses and the upreaching spires of the ziggurats. The citizens of his capital were preparing for another day.

Nebuchadrezzar liked the mornings best — when a night's rest gave a gauzy innocence to the newly awakening world, and before the heat of the day settled in like a burning blanket of brass.

The business of ruling an empire proved far less thrilling than the process of winning one. Each day his counselors brought him an endless list of matters requiring his approval or supervision. Now he felt pulled and stretched, tugged this way and that by diverse and unceasing exigencies. Raids upon outlying territories, petty disputes among vassal princes, encroachment by enemies upon his domain — so unlike the days of the campaign. The vigorous clarity of war contrasted sharply with the messy ambiguities of governance.

He sighed and leaned against the trunk of a miniature date palm imported from Egypt for his sky garden. Idly he plucked a long, thin frond from the immature tree. It would be six seasons before this palm produced fruit; then it might bear for two or three generations.

He wondered how many generations Babylon would bear fruit. His sons exasperated him with their dilettante ways; they seemed more concerned with creating grand impressions than with learning the business of empire.

Again he looked at the tree. And Egypt. What of her? Neco had been quiet since the thrashing administered at Carchemish, but Nebuchadrezzar doubted that Pharaoh had surrendered all notions of aggrandizing his dominion. Perhaps the old lion was asleep; but who knew what her dreams were, or when she might awake? Surely Neco coveted the seaports of Phoenicia, and the flat, fertile plains of Philistia. And Judah...

Through the dense foliage of the garden behind him, Nebuchadrezzar heard footsteps coming toward him.

Nebuzaradan spied the emperor and approached, making obeisance. "My king," he said, "Lord Sheshach has returned from his mission to Jerusalem. He awaits in the council chamber. I thought I might find you here, and so I came to tell you."

Nebuchadrezzar nodded, looking once again out over his city. He sighed, unwilling to assume today's drudgery of rulership, yet unable to avoid it any longer. He looked back at his trusted commander with a weak smile. "Well, Zaradan, let us not keep the road-weary Sheshach waiting. Lead on." The two men threaded their way through the greenery to the central stairway.

Sheshach sat at an intricately carved marble table, embossed in bas-relief with the lion-and-bull symbol of the empire. The ambassador's eyes were red and swollen — he had traveled all night to bring his report. His elbow was propped on the table, his face resting on his palm.

He was jolted from a nodding doze by the voice of the commander of the guards. "His imperial highness, the son of Marduk, Nebuchadrezzar, emperor of Babylon," announced Nebuzaradan, as the tired minister hastily roused himself from his near-slumber, falling to his knees on the cedar-planked floor.

"Rise, Nebel-Sheshach," Nebuchadrezzar curtly commanded as he strode in, taking his place at the head of the massive table. "You have come from Jerusalem?"

"Yes, my king."

"And did you secure the tribute of Judah, now an entire season in arrears?"

"No," he said, after an uncomfortable pause. "No, your worship, I did not."

Nebuchadrezzar allowed a vast, hushed chasm to separate him from the emissary who wilted before his icy query: "Presumably you have some excuse?"

The hapless ambassador began to babble. "My king... The people in Judah are poor... They paid heavy extortion to the upstart Neco, before your just and merciful reign began. They...they have little left to offer, other than—"

"Are there no crops in Judah?" Nebuchadrezzar's voice sliced like a cold blade into Sheshach's bumbling apology. "Have they no daughters, no sons? And what of this temple of theirs? It has stood atop that rocky little hill for five hundred years or more — do the people of Judah not make offerings to their god?"

Again the emperor dropped a frigid slab of silence upon the shoulders of the cowering noble.

"Your main fault, Sheshach," continued Nebuchadrezzar,

after a suitably uneasy interlude, "is that you have small ambitions, narrow vision." He drummed his fingers on the marble, and in the still chamber they sounded as loud to Sheshach as the tramp of a marching army. "Perhaps it is time for me to visit Jerusalem personally, to oversee the administration of this small, poor, and yet apparently very troublesome district.

"You may go..." he said finally.

The wretched minister dropped gratefully to his stomach, glad to escape the chamber with his life.

"But," continued Nebuchadrezzar as the envoy prepared to take his leave, "hold yourself in readiness. I may have other missions for you. Less strenuous missions."

"I am yours to command, my king," oozed the noble.

"Indeed," drawled the emperor. "Now leave me at once."

When they were alone in the chamber, Nebuchadrezzar arched an eyebrow at his commander, who shrugged slightly in reply.

"Perhaps he takes a bribe from them — who knows?" observed Nebuzaradan. "As you say, he has limited vision. Perhaps it is not only his weakness, but also his strength."

Nebuchadrezzar chuckled at the cogency of the commander's assessment. "Well said. Yet I wonder: Could it be that Egypt encourages disobedience with vague promises of protection?"

"Why should Neco wish to incur your overt hostility? He has had ample opportunity to learn the consequences of such an action."

"True. Still, I cannot avoid the sense that Judah's intransigence is somehow linked to the lurking presence on her southern border."

Just then the emperor's chief eunuch, Ashpenaz, hesitantly cleared his throat in the doorway. Nebuchadrezzar glanced up. "Enter," he commanded.

Rising from the floor, Ashpenaz said, "My lord king, you have commanded me to make a report to you on the progress of the Hebrew youths in their training."

"Yes, I recall this. What is it you wish to say?"

"Only this: Some time ago Belteshazzar, named among them Daniel, refused to eat the ration you commanded for the young men..."

Nebuchadrezzar stiffened, but said nothing.

"...and naturally I was fearful, knowing the consequences of such disobedience."

"Well might you have been," intoned the emperor. "Continue."

"My lord," resumed the eunuch, "this Belteshazzar made an earnest plea, objecting to the food because of his religion. Therefore — and may the king be merciful to me — I took it upon myself to conduct a trial of the question."

Nebuchadrezzar stared at the eunuch. Ashpenaz stumbled on.

"For ten days I allowed the Hebrew youths to eat what they would — little other than vegetables and water — and the other boys ate the prescribed ration. At the end of the time, to my amazement, the Hebrew youths were superior in all respects: their teeth were healthier, their eyes clearer, their flesh more plump than any of the others. Because their god had so obviously blessed them, I allowed their special diet to become permanent. And now may the king do with me as he wishes for presuming to abrogate the least of his gracious and wise commands..." The eunuch prostrated himself on the floor.

Nebuchadrezzar mused. What was it that caused Judah to nag at his notice like a persistent beggar? Why did he sense that — for some reason, ludicrous though it seemed — this insignificant corner of his empire had become a touchstone of his fate? It was time to gain a more thorough understanding of this incongruous people.

"Ashpenaz," he said, "bring these Hebrew youths to me. I wish to speak with them."

25

JEREMIAH LEFT the house of the seller of purple after first looking up and down the street for any sign of surveillance. Drawing his mantle over his head and shadowing his face as best he could, he slipped along in the shadows toward the nondescript house where he, Baruch, and Squint had taken lodging.

He came to the narrow alley which led to their quarters, above a coppersmith's shop. Glancing over his shoulder to see that he was not followed, he turned into the small, dark way.

He wondered how much longer the three of them would have to creep about like furtive beasts. As he was copying out documents wanted by the cloth merchant, he had overheard the man talking to a customer about the rumors being whispered through the streets of Jerusalem: Jehoiakim had not been seen outside the palace compound for some weeks now. The gossip intimated he was taken ill, perhaps already dead. Apparently some squabble within the royal family delayed the succession to the throne. Or so the tales ran.

Jeremiah again looked in front and behind before ducking through the low doorway into the coppersmith's shop. He walked to the back of the small, smoky room, nodding to the proprietor. In all the time they had been here, the man had spoken perhaps ten words. Now the smith raised up from the forge where he fashioned a bracelet. Jeremiah saw the unspoken request on his sooty, sweaty face. He wanted the money for this week's lodging. Was it time again already? Jeremiah sighed, reaching into his wallet. Ten gerah. The entire sum he had earned from the seller of purple. He held the coin out to the coppersmith, who quickly pocketed it without looking again at Jeremiah. He turned back to his forge. For a moment Jeremiah regarded his landlord's stooped shoulders as he tapped with a small hammer on the bracelet. The fellow had no family, and was fallen on hard times — not uncommon in Judah in these days. He took their money and asked no questions, for which Jeremiah was grateful. But the prophet could not help wondering what went on behind the bushy black eyebrows of the taciturn artisan.

Climbing the steps to the upper room, he paused. Unfamiliar voices came from within their quarters. Cautiously Jeremiah peeked through a crack in the door.

Baruch was huddled at the table with two other men. One was very old, with a face like a dried fig, wrinkled and dried by the sun. The other was somewhat younger, about Jeremiah's age. The three men appeared to be engaged in earnest conversation. Baruch had his writing materials out, and seemed to be taking dictation from the older man.

Jeremiah eased the door open. At its rusty creak, the three in the room swiveled to face him.

"Jeremiah!" called Baruch, "these men— "

"This is Jeremiah of Anathoth, the prophet of God?" interrupted the old man in a voice like the sighing of wind through a cedar bough. Carefully he rose from his seat, his hands in front of him as he fended the air, seeking Jeremiah.

As he drew nearer, Jeremiah could see the clouded irises of the old man's eyes. He was blind. Jeremiah reached out to catch the nearest waving, wrinkled hand. The old man carefully felt his face, his neck, his shoulders. He raised a hand above Jeremiah's head, as if to swear an oath.

Tilting his own face upward, he spoke in a wavering, hoary voice: "May this man be blessed of the Most High! For he speaks the oracles of Adonai Elohim, and warns the people of the great and terrible Day of the Lord. May his hand be lifted up, and may his eye not waver from the sin of this people. May Adonai raise him up, and may the mighty hand of El Shaddai be upon him, all the days of his life."

The old man embraced Jeremiah for a moment, then slowly turned and feebly sought his place at the table he had just left.

Jeremiah, deeply moved by the benediction of the aged blind man, looked quizzically at the still unnamed guests. The younger man rose to greet him.

"I am Habakkuk, son of Nebat, and this is Zephaniah, son of Cushi. We, too, are prophets of the Most High."

"I have been busy this day, friend Jeremiah," smiled Baruch. "Come, and see what we have done."

Jeremiah walked over to the table. Beside the scroll on which Baruch was working, two other rolls were bound and wrapped.

"I have copied the words God has given these men," said Baruch. "They, too, have seen the day of wrath which approaches."

Jeremiah studied the two men carefully. Their faces were drawn, tired. Even about the eyes of the younger, the sadness of knowing etched deep lines of care. Absent was the smugness, the conspicuous air of piety assumed by the street corner charlatans. Absent, too, were coin purses stuffed with the proceeds of larceny practiced upon the people in the name of Yahweh. Jeremiah recognized in their faces — and felt the resonance of confirmation deep within his soul — that these men were brothers, joined to him by a common calling, a common sorrow, a common strength.

He sat down with them. "You and I have much to say," he began.

MATTANIAH CRASHED his fist onto the table, glaring at the calm, collected figure seated across from him.

"I should be king!" he grated, baring his teeth in rage and frustration. "Jeconiah is a gutless, dandified simpleton who has no more notion of being a king than...than..." — he cast about, sputtering — "than my infant son, still pulling on the teat!" He thrust himself onto his feet and away from the table, stalking the apartment of Hananiah like a caged lion.

Hananiah allowed him to fume and pace for a few moments before he replied, in a low, reasonable voice calculated to soothe the hot-blooded ire of the prince. "My lord," he began, "forgive me for saying this, but is it possible that you are overlooking a very important fact?"

"What do you mean?" demanded Mattaniah, wheeling to look at the older man.

"Simply this: Upon his death, your brother King Jehoiakim was almost a full year delinquent in sending the required taxes to Babylon. Do you imagine this has escaped the notice of Neb-uchadrezzar?" Hananiah allowed the question to hang in the air. Mattaniah stopped pacing, peering thoughtfully at Hana-niah as he continued.

"The diplomatic efforts attempted by the late and lamented king appear to be coming to naught. And in any case, as you suggest, your nephew Jeconiah is regrettably not the man to pursue such ventures." Hananiah carefully studied his finger-nails as Mattaniah slowly returned to the table. The silence deepened in the room as he allowed Mattaniah's mind to spin along the paths his comments suggested.

Presently the prince jerked his face up from his study with a look of illumination. "Then you are saying," he blurted, "that I should allow Jeconiah...to take the blame..."

Hananiah began to nod slowly, "For his father's poor deci-sions — yes. Precisely." He smiled at the prince. "Would you rather be king only until the spring, when the Chaldeans are al-most certain to send a punitive expedition to Judah, or, by being patient, be king for the rest of your life?"

FOR JEREMIAH, the meeting with Habakkuk and Zephaniah came like unexpected rain during a drought. Sending them on their way, he felt the moving of the Lord within his spirit. Lying on his pallet that night, he stared at the dark ceiling, thoughts running like a tangled skein of thread through his mind.

"Sovereign Lord," he prayed, "forgive me." He realized that his eyes and ears had been attuned more to his own woes and difficulties than to the Voice. The encouragement brought by two other servants of the Most High had caused him to remem-ber the promises of strength made to him at his first calling. He now felt that strength flowing through the passageways of his soul. Once more in his heart there rushed a river whose streams he had almost forgotten in these last dry months.

Tomorrow, he thought, as at last he began drifting toward sleep, *I must go to the Benjamin Gate. I must tell the people...*

"'WOE TO THE SHEPHERDS who destroy and scatter the sheep of My pasture!' says the Lord..."

Jeremiah stood in the square before the Benjamin Gate, a

stone's throw from the main gate of the Temple courtyard. His voice was clear and strong as he spoke.

"'You have scattered My flock, and driven them away. You have not attended to them. Therefore I will attend to you for your misdeeds,' says the Lord.

"'And I will gather the remnant of My flock from the lands to which they have scattered, and I will set shepherds over them who will care for them, and they will no longer be afraid or terrified, nor will any be missing,' declares the Lord..."

"'Behold! The day comes when I will raise up for David a righteous branch, and he shall reign as king and execute justice in the land. In his days, Judah will be saved. And this is his name: Zedekiah!'"

The crowd murmured in puzzlement. Who could this be — this Zedekiah? The name meant "the Lord is righteousness." But of whom was it spoken? Jeconiah now sat upon the throne of Judah. But the description of this preacher hardly applied to the weak-jawed son of Jehoiakim. In his few public appearances Jeconiah evidenced a distinctly tentative air, as if he would greatly have preferred to avoid all this notice. Who could this prophet be referring to?

From the back of the crowd, a man shouted at Jeremiah, "Hey, preacher! When will these things happen — this king, these good days?" Avidly the eyes of the crowd turned back to Jeremiah, waiting for an answer.

Jeremiah looked at them. He had often, as he spoke to the people, been heckled, been jeered at. But rarely had he seen honest questioning in the eyes of the people.

Storm clouds gathered over Judah. From the cracks in the palace walls leaked rumors of Jehoiakim's failure to send tribute to Babylon. Speculation was rife of the imminent coming of Nebuchadrezzar — a coming which could have but one result. In these days of uncertainty, the folk in the streets were eager for anything which seemed hopeful.

They waited for the prophet's reply to the questioner. Their eyes asked silently: When? When may we no longer live in fear?

He gathered his breath to answer.

"'In those days,' says the Lord, 'people will no longer say,

"As surely as the Lord lives, who brought His people out of Egypt..." Instead, they will say, "As surely as the Lord lives, who brought His people back from the land of the north and out of all the countries where He had banished them..." Then they will live in their own land...'"

The people wandered away, pondering the enigmatic words of the oracle. The prophet Hananiah stood to one side, stroking his beard with thoughtfully narrowed eyes. *Zedekiah*, he thought. What use could be made of this troublemaker's words?

As Jeremiah prepared to leave, a figure clad in the white linen and gold sash of the priests approached him. The prophet stiffened, fearing a reprisal by Pashhur and his minions. But the fine-boned, earnest-faced young man drew near to him, and Jeremiah could see the anguish written on his visage.

"Teacher..." the young priest began.

It had been long since Jeremiah had been addressed with such a respectful title. He placed his hand firmly on the priest's shoulder, with his eyes encouraging the younger man to continue.

"...I am deeply troubled in spirit. The words you have been speaking — for many days now they strike a chord within me that I can neither ignore nor fully understand. I sense inevitability in your message, and it fills me with a sadness almost too great to bear. If I talk of these things with my brother priests, I will be despised. Yet if I do not speak, I despise myself." He paused, searching within for words he did not know.

"Who are you, my son?" asked Jeremiah softly.

"I am Ezekiel, son of Buzi."

"Then listen to me, Ezekiel son of Buzi," said Jeremiah. "Do not quench the voice within your heart. Attend carefully; drink deeply. It may be you are being taught lessons you will be called upon later to give to others."

"When? What others?"

Jeremiah scanned the face of Ezekiel.

"That I cannot say. It lies beyond my vision." He gripped the younger man's shoulder a last time, and walked away. Ezekiel looked after him — then turned his steps toward the gate of the Temple.

JEREMIAH STOOD in the Street of the Winesellers, his voice raised to the crowd which had gathered to listen: "This is what the Lord says to the men of Judah and to Jerusalem: 'Break up your fallow ground, and don't sow among thorns! Circumcise yourselves to the Lord! Circumcise your hearts, you men of Judah and Jerusalem, or My wrath will break out and burn like fire because of the evil you have done...'"

As his voice fell silent and the crowd began to drift away, a dusty, tired-looking man approached him, staring curiously. Squint interposed himself between Jeremiah and the stranger, but the prophet placed a hand on Squint's shoulder.

"It's all right, Squint," he said, his brow wrinkled as he studied the man who stood before him now. Something was oddly familiar about him.

"Are...are you Jeremiah...of Anathoth?" the man asked.

Recognition burst across his mind like a sudden vision. "Othniel!" His mind spun. The last time he had seen Joash's youngest son was...was some twenty-five years before, at the ill-fated Passover feast in his father's house. A cloak of sadness fell about his shoulders as he contemplated the years and distance between himself and his kin.

He turned again to his nephew. "How goes it with your father?"

"He is dead." Othniel's voice was weak, bleached of life, but it seemed to strike Jeremiah with blindness. With a pang he saw only the moment of his last words spoken in Joash's hearing, words of condemnation and judgment. Though the oracle had been directed at Lemuel and not Joash, Jeremiah could not help regretting that his oldest brother's last memories of him were an angry voice and a wrathful countenance.

A long silence trod by like a line of mourners, as Jeremiah grieved for a brother he had never really known.

Then he saw again his nephew standing before him. Othniel waited impassively. Finally he reached into his robe and produced a wallet, which he held out toward his uncle. "Here... take this." Jeremiah glanced from the wallet to Othniel, uncomprehending.

Othniel explained. "Each year, my father laid up a portion for you, according to a promise he said he made before you left.

On his deathbed, he made me lay my hand on his thigh and swear I would deliver this to you and fulfill his oath. Now take it. He said it was yours."

The young man offered the purse. Jeremiah could hear the muffled rattle of coins inside. As he slowly, almost mindlessly, began reaching out to take the wallet, he thought he saw a trace of irritation, or perhaps resentment, in the face of his nephew. His fingers pulled back.

Othniel saw his uncle's hesitation; it was enough to unleash the bitter words in his heart: "But why should my father do anything good for you? What good have you ever done your family? Your name is a reproach in Anathoth. Your father and mother were taunted into their graves by the shame you brought upon them. My father's sweat and sinew are in this bag, and you do not deserve to share in it." The young man paused, his chest heaving.

"Yet I would not have my father forsworn," he continued. "Though my older brothers will beat me if they discover what I have done, for my father's sake I will give you what you have not earned." He threw the wallet contemptuously on the ground, spun on his heel, and walked quickly away into the gathering dusk.

In stunned silence Jeremiah began moving haltingly toward his house, a hand on each side of his face. Squint stared after him for a moment — then hastily snatched the wallet from the ground, and followed.

26

THE TENTH OF NISAN was a bright blue day awash in sunlight and the frenetic jubilation of spring. Birds drenched the air over Jerusalem with song, incongruous with the grieving quiet of the city and the taciturn discipline of the Chaldean host gathered rank upon glittering rank before the walls of Zion.

The army's vast silence was more frightening than shouted war cries — as if by its very presence it conquered. Nebuchadrezzar himself was there, standing like an avenging deity clad in polished bronze armor beneath a canopy of brilliant red silk — a splash of blood on the plateau before the Ephraim Gate.

Jeconiah walked on wobbly legs down the side of Mount Moriah. Passing like a shade through the streets of the city, past the aghast faces of his subjects, he made his way to the square before the Ephraim Gate. Giving the order to the guards, he waited as the huge gates creaked heavily open, then walked out alone.

Mattaniah watched from the Hanameel Tower as his nephew tiptoed toward the pavilion of the Chaldean ruler. He was a pathetic sight as he made his pilgrimage of defeat — even on this day Jeconiah tried to avoid unnecessary notice. Despite his jealousy of even the short time his brother's son had sat upon the throne, Mattaniah could hardly bear to see the shame of the king.

It was a voiceless tableau of futility: Jerusalem wishing to turn her face away from the sight, yet watching as one weeping soul while her king groveled before the angry emperor.

Nebuchadrezzar looked down at the pitiful figure on the ground before him. Oddly, he felt disappointed. This meek compliance was anticlimactic. He had come here prepared to wreak an awful vengeance on the conniving Jehoiakim, only to find himself cheated by the wretch's untimely death. And now his son opened the gates of his capital and crawled on his belly, depriving Nebuchadrezzar of the satisfaction of razing this rebellious city's walls. Still, he could not allow Jehoiakim's cheating to go unpunished.

He motioned to the scribe at the rear of the pavilion. The cleric bowed, offering the emperor a clay tablet, still wet, awaiting the impression of the signet ring on the emperor's finger.

"In consequence of your disobedience," Nebuchadrezzar read in a harsh voice, "your land will pay not only the tribute in arrears, but a penalty of seven times the amount which should have been sent."

A faint gasp came from the prone figure of Jeconiah, but he did not move or raise his head.

"Further, this rebellious people will be dispersed to such other portions of our dominion as may please us. No longer shall they live in this land, since they have mocked our decrees and our just rule.

"A tally shall be made of all the people in this country — their flocks, their herds, their crops, their children, their wives, their servants. To the land of Chaldea we shall take such of these as please us. They will live there and await our pleasure and that of our loyal subjects.

"So let it be done," he finished, and pressed the crest of his ring into the damp clay.

He looked down once more at the dishonored king. "Get up," he said, "and go tell your people what you have brought upon them." He turned away in disgust.

Jeconiah rose and limped back toward the city's open gates.

JEREMIAH WALKED past the house of the seller of purple — one of his former employers. A woman sat in the street beside the house, wailing and tossing dust on her head. People hurried past, sneaking furtive glances at her, not wanting to acknowledge her or share in any measure of her pain. Her plight was too common in Jerusalem these days.

Nailed to the doorpost of the spacious house was a notice, written on parchment in the script of both the Hebrews and the Chaldeans: Under penalty of death, the occupants of this house were ordered to gather such possessions as might be carried with them, and to appear immediately before Nebuzaradan, the commander of the royal guard of Nebuchadrezzar, for escort to Babylon.

Jeremiah approached the moaning woman. He recognized the wife of the cloth merchant. "Zipporah," he said, squatting in front of her, "why are you here, and not with your husband?"

"They were here when I left this morning to go to the house of my son," she whimpered, shaking her head. "But when I returned just now, the house was empty — and they are gone ...all gone!"

She hid her face in her hands and rocked back and forth in the dust, weeping in great, wet groans of misery.

Jeremiah stepped inside the house. It had been stripped — again, not an unusual occurrence these days. Moments after a house's owners were evicted, anything left inside was plundered by the poor or, more often, by greedy neighbors.

A confused social shift was taking place. Whole sections of the upper echelons of Judean society were being scooped up in the net cast by Nebuchadrezzar's decree, and those left behind were eagerly scrambling to take the places of their less fortunate betters. The avarice and self-serving scavengery taking place, even in the face of such a rending event as this reverse exodus into slavery, sickened Jeremiah to the heart.

He went outside to help Zipporah look for her family.

PASHHUR KNELT beside the altar of incense in the outer sanctuary. For hours now he had been trying to pray — to summon words which would make Yahweh intervene. Did He not see what passed here, in the very city of His Name? Infidels strode through her streets, casually wreaking havoc on every decent family, every respectable house. Her king, the heir of David and Solomon, was to be carried to Babylon like a bird in a cage. Did the Almighty have no regard for His people? Was it for nothing that Pashhur had offered up sacrifices night and day, until the smoke of the burning was in his nostrils even when he slept? He had followed the prescribed forms, had scrupulously kept the ordinances. Why had the Eternal allowed this immense calamity to happen?

As he struggled for words to express the confusion in his soul, he heard the sound of marching footsteps. A ringing of voices broke out in the courtyard. Rising from his place, he ran to the doorway and froze in horror at the sight: A detachment of Babylonian infantry marched toward him — unclean ones entering the house of the Lord!

A group of Levites rushed at the soldiers. As Pashhur watched, the Chaldeans mowed them down in swift, efficient order.

As the last Levite corpse fell in a bloodied heap, the commander of the patrol strode arrogantly up to where Pashhur stood, leaning weakly against the pillar of Jachin. "Show me where you keep the gold and silver," the officer demanded brusquely. "You and it will be coming to Babylon."

Pashhur stared from the tangled pile of bodies in the courtyard to the blunt, businesslike face of the commander. He could not speak. The commander turned and called to some of his men. They came and struck the aged priest on the mouth, then clapped manacles on his wrists.

Calmly the commander strolled inside the outer sanctuary, inspecting the equipment and furnishings with a practiced eye. He began pointing this way and that, and the soldiers were soon busily at work, prying the gold and precious stones loose from artifacts consecrated to the Lord centuries before by the great King Solomon.

With no more remorse than that of thieves, they broke open the vault and bundled up the censers, the gold and silver utensils, and the ceremonial implements guarded so carefully by the Levites and priests, some since the time of Moses himself.

As Pashhur watched in helpless revulsion, the Chaldeans quickly and efficiently ravished the soul of the nation.

IN THE COURTYARD of the Porch of Pillars, Jeremiah watched as Jeconiah, Nehushta the queen mother, and other members of the royal household prepared to leave Jerusalem forever. In these days the prophet went about as he pleased. So bitter was the cup Nebuchadrezzar had forced upon the city that no one had the energy or the will to care what Jeremiah did or said.

The commander Nebuzaradan supervised the eviction of

the royal household. He stood nearby, watching the loading of the family's provisions with a baleful eye.

Jeconiah looked ashen as he gazed about like a soul wandering from its grave. For three months he had tasted kingship. Now he appeared as one who had eaten wormwood.

The prophet approached quietly and laid a hand on the arm of the fearful boy-king. Jeconiah flinched away from the touch.

"Who are you?" he demanded warily.

"I am Jeremiah," he replied gently, "a prophet of the Most High."

"You! You are he who denounced my father all the days of his life, and who kept preaching the downfall of this city! What have I to do with you?" The young man's eyes issued a frightened challenge.

Jeremiah's eyes were deep wells of sorrow. "Do you think I derive pleasure from proclaiming distress for my people? In the days before the Lord's judgment came upon the land, I was thought a madman, a traitor. Now it is even worse. In these days I am like a man who predicts the onset of his own leprosy. Being correct is far worse than being wrong."

With a sigh Jeremiah stretched his arms wide. "I have experienced the agony of this day for thirty years, my king. For a generation I have carried the shame of the exile of my people within my breast like a malignant disease. And now that the time has come, how can you imagine that I rejoice in the fulfillment of the words I have spoken?

He moved half a step closer to the king and looked earnestly into his eyes. "But this is not what I wished to say to you, my king. The days will not always be as evil as this. The Lord has shown me this, too: A time will come when He will redeem a remnant of His people. Again shall He look with favor on the house of Judah. Remember this, my king. And cling to this hope."

Their eyes locked. "Is this all, then?" queried Jeconiah. It was not a demand — it was the plea of a child for reassurance.

"Better comfort I cannot give, my king," said Jeremiah sadly. "I speak only the words I know."

Nebuzaradan strode up and barked, "All right, then. Let's get moving!

"Who's this?" he demanded, pointing at Jeremiah.

"It's all right, sir," assured Jeconiah. "This is..."—he looked again at Jeremiah—"a prophet. A holy man of our God. He came to comfort me."

"Indeed?" sniffed Nebuzaradan, inspecting Jeremiah dubiously. "And what sort of god might yours be?"

"He is the Lord, the One God of heaven and earth," said Jeremiah in a low, firm voice. "It is He who has raised up your master as a punishment for the sins of His people Israel. It is He who establishes kings, and He who appoints the hour of their downfall. He has given Jerusalem into your hands, until the hour of His judgment is fulfilled."

Nebuzaradan opened his mouth several times to answer, but thought better of it. At last, he cleared his throat and turned away from Jeremiah. "Let's be off!" he shouted. "We've wasted enough time, and the day grows no longer." Casting a long, last look at the prophet, the commander strode away to oversee the the pack train's departure.

Jeconiah rejoined the others of his household, who now were weeping. He glanced over his shoulder to look back once more at the plain, tired-looking preacher with the sorrowful eyes. But Jeremiah was gone.

NEBUCHADREZZAR, despoiler of Assyria, scourge of Egypt, emperor of the Land of the Two Rivers, sat at his ease upon the throne of David in the Great Hall of Solomon, showing no awareness of the ill-concealed hostility among the Judeans in attendance. Let them gnash their teeth and clench their fists, he had decided; this act was necessary to demonstrate his absolute dominion over their troublesome little country. Besides, his hand-picked guards, standing in ranks all about the hall, were poised to react swiftly and with finality to any overt challenge.

A Babylonian satrap was reading a proclamation to the small, faded-looking group of Hebrews. Among them stood Mattaniah, younger brother of the rebellious Jehoiakim, whose death had cheated Nebuchadrezzar of exacting a more personal retribution for his violation. Nebuchadrezzar believed he could work with this young man. Time, of course, would tell.

"And because of his clemency," the reader continued in his

nasal voice, "the grand and mighty Nebuchadrezzar purposes that Judah shall have a leader from among her own people. This leader shall use the title of king, and shall reign over his people, the servants of Nebuchadrezzar, emperor of Babylon, in the name and with the protection of Nebuchadrezzar. Insofar as he maintains faith with the good and gracious emperor, he shall be maintained in all manner and likeness as king of his people.

"But shall he default in his loyalty to the just and wise rule of Nebuchadrezzar"—the satrap's voice dipped in an inflection of caution—"or fail to secure in his subjects, the servants of Nebuchadrezzar, their loyalty, or break or cause to be broken any of the just and wise ordinances of the emperor, he shall cede any further protection and favor of the emperor, and shall incur the swift and terrible punishment of Nebuchadrezzar.

"So let it be done," he concluded matter-of-factly.

The emperor nodded, his lidded gaze gliding coolly from one Hebrew face to the next. Their eyes were all carefully downcast.

Finally he studied Mattaniah. "Come, Mattaniah," he said at last, "and take the throne I have given you."

Nebuchadrezzar rose and stood to one side.

Mattaniah came immediately forward, carefully mounting the dais to the throne. Reaching the topmost level, he first made obeisance toward Nebuchadrezzar, then stood in front of the throne.

"In what name," asked the satrap, his pen poised above a tablet, "do you take the throne so graciously bestowed upon you by the high and exalted Emperor Nebuchadrezzar?"

Mattaniah glanced toward Hananiah, standing quietly at the foot of the dais. Slowly the prophet nodded his head. Taking a deep breath and facing the satrap, Mattaniah announced, "From this day on I will reign and be known as Zedekiah." With a shrug, the satrap scribbled the name in his records.

At the foot of the dais, Hananiah smiled secretly. There! From the troublemaker's own lips had come the name of the new king. Let the man from Anathoth chew on that.

PART III

The
Lament

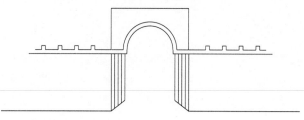

27

NATHAN STOOD in the courtyard before the Ephraim Gate, surveying the scurrying crowds. Though his vision was not as keen as in his apprenticeship under his old master Jehiel, his eye for human nature had intensified with age, and the sweeping changes in Judah had created a whole new market for his product. Times had never been better.

The prophet entered middle age gracefully; his silvery beard flowed down his chest in a silken, rippling cascade. His paunch had grown through the years, an evidence of his prosperity.

Catching the eye of Benjamin, his assistant, standing among the thronging crowds, he nodded, and stepped up onto a low stone wall. Flinging his arms wide, he raised his face to the sky, eyes closed, and in a practiced, powerful voice, began to ply his trade.

"People of Jerusalem! Hear the burden of the Lord, which He has placed upon my heart! Listen now as His words are proclaimed!"

Gradually the bustle slowed, as the people of Jerusalem turned to hear the message of Nathan.

"This is what the Lord says: 'Behold! I have punished the children of Jacob, and I have beaten the sons of Israel with many stripes! The sound of weeping is heard in the land, mothers crying aloud for their sons swallowed up by the Two Rivers! A brother wanders the streets, asking, "Where is my sister?" A wife groans on her bed at night, saying, "Where is my husband?" But listen to Me,' says the Lord!

"'I will not always turn My face from Judah. Those I have sent away bear with them My wrath. I have purified Jacob, and now I will bless this land which I have promised to you and to your fathers. Lift up your faces, for I will surely establish you,' says the Lord!

"'As surely as My temple stands in this place, I will relent of the evil I have done in the land, and I will hear your prayers. I will bring back the captives, and I will restore the sons of David,' says the Lord Almighty…"

The listeners nodded to themselves, acknowledging the self-evident logic of Nathan's oracle. The prophet calculated their mood as he spoke. He felt himself to be riding the wave-crests of their emotions, running before the irresistible winds of the people and the times. He felt invincible, omniscient. He was in control.

JEREMIAH WANDERED aimlessly through the busy market-place of Jerusalem. Sellers and buyers scuttled everywhere, but the prophet's thoughts were far removed from the agitated stir of commerce. He was an island of restless malaise in a rambunctious sea of enterprise.

Jeremiah's heart felt cold. Months had passed since Nebuchadrezzar's abduction of the cream of Judah's citizens, but the time had done little to heal the ragged wound in his spirit. All about him the people gathered themselves together and went on with their lives, but Jeremiah felt a cavity, a nagging absence within which persistently whispered that what had passed was not a conclusion, but a prelude. His deep sense of foreboding gave the lie to the city's hectic hustle, which seemed to him a sort of false optimism by the sickbed — a forced cheerfulness intended to soothe the ill, but empty of healing.

As he walked through the crowded mazes of the bazaar, his eye fell upon a stall occupied by a seller of figs. The owner and his son were busily sorting through a mound of the fruit, culling the unsuitable figs into one basket, the edible fruit into another. For some reason the sight of the two baskets of fruit resonated with something deep inside his mind. He stopped his random promenade through the marketplace, stared at the figs, and searched within himself… Two baskets of figs — one good and one bad…

And then the Voice spoke with a soundless thunder inside his mind.

"Jeremiah! What do you see?"

"Two baskets of figs," Jeremiah replied. "One good, full of desirable fruit, the other full of fruit so bad that it is useless."

A passer-by glanced oddly at the old man who stood in the middle of the marketplace, talking to himself. He shook his head and hurried on.

"You have seen correctly. And like the good figs, so I regard the exiles from Judah whom I sent away from this place to the land of the Babylonians. My eyes watch over them for their good, and I will bring them back to this land...

"I will give them a heart to know Me, that I am the Lord. They will be My people, and I will be their God, for they will return to Me with all their heart.

"But like the poor figs, so I will deal with Zedekiah king of Judah, his officials, and the survivors in Jerusalem, whether they remain in this land or live in Egypt. I will make them abhorrent and offensive to all the kingdoms of the earth, a reproach and a byword...

"I will send the sword, famine and plague against them until they are destroyed from the land I gave to them and their fathers."

KING ZEDEKIAH huddled with his advisers in a chamber in the House of Lebanon. It was night, and the room was thick with the smoke from the oil lamps and the cloying, heady scent of intrigue.

"I did not take the throne of David to sit meekly by while Nebuchadrezzar runs roughshod over the people of this land!" the king said hotly. "My father was bold, but overly trusting in the vagaries of fortune. I propose to be as bold as he, but with more careful planning, more craft, more attention to detail." Intently he gazed at the underlit faces around the table, willing them to agree with his vision of himself.

"For every cruelty practiced by the Chaldeans upon this land, other nations have grievances as great against the king of Babylon. All the lands round about — Edom, Moab, Tyre; yes, and Philistia too — all have felt the heel of Nebuchadrezzar. Judah is not alone in her misery!

"What I propose," said the king, leaning closer, drawing them in, knitting them to his purpose, "is that we forge an alliance. Let us play upon the anger of all the surrounding kingdoms toward Chaldea, alloy their wrath with ours into a weapon that can be wielded against our common foe. What could be more natural? Singly none of us could hope to stand against the might of Babylon. But together...together with a single will, a single purpose — to resist the heavy-handed oppression — we might wrest freedom from the jaws of tyranny. How can we not press toward such a worthy goal?"

His shining stare, fierce with the blood of the sons of David, rang its challenge at them. None of the counselors made reply, but they were careful to avoid the appearance of dissent. They all nodded thoughtfully, stroking their beards and squinting in calculation — all, that is, except the aged Elnathan. Slowly he began to shake his ancient, grizzled head. An uncomfortable pause ensued, as everyone waited for the king to react to this contradiction from his oldest adviser.

"Son of Achbor, you have misgivings?" the king asked, reluctant to surrender control of the palaver, yet unable to think of a suitable alternative.

"I distrust this plan of treating with the surrounding kings," began Elnathan in a worn, cracking voice. "For all the history of our people they have been hostile to us, oppressing us when they can, sabotaging us when they dared not act openly. And besides, I have heard the prophet Jeremiah say..."

"Ah, the prophet Jeremiah!" Hananiah spoke for the first time. "If all one does is predict doom, soon or late one must be proved correct!"

The attention in the room shifted to the suave and well-manicured prophet, who sat at a slight remove from the others, flicking an imaginary piece of lint from his finely spun robes.

He raised his eyes to meet theirs. "We live in rapidly changing times, my brothers," he said smoothly, "and change is never comfortable. Yet with the discomfort comes opportunity, for those with the vision to see it.

"This ragtag preacher from Anathoth has a persistent bellyache, and he has filled Jerusalem with his whining for over thirty years now. Yet there are other voices, other messages, from sources with as much right to be heard." Modestly he studied the backs of his hands, as he allowed the tone and content of his words to take their effect. More than anything else, he knew what the king wanted to hear. This was his particular genius, and he employed it with great effect. Timing was all, and it had carried the day for him on numerous occasions.

"Well said, Hananiah!" pronounced Zedekiah, beaming. "We should always be willing to weigh all the factors, shouldn't we?" The king allowed a brief silence to endorse his assessment. Then he slapped the table decisively, and went on: "Let us study this matter, and I will wish to hear more from you soon." He rose, signaling that the conference was at an end.

Grumbling into his beard, Elnathan levered himself to his feet and tottered away, his cane tapping feebly against the stone floor. As Zedekiah watched him go, Hananiah glided smoothly up beside the king.

"When one approaches dotage," the prophet observed quietly, "the voices of the grave whisper so loudly one can hear little else."

THE DAY WAS HOT, and Squint straightened from his crouch over the brick molds, wincing as the muscles in his lower back and calves twanged with the sharp, brief pains of relief. He scraped the thick brownish-red mud from his palms with a flat stick, then wiped his forehead and pate with the sleeve of his garment. He stood in the gate of a large house in a well-to-do quarter of the city.

He had hired himself out as a mason's helper. They had laid three courses of mud brick for the merchant's guest house, and the fourth was drying in the molds he tended. This had been a good job; the pay was fair and the work would be steady for another few days.

As he massaged the fatigued muscles of his neck, he noticed a rider coming down the street toward him, his face covered with a burnoose after the manner of the bedouins of the Arabah. The rider dismounted, knocking in an odd rhythm at a small gate set in the wall, which separated the street from the back of the palace compound. The door opened a small crack, and the hooded rider muttered some sort of password. Squint recognized the accent as Moabite. Thoughtfully he returned to his work.

SAKHRI SAT on the sunbaked terrace, gratefully feeling the heat seep into his aching, aged joints. In these blazing summer months, younger men occupied themselves in trying to keep cool; the ambassador's rheumatic bones, however, craved warmth above all else. The hot discomfort on his skin was more than compensated by the relief it gave his weary old joints.

He heard the soft pad of a servant's bare feet behind him. He shifted on the reed mat, craning his neck to see who approached. The young male slave bowed his head. "Honored master, a visitor seeks an audience with you."

"Well are you going to tell me who it is," snapped the ambassador peevishly, "or shall I begin guessing?"

"He would not give his name, nor state the nature of his errand," the slave murmured. "But..."

"Yes, what is it?"

"To your humble servant's ear, his accent sounded Hebrew."

"Indeed..." Sakhri squinted, pursing his lips in reflection. "Very well, send him to me." The slave padded away, and Sakhri shifted himself heavily on the mat, seeking a more comfortable position.

He listened patiently as the shifty-eyed envoy from Jerusalem stated his case. Prince Mattaniah, now King Zedekiah, wished to remind the worthy and well-esteemed Pharaoh of the understandings reached several years before between their two nations...

"Yes, yes, yes," interrupted Sakhri. "I don't need some tiresome rehearsal of the past to remind me that I made a bargain which promised nothing and gained less."

"But — but my lord," stammered the envoy after a startled pause, "you agreed to suggest that the Pharaoh support King Jehoiakim in his effort to wrest control of Judah from Babylon, in exchange for certain strategic considerations—"

"And your king expected the Pharaoh to take the field against Nebuchadrezzar for no greater gain than that?" cut in Sakhri sharply. "When did Judah become a province of Egypt, that she deserves such unilateral intervention from the prince of the Nile? Next I suppose you'll blame me that Jehoiakim had the poor sense to die before the uprising could be born." The ambassador snorted and looked away. These Hebrews were a presumptuous lot! Besides, Sakhri had not exactly mentioned the Judean affair to Pharaoh, not in so many words. Oh, they had discussed the theoretical possibilities perhaps...but nothing more. Since then, Hophra the Younger had ascended the throne in Egypt, and here came Jehoiakim's younger brother — one more Hebrew king whining to Pharaoh for deliverance from an unwanted yoke.

Sakhri listened with a bit more interest — although he was careful to give no outward evidence — as the Hebrew haltingly described the embryonic alliance Zedekiah sought to fashion among the half-heathen desert kingdoms of the Arabah and the country east of the Salt Sea. This was slightly more promising than the vague commitment of puny Judah alone. Perhaps if the barbarians did indeed remain firm in their resolve...

Sakhri again interrupted the nervous emissary. "I have heard you, and I will consider what you have said. Perhaps I will mention it to the exalted Pharaoh Hophra. And it may be that he will decide to intercede in this matter. I do not know. You may tell your master so much, and no more."

Nervously the envoy bowed his way from Sakhri's presence. The ambassador sighed. He had outlived two pharaohs. He was too old for the serpentine intricacies of diplomacy. Still, Hophra would perhaps be interested in the alliance, if a joining of such unequal parts could be so characterized.

Sakhri turned his head as far as his arthritic joints and his flabby bulk would allow. "Boy," he said to the young slave attending him, "bring my writing supplies. I must compose a message for the Pharaoh."

28

THE *SHOFARIM* BLARED in the winter air as the crowds cheered the appearance of each delegation. Jerusalem was decked in her finest. Banners hung in a profligate chaos of color from every wall. The Mishnah Gate was a bedlam of waving arms and shouting voices. Enthusiastic mobs lined the streets leading from the gate to the palace, chanting their support for the kings of the grand alliance as their servants and ministers made their ceremonial way to the Porch of Pillars, where a magnificent feast was spread to celebrate the founding of the league which would enable the region to throw off the hated shackles of Babylon.

Hamesh, envoy and brother of the king of the Edomites, rode a coal-black charger which snorted and pranced, its nostrils showing red and the whites of its eyes shining in stark contrast to its gleaming ebony hide. Hamesh wore a coat of whitest fleece against the day's chill, and a wide leather belt cinched about his waist supported a shining broadsword with a hilt of carved ivory. About him marched thirty handpicked guards, each clad like their commander.

Jehozabad, son of the king of Moab, rode in a chariot carved from a single huge section of the trunk of an oak. The finely polished wood glistened in the sun, and the metal spokes of the wheels flashed fire. Every so often the prince would reach into a small pouch at his side and scatter a few small silver coins to the crowds along the way. He looked invincible as he rode, laughing and jesting with the cheering multitudes.

Even the kings of Philistia had sent their ambassadors, riding in palanquins of ebony wood, draped with rich, gold-trimmed purple linen. Tyre and Sidon, too, had thrown in with the nations of the confederation, and Judah was shouting the praises of Zedekiah, the wise king who had conceived the bold master plan.

Adding to optimism was the news of a rebellion within the ranks of Nebuchadrezzar's army. Certain generals, disaffected by their leader's dispensation of several coveted territories, had taken up arms against the ruler of Chaldea.

This was a day for celebration, for martial pride, for the swearing of oaths and the rattling of swords. Great things were afoot in Judah, and anything was possible.

The emissaries wound their way up Mount Moriah. With great pomp and much exchanging of gifts, each delegation assumed its place around the huge banquet table spread on the portico opening onto the largest courtyard in the palace compound. The courtyard, normally forbidden to all except the royal and noble families, was on this day crowded with a jostling, milling mob of eager onlookers. Zedekiah had given orders that as many people as possible be allowed to witness this triumph of diplomacy. Accordingly, the courtyard was filled to capacity — even the tops of the walls surrounding the square were lined with spectators.

After the meal, surely the most public in the history of Judah, each envoy rose to make a speech concluded by the pledging of a cup. Each oration seemed more eloquent than the last, the loud huzzahs of the admiring crowd more and more exuberant. At last it was Zedekiah's turn, as host, to make the final pledge. As he rose from his place at the center of the table, his glance roved over the mass of his people gathered to watch as he took his place in history.

At the back, near the gate of the courtyard, a swirling eddy in the sea of faces evidenced some disturbance. As the king looked on, he could trace the progress through the throng of a single oddly postured figure. As the fellow neared the front, Zedekiah was astounded to find him a tall, slender, gray-haired man with, of all things, a yoke strapped about his neck and shoulders.

The king stood silent, his mouth agape. The strange figure, with eyes never deviating from their stern grip on his own, strode purposefully toward the steps of the portico. Oddly, even the guards at the base of the steps did not bar the man's

way, so startling was his appearance. Zedekiah heard Hananiah, seated just behind his left shoulder, muttering quietly,
"My king, this is Jeremiah, the troublemaker from Anathoth. He
should not be permitted— "

Then Jeremiah spoke, in a voice like the unsheathing of a
sword.

"This is what the Lord Almighty, the God of Israel says."
The prophet's gaze swept the banquet table, pausing in turn at
each of the envoys. "Tell this to your masters: 'With My great
power and outstretched arm I made the earth and its people
and the animals that are on it, and I give it to anyone I please.
Now I will hand all your countries over to My servant Nebuchadrezzar, king of Babylon. I will make even the wild animals subject to him. All nations will serve him and his son and
his grandson until the time for his land comes; then many nations and great kings will subjugate him.

"'If, however, any nation or kingdom will not serve Nebuchadrezzar, king of Babylon, or bow its neck under his yoke, I
will punish that nation with the sword, famine and plague,' declares the Lord, 'until I destroy it by his hand...'"

A dagger slithered from the sheath of one of the bodyguards of Hamesh of Edom, but the prince placed a hand on his
man's wrist. Even among Edomites it was ill fortune to slay in
cold blood a messenger of the gods.

"'So do not listen to your prophets, your diviners, your in-
terpreters of dreams, your mediums, or your sorcerers who tell
you, "You will not serve the king of Babylon." They prophesy
lies to you that will only serve to remove you far from your
lands. I will banish you, and you will perish.

"'But if any nation will bow its neck under the yoke of the
king of Babylon and serve him, I will let that nation remain in
its own land to till it and to live there,' declares the Lord."

The prophet challenged them with his steely gaze for a moment more, then turned and walked back the way he had come.
The crowd parted before him, as if afraid of contact.

Haltingly, Zedekiah made the address he had planned, but
his words sounded shrill, hollow — even to himself. He finished
with what should have been a rousing appeal to nationalistic
pride, but the muted response from the crowd only confirmed

the pall cast over the proceedings by the strange preacher, who had appeared like a vision and vanished just as suddenly. The faint echo of his words seemed to hang in the clear air of the courtyard, as if even the stones in the walls whispered their endorsement: "Serve the king of Babylon!"

HANANIAH was truly confounded. He had just come from the palace where the king sat in a blue funk within his chambers, fuming and fretting over Jeremiah's words. Despite all the elaborate preparation, despite the overwhelming and even frenzied concurrence of the populace of Judah, despite the clear logic of the accord with the surrounding nations — one man, acting alone, had been able with a few words to unravel the carefully woven tapestry of Zedekiah's resolve.

What gave this fellow his uncanny sense of timing? And the yoke he wore as he uttered his grim predictions — very effective. Grudgingly Hananiah was forced to admire the man who, even now, days later, still wandered the streets in his queer garb, preaching submission to Nebuchadrezzar at the top of his voice. Hananiah's eloquence and carefully cultivated contacts had never produced as strong an effect as that of the unpredictable blurtings from this deranged malcontent.

But how to neutralize the fellow? Hananiah had followed with interest Jeremiah's career — tracking, as it did, so close to his own. What could sway the prophet's future steps?

Pashhur's stocks had not quieted the raging preacher. Hananiah paused, remembering with momentary discomfort the rumors of Jeremiah's prediction of Pashhur's forced relocation to Babylon. An odd coincidence, that...

Jehoiakim's threats and repressions had not solved the problem either, at least not in any final sense. When the ill-tempered king died, there was Jeremiah — ready as always to preach his tidings of death and destruction.

No, Hananiah did not believe the key to the puzzle lay in the use of force. There had to be some other way.

They were living, he reminded himself, at a critical juncture in the history of Judah. It would not do for the delicate balance to be upset by a roving doomsayer and the consternation that followed in his wake. Charting the country's course was a task for calm, reasonable people, those who could see clearly the pieces on the gameboard — people like himself.

He rose and paced the length of his room, running his fingers thoughtfully through his carefully combed beard. Perhaps he would pay a visit to this man, to learn how he might disarm this menace to the nation's well-being.

Yes, he decided. It was time to get better acquainted with Jeremiah of Anathoth.

THEIR MEAGER SUPPER concluded, the three men set about various means of occupying the idle time between the evening meal and sleep: Baruch mixing lampblack and gall to make ink, Squint mending the strap of a thong, Jeremiah reading the words of the prophet Hosea preserved by Mahseiah among the precious scrolls in the clay jar.

A knock came on the door. The three looked at each other in suspicion. By tacit agreement, Squint rose and stepped carefully to the entrance. Planting his sturdy frame squarely, he placed himself so as to block the door with his shoulder as he opened it slowly, cautiously.

"Is this the place of Jeremiah?" asked the well-modulated voice of the stranger. Silence answered.

"Come now," reasoned the caller, "if I wished to harm you, would I not have brought a patrol of guards with me, and simply broken the door down?"

Squint stood still.

"It is Hananiah bar-Azzur who speaks to you. Will you not allow me in?"

"Squint," said Jeremiah after several moments' reflection, "let him in."

Squint opened the door enough to admit Hananiah, whose gaze flicked past Squint, lit for several moments on Baruch, then came finally to rest on Jeremiah.

"Ah. There you are."

The two men stared at each other: Hananiah standing, clad in well-wrought white linen garments with a cloak of pale yellow silk; Jeremiah sitting at the table, still holding the scroll he had been reading, wearing his simple gray tunic of homespun wool, somewhat the worse for wear. In those instants each of the men took the measure of the other. Finally Jeremiah spoke, breaking the spell.

"Would you sit down?"

"Thank you." Hananiah folded his legs and squatted on the other side of the low table, the oil lamp flickering between them.

"Why have you come?" asked Jeremiah. It was a simple query, framed in genuine puzzlement and without hostility.

"I wished to speak to you." Hananiah gazed frankly back at Jeremiah. "I wish to understand why and how you speak as you do."

Another several moments passed as the two men fenced wordlessly with their eyes.

"I speak because I must," said Jeremiah finally. "The Spirit of the Lord compels me..."

"This I understand," said Hananiah. "To know the urging of the Almighty — it is a fearsome thing. And everyone in Jerusalem has surely felt the heat of your blaze, whether he will admit it or not."

He grinned self-deprecatingly. "I must confess, at times I have chafed under the sting of your reproof — and on later reflection been forced to admit some truth in it."

Earnestly, Hananiah sought Jeremiah's eyes as he continued: "You are a good man, Jeremiah, perhaps even a great one — and you have much to teach. But why must your words always be so...so unremittingly pessimistic? This is the land of the promise! Surely Adonai must give you some word that is not gloom and disaster. Doesn't it tire you to always bring messages of such woe?"

"Yes." Jeremiah's shoulders slumped and his gaze fell to the backs of his hands, resting on the table top. "I am weary beyond weariness..." Why did he feel himself on the point of unburdening himself to this man he hardly knew, except by reputation? Hananiah had been the companion and adviser of kings. His circles were those of the great and renowned. Yet tonight, across the table in this dark little upper room, his face was a portrait of compassion. Could it be that he really understood Jeremiah's plight — or wanted to? He claimed to be a prophet. Might he not at times have felt the awful loneliness — the sense of isolation?

"At times I feel as though…as though my only reward for speaking the words of God is to be hated and cursed. So many times I have regretted the day of my birth…"

Hananiah nodded, his brow knit in concern. "Anyone can see," he said with encouragement, "that the burden you bear is too great for human endurance."

"Yes," agreed Jeremiah, "It crushes me at times. But at other times, when He burns in my heart like fire…" Jeremiah rose from the table and walked across the room, trying to master his emotions. After a moment, he turned to face Hananiah, a tremulous sigh wavering in and out of his chest. "When one has tasted the sweet presence of the Lord, no burden seems too great, in order to drink more of His Spirit. And so I must go on speaking." Jeremiah shrugged, shaking his head helplessly.

Hananiah sat quietly, considering the other man's words. Presently, he rose, crossed to Jeremiah, and gripped his shoulder.

"I, too, bear a burden — for this land, this people. So difficult are her days, so diverse her choices. Jeremiah…" Hananiah's voice was weighted with emotion. "I pray night and day for the well-being of our people. And I do not, *cannot* believe that the Lord will forsake those He once promised to make as many as the grains of sand on the seashore."

Jeremiah looked carefully into Hananiah's face. "I hear your words. Yet these are evil days, and the heart of the people is not wholly turned toward the Lord. He will not tolerate pretense, Hananiah, and you should know this well—" Hananiah's face tightened the slightest bit, but he said nothing. "These people have returned to Him only with their lips," Jeremiah continued. "Their hearts are far from Him. Until and unless they return — completely return — I fear there is little hope."

Again the two men's gazes grappled silently, this time until Hananiah spoke first: "I will think deeply about what you have said, Jeremiah of Anathoth. And I will pray to the Lord for words of comfort — for the land…and for you."

"Thank you for your kindness." Jeremiah inclined his head in gratitude.

Hananiah took a last look about the room and its occupants, and slipped out quietly.

Closing the door, Jeremiah regarded his two companions.

Baruch gave a sad little shrug. Squint mutely returned to his mending.

Jeremiah walked slowly to the table, placing his finger alongside the place he had been reading when Hananiah's knock intruded:

> *"Shall I ransom them from the power of Sheol?*
> *Shall I redeem them from death?"*

WALKING BACK to the palace, Hananiah reflected on what he had learned. The man from Anathoth was weary. Indeed, he longed to lay down his burden.

Perhaps a way could be found to help him to do just that...

29

JEREMIAH STOOD in the court of the Temple, his arms spread out as though embracing the city. Still wearing the yoke clamped about him, he preached.

"Submit to the king of Babylon! God has given him dominion over you for a time, until he has accomplished all that the Lord has designed. Serve Nebuchadrezzar, for this is the will of Adonai concerning you..."

As Jeremiah spoke, Hananiah strode through the crowd, a fixed stare of righteous resolve carved onto his features. Jeremiah fell silent as the other prophet, his eyes blazing with fervor, approached him.

Standing beside Jeremiah, Hananiah turned to the throng and said in a loud voice, "This is what the Lord Almighty, the God of Israel says: 'I will break the yoke of the king of Babylon. Within two years I will bring back to this place all the utensils of the Lord's house that Nebuchadrezzar removed to Babylon. I will also bring back to this place Jeconiah, son of Jehoiakim king of Judah, with all the other exiles from Judah who went to Babylon,' declares the Lord. 'For I will break the yoke of the king of Babylon.'"

He turned and gave Jeremiah a glance of steel. The whole of the Temple courtyard was motionless, watching as the silent sparks flew from this confrontation of visions.

After an eternity, Jeremiah inclined his head to Hananiah. "May it be so!" he pronounced, as a sigh of relief whispered through the crowd. "May the Lord do just as you have said, Hananiah."

"Nevertheless, listen to what I say in your hearing and in that of this assembly." Again a hush fell like an invisible shroud over the gathering. "From the earliest days, the prophets who preceded me and you, Hananiah, have pronounced war, disaster, and plagues against many countries and great kingdoms. But to prophesy peace, especially in these days — such a prophet will be validated only when his words have come to pass." His last phrase ringing a warning, Jeremiah fell silent, waiting for Hananiah's response.

Hananiah took hold of the yoke on Jeremiah's neck, lifted it over the other man's head and threw it to the ground. He then grasped the wooden crosspieces and cracked them in pieces over his knees. Raising the broken yoke over his head, he said in a resounding voice, "The Lord says this: 'In the same way, within two years I will break the yoke of Nebuchadrezzar king of Babylon from around the necks of all the nations.'"

Jeremiah answered in a low voice, "I pray to God with all my heart that your vision is sure." Then he walked away through the crowd.

Watching him go, Hananiah smiled inwardly. Using Jeremiah's own prop against him had been as effective as he had hoped. Now let the man of Anathoth be the one to puzzle over an oracle, for a change.

"O LORD GOD," prayed Jeremiah as he wandered the streets of Jerusalem that night, "have I been so wrong? Have I spoken falsely to the people?" He could not dismiss the prophecy uttered so boldly and powerfully by Hananiah, and now felt a churning cauldron of confusion within.

In the years since he had entered the gauntlet of God's calling, he had endured the lash of rejection, the numbing ache of loneliness. He had often doubted his ability to hew to the course Adonai set for him. He had known fear, and the courage to which fear was midwife. He had felt scalding anger — at wrong-spirited people, at stubborn kings...and yes, even at God upon occasion. But never, until this day, had he doubted the unerring relevance of his vision. He had spoken with invulnerable certainty of seventy years in exile, of Jerusalem destroyed, of sons of Judah who would never again see the land of their fathers. Now, however, his feet had been cut from under him by Hananiah's confident words of a soon-coming restoration.

He agonized: "To whose voice have I been listening,

Sovereign Lord, if not to Yours? For what purpose have I endured, if not Your call? Why must I speak words of loathsome substance, if within two years all that Hananiah has said will come to pass?

By the Ophel Tower he leaned against the wall, listening to wild dogs yipping outside in the moonless night.

"For a score of years and half another score, I have preached wrath and violence against this place. Now I am old; my body withers with age; I hear at my back the footsteps of death. And now must I learn that my life has been given to a falsehood? To think this, O my God — it is a spike in my heart!

"Heal me, O Lord, and I will be healed; save me and I will be truly saved. You are the One I praise. Yet men keep saying to me, 'Where is this word of the Lord? Let it now be fulfilled!'"

He walked on, longing for a light that would shine now and reveal the rightness — or the wrongness — of his whole life.

In the city's night his eye caught a glow, there on a nearby rooftop. He had seen a last leap of flame among the dying embers in a brazier. At once he knew that incense to Ashtaroth or Marduk had been offered there only moments before.

His loathing struck in a different, higher jab of pain that surged beyond his earlier hurt. "They mock, Holy God! Though I do not keep silent, though I cry aloud Your words, and have not run away from being a shepherd for Your flock — still they do not believe!"

He fell to his knees. "My God, you know I have not desired the day of despair. Therefore, do not be a terror to me, but instead be my refuge in the day of disaster.

"O Lord Almighty!" he cried, his head upon the dust of the deserted street. "Preserve me from shame and dread..."

THE FIRST BRIGHT pigments of spring had barely appeared on Judah's hillsides when dreadful news limped into Zedekiah's court on the staggering, bleeding legs of a messenger from Moab.

Hastily Zedekiah convened a privy council in an apartment of the winter palace, to listen to the half-dead Moabite.

"The onslaught was fierce and sudden, my lord," he said, his breath still labored. "They came against Kir-Moab without warning, and the capital now lies in ruins…" His voice failed him. Impatiently, Zedekiah signaled a valet to give the fellow a drink. Weakly the messenger sipped a few swallows, spilling most of what was offered to him. Leaning back against the cushion on which he sat, he continued, his voice a bit stronger.

"I myself saw the death of the king, at the hand of the Chaldean commander. And Prince Jehozabad…" Again the man's voice failed, but he waved away the cup, his chest heaving with emotion. After some moments he gained enough control of himself to speak. "Him they emasculated," he whispered hoarsely.

Silence darkened the room.

WITH ALARMING RAPIDITY, similar tidings came from Tyre, from Sidon, from Edom. The emperor's reprisal against the alliance was swift and upon all fronts. Judah had no chance of fielding an army to assist her allies.

By the time news of the Babylonian offensive was but a few days old in Jerusalem, a battalion of Chaldean infantry arrived at her gates. They were only the vanguard. A more massive force was just a few days' march to the north.

ALONE IN THE HALL OF JUDGMENT, Zedekiah sat remembering the ignoble sight of his nephew, Jeconiah, capitulating to Nebuchadrezzar. Today was the day for Zedekiah to make that same journey.

His dreams of independence echoing through his mind in brutal mockery, Zedekiah arose, straightening his clothing. He had put aside his customary robes of purple and gold linen; today he wore a crude shift of rough, hempen sackcloth. His normally carefully braided hair hung in loose, bedraggled hanks, smeared with ashes rather than expensive oils. His feet were bare, and his face streaked with the dust he had tossed upon his head.

Not as a king, but as a beggar, would he go out to the Chaldeans.

"AND SO, your exalted lordship," Zedekiah was saying, his face pressed into the grimy, sweaty sandals of the Chaldean commander, "the rebellious kings of the lands surrounding Judah prevailed upon me, threatening your humble servant with war and mayhem if I did not support their foolish plan. As you have seen, no Hebrew troops opposed you in any of the battles you fought with the ungrateful wretches. Will you not repent of your righteous anger, and spare your humble servant and his people from the fierce wrath of the mighty Nebuchadrezzar?"

Nebuzaradan's lip curled in contempt. This tasted wrong, this whining plea of coercion. But Nebuchadrezzar had deigned to allow this obdurate people yet another chance to prove loyal. Perhaps the boys in the royal court had turned the emperor's ears.

In any case, the commander had no option but to let them off with nothing more severe than another exaction of heavy tribute, and a warning. He yanked his feet from beneath the face of Zedekiah, allowing the Hebrew's face to fall into the dust.

"Get out of my camp," the commander growled. "Your pleas are heard."

JEREMIAH WAS WALKING down the Street of the Potters when the Voice broke long silence and spoke in noiseless peals within his spirit.

"Go to Hananiah, the son of Azzur of Gibeon, and tell him, 'This is what the Lord says: "You have broken a wooden yoke, but in its place you will get a yoke of iron..."

Azzur. Gibeon. The names struck within his mind like a hammer on a spike. He remembered what he had known, but forgotten: the face of Samuel, the human donkey; the blithe callousness with which Azzur, his master, had treated a fellow Hebrew.

In the same way Azzur had used Samuel, so had his son Hananiah used the people and kings of Israel — to further his own interests, with no regard for truth or justice. He had spoken lies to the people in the name of God.

Jeremiah walked to the apartment of Hananiah within the palace of the king, and stepped boldly into his chamber. The surprised prophet jerked about from the window; he had been looking out to the gates where Babylon's army was arrayed.

"Listen, Hananiah!" Jeremiah's eyes were dark, glowing points of holy fury. "The Lord has not sent you, yet you have persuaded this nation to trust in lies. Therefore, this is what the Lord says: 'I am about to remove you from the face of the earth. This very year you are going to die, because you have preached rebellion against the Lord.'"

Hananiah, normally so calm and assured, fell back on his couch as if already stricken. He opened his mouth to speak, but the resonant voice was mute.

Jeremiah wheeled and left the wordless, doomed man among his finery.

AFTER ENOUGH DAYS had passed for Zedekiah's nervous trembling to subside, he sent for Hananiah. He meant to take the prophet severely to task for lending prophetic credence to the confederation gambit. Why, he wanted to know, had the prophet so confidently predicted good fortune for Judah when all that came to pass was disaster?

Impatiently striding to and fro in his council chamber, he awaited the arrival of Hananiah.

Hearing the sound of footsteps behind him, he whirled and was piqued to see not Hananiah, but the valet he had sent to fetch the seer. "Where is Hananiah?" he demanded brusquely.

The servant bowed low. "My king, your humble servant went to the quarters of the prophet Hananiah, just as you commanded. Yet when I arrived, to my great distress I found the illustrious Hananiah ill and fast abed. So ill, indeed, that he cannot rise to meet the summons of the king."

"Ill, is he? We shall see about that." Zedekiah stepped hotly out the chamber door and through the palace halls toward Hananiah's apartment. To think he had sheltered this fool in his own house! Even worse, to think he had listened to such worthless counsel!

Reaching the apartment he flung open the door, strode into the bed chamber — and gasped. The prophet, hale and hearty only days before, lay upon his bed with sunken cheeks, his skin the color of old parchment, his open eyes receding into their sockets.

Hananiah's chest rose and fell in short, shallow gasps. He

turned his wasted eyes and stared at Zedekiah, fear etched on every feature.

Unable to face what he could not understand, Zedekiah shuddered and went out, half-walking, half-running.

30

EZEKIEL HAD JUST finished reading the section of *torah* for the day's devotions. He reverently rewrapped the scroll, kissed it and replaced it in the wooden ark.

Turning to the small group gathered beside the canal, he spread his arms and intoned the *Shema:*

> *"Hear, O Israel — the Lord our God, the Lord is One.*
> *And thou shalt love the Lord thy God, with all thy heart,*
> *with all thy soul, with all thy strength*
> *and with all thy mind..."*

The small congregation chanted in response the haunting anthem of Israel's identity. Outside, the sun began to peek over the flat rim of the delta country of Chaldea.

When the hymn was concluded, Ezekiel nodded to Elasah, son of the revered scribe Shaphan and younger brother of Ahikam, signaling that it was time to read the letter he had brought from Jerusalem.

Forcibly stripped of the surroundings and habits of their native land, the exiles from Judah urgently banded together in this strange new country, drawing mutual support and cultural survival from their new fellowship. They had no more Temple, but they had each other in a way they never had before.

Elasah stood and unrolled the parchment. He briefly glanced at the assembly and announced, "These are the words of Jeremiah of Anathoth, the prophet in Jerusalem, concerning you, the exiles of Judah." The listeners stirred. Jeremiah's words were granted a retrospective deference here in Babylon that they did not enjoy in Judah.

Elasah began to read:

"This is what the Lord Almighty, the God of Israel, says to all those carried into exile from Jerusalem to Babylon:

"'Build houses and settle down. Plant gardens and eat what they produce. Marry and have sons and daughters; find wives for your sons and give your daughters in marriage, so that they too may have sons and daughters. Increase in number there, do not decrease.

"'And seek the peace and prosperity of the city to which I have carried you into exile. Pray to the Lord for it, because if it prospers, you too will prosper.'

"Yes, this is what the Lord Almighty says: 'Do not let the prophets and diviners among you deceive you. Do not listen to the dreams you urge them to have. They speak lies to you in My name. I have not sent them,' declares the Lord.

"The Lord says this: 'When seventy years are completed for Babylon, I will come to you and fulfill My gracious promise to bring you back to this place. For I know the plans I have for you,' declares the Lord, 'plans to prosper you and not to harm you; plans to give you hope and a future...'

"You may say, 'But the Lord has raised up prophets for us in Babylon, and they have said this and that.' But this is what the Lord says about the king who now sits on the throne of David in Jerusalem, and about your countrymen who are still in Judah: 'I will send the sword, famine and plague against them, and I will make them like poor figs which are so bad they are inedible... For they have not listened to My words,' says the Lord."

"ALL MY BONES TREMBLE, and I am as a drunken man, because of the words of the Lord!" Jeremiah stood by the Benjamin Gate of the Temple, and tears coursed unheeded down his face as he spoke.

"My heart is broken within me!" he cried. "The land is filled with adulterers, and is cursed. The prophets follow evil and use their influence unjustly. Both prophet and priest are godless; 'Even in My House I find their wickedness,' says the Lord.

"Therefore their path will become slippery"—Jeremiah recalled a young boy's grief at seeing his straying pet plunge to destruction off a treacherous path—"and they will be banished to darkness and there they will fall..."

224

The crowd began drifting away. Again today, his message was nothing new.

Valiantly Jeremiah tried to pierce the armor of their ears with one last plea.

"Do not listen to what the prophets are saying to you. They fill you with false hopes. They speak visions from their own minds, not from the mouth of the Lord. The Lord says, 'They keep saying to those who despise Me, "The Lord says you will have peace." And to those who follow the stubbornness of their own hearts they say, "No harm will come to you." ' "

The last of the hearers was wandering away. Jeremiah continued, " 'Am I only a God nearby,' declares the Lord, 'and not a God far away? Can anyone hide in a place I cannot see? Do I not fill heaven and earth?' "

Alone, he was about to turn in disgust and make his way homeward when a priest approached him, carrying a vellum scroll. Jeremiah recognized Zephaniah. This man had a sincere heart, Jeremiah believed. He was the successor to the banished Pashhur, and of a far more genuine temperament than Jeremiah's old nemesis. The priest, with worry on his brow, hurried to the prophet.

"A dispatch has come back to us from the elders of the exiles," he said. "You are mentioned." The priest unrolled the letter and began reading:

"From Shemaiah the Nehelamite to Zephaniah, son of Maaseiah, chief officer of the Temple of the Lord in Jerusalem: greeting.

"The Lord has appointed you priest after the manner of Jehoiada, who zealously strove against evildoers in the days of King Joash. Now therefore, why have you not punished this Jeremiah of Anathoth, who affects the manner of a prophet, and raves against the people of the Lord, saying, 'Your exile will be long; plant gardens, settle down, marry and give your children in marriage...'? Such a madman ought to be put in the stocks and neck irons."

There was more, but Zephaniah did not read it. He looked at Jeremiah. "Man of Anathoth, I know you are not mad. Troublesome, yes. Disturbing, certainly. Whatever else you may be, I can feel the temper of your spirit, and I know your sincerity, as certainly as I know my own. But are you certain it is wise to send such words as these to our kindred in the strange land; words which could be considered treasonous?"

Jeremiah peered deeply into the eyes of the chief officer. "Good Zephaniah, I thank you for your kindness in showing me the charges uttered against me. But I cannot retract a single syllable of what I have said, for to do so would be treason against the Eternal. You do as you must, and I will do the same, for the time grows short."

Zephaniah glanced sharply at the prophet. "What have you seen?"

A long and intimate sorrow, inconsolable by human means, contorted the features of the prophet as he looked toward the walls of the Temple. He shook his head regretfully, turned, and walked away.

PHARAOH HOPHRA looked for the hundredth time at the chart of the lands between Egypt and Chaldea. There in the middle sat Judah, like a plum dangled between two outstretched hands. He strode away to his balcony. From here, in the upper terraces of his palace, he had a view of the Nile undulating away to the north.

He remembered the words of old Sakhri, now dead: "Go cautiously against the Chaldeans. Nebuchadrezzar is a crafty warrior. Take double the troops and triple the precaution when you take the field against him..."

But Hophra chafed against such warnings. Why was it always assumed he was limited by the shortcomings of Neco? Was he not Pharaoh in his own right? Might he not succeed where others had failed?

He paced back into his chamber. "Send in a scribe," he commanded a servant. "I wish to send a letter to the king of Judah."

"REPENT! THE DAY of the Lord's wrath is soon to come!"

Those passing by glanced briefly at the tall, slightly stooped old man shouting in the Street of Bakers, then went on their way. It was near the time of the Passover feast, and they hurried to purchase the needed provisions before supplies were gone. This fellow had been roaming the streets of Jerusalem for as long as almost anyone could remember, delivering his dour message with monotonous persistence. But death and destruction would have to wait for another time — Passover was almost upon them.

Jeremiah watched them. Why the dogged fixation on Passover preparations? Of what use was the empty keeping of a ritual when God was bringing such complete destruction that not one stone here would be left upon another?

He considered how the good intentions of Josiah thirty years before had, in a perverse way, worsened the situation. Many who might otherwise be more attentive to the prophet's message now congratulated themselves on their punctuality in keeping the feasts of the Covenant — while blithely ignoring its claim on their lives. They made no distinction in kind between the liturgies of the Law and those of the worthless gods they prayed to upon their rooftops, or the far more subtle gods of their appetites. Josiah had tried to do righteousness, but no king of men, Jeremiah realized, could abolish the darkness in the hearts of his people.

For more than thirty years now he had stood in their streets and their marketplaces, pleading with them to turn. Among some he had seen the right response. He could remember most of them: his friend Baruch, Ezekiel the priest, Daniel the young prince, Shaphan, Ahikam, Elnathan, and a handful more. But they were a tiny scattering of sparks against the cold, dark ignorance of this nation.

Sadly, he left the marketplace. When he came to their room that night, he found Squint already asleep and Baruch copying a scroll by the light of the tallow lamp. Softly he closed the door, quietly he seated himself across from the scribe.

Baruch glanced across at him, quickly reading the attitude of the slumped shoulders, the bowed head. He returned to his writing. "You cannot force them to see," he commented quietly, "if they wish to remain blind."

Jeremiah stirred, looked up at his friend, then away. "They do not even realize their blindness. If they did, I might offer them light."

Several moments passed with the scratching of Baruch's stylus the only sound. "Why do you go on?" the scribe asked.

"Because I must!" returned the prophet immediately. "You, of all people, should know that!"

"I do." said Baruch softly. "I asked for you, not for me."

Jeremiah squinted his eyes at the studious form of his friend. A tiny smile teased at the prophet's weary face. "What are you copying?"

"Hosea."

"What section?"

Baruch tilted his grandfather's old, faded scroll toward the light, adjusting the angle to accommodate his aging eyesight. Then he read:

> *"What will you do on the day of your appointed feasts,*
> *   on the festival days of the Lord?*
> *Even if they escape from destruction,*
> *   Egypt will gather them,*
> *   and Memphis will bury them.*
> *Their treasures of silver will be taken over by briers,*
> *   and thorns will overrun their tents..."*

Jeremiah thought again of the crowds hastening homeward to keep what, to them, was a quaint ritual, little more. He remembered the rest of the passage:

> *"The days of punishment are coming,*
> *   the days of reckoning are at hand.*
> *Let Israel know this.*
> *Because your sins are so many, and your hostility is so great,*
> *   the prophet is considered a fool,*
> *   and the inspired man a maniac..."*

He stared away in thought until Baruch blew out the lamp.

THE SOLDIER JASIEL stood at his station in the Tower of Meah, watching the column marching through the Gate of Mustering as they left to reinforce Jericho. The day was overcast, unusual in the summer months, and a strangely cool breeze from the north swirled and eddied about the walls of Jerusalem. Jasiel, his watch station unsheltered from the sun, should have been glad of the shade and the breeze. But they only added to his vague restiveness.

Under King Zedekiah's orders, the cities of Judah were being refortified. Jerusalem buzzed with speculation; some were apprehensive, some eagerly belligerent. Messengers from the Pharaoh's court were seen entering and leaving the palace almost weekly, and Jasiel had noted certain of the nobility affecting a new haughtiness.

Since the deportation of Jeconiah and many of his lords, the voices closest to the king's ear were those most anxious to make a name for themselves, hoping to bolster their tenuous hold upon respect in Judah. And their advice had its effect, if the preparations of the last few weeks were any indication. But others — wiser heads in Jasiel's opinion — advised caution.

The soldier had no illusions about who would do the earliest dying if war came. It was all well and good for kings and princes to boast of valor and the honor of Judah. But the common man would be the first to stare into the faces of Chaldean regiments when they came, and his belly the first to be gashed.

And this tower on which Jasiel was stationed — and others like them — would be among the first objects of the assault. These lofty fortifications were built during the reign of Uzziah, king in Jerusalem before the days of Hezekiah. They had withstood many assaults through the nearly two centuries of their existence — from the Moabites, the Syrians, the Amorites, even the Assyrians. All had come, had tested their mettle against the ramparts of the city of the Name — and left the towers intact.

Jasiel should have taken comfort in the rugged history of the walls of Jerusalem. But something was different this time — disturbingly so. Perhaps the preaching of that old man with the sad eyes had affected him more than he thought.

31

FRANTICALLY the harried militiaman counted goats as they were herded into pens along the city's outer wall. He was choking on dust raised by the hoofs of the skittish beasts who scurried by, then milled madly within the hastily constructed enclosures.

Scarcely had he made his tally marks on the tablet than another herd approached.

His commander came pacing by. "How many head so far, Jabesh?" he demanded.

Quickly Jabesh consulted his tablet. "Already twelve score," he reported.

The commander grunted. "Few enough to feed so many mouths if the Chaldeans come." Off he strode, grumbling.

Despite the nearing herd, Jabesh paused to look toward the Gate of Mustering through which, hardly a month before, regiments had bravely marched out to fortify the walled cities and towns of Judah. Now all traffic was inward; a steady stream of broken and bleeding refugees limped into Jerusalem from the defeated strongholds to the north. Around the watchfires at night Jabesh heard morbid accounts of wives and daughters raped, sons castrated, farms and villages torched. And atop the walls at night one could scent the smoke on the wind — the smell of Judah burning.

Something jabbed him in the ribs — a shepherd's crook. "Are you going to stand there all day mooning about!" the drover was saying, the first of his herd already frisking by. Hurriedly Jabesh returned to his task, grateful to be busy. Perhaps it would quiet the dread which pulled at him.

Within two weeks, Jerusalem lay under siege.

JEREMIAH SADLY WATCHED the frenzied activity in the Temple courtyard. For weeks now, since the commencement of the siege, the priests had been offering sacrifices night and day by order of the king. The coals on the altar glowed so hot and so constantly that the altar's brass horns melted. In the streets children were already starving, but Zedekiah thought he could sway the favor of God by feeding this altar instead.

In some quarters were those who insisted with rabid fervor that God would yet deliver Jerusalem. But Jeremiah knew, with the certainty of the hunger pangs in his belly, that this siege would not be ended by the intervention of God.

Wincing with the grinding pain in his gut, he shook his head and turned away, while the sizzling fat of bulls and rams ran down the sides of the altar.

ZEDEKIAH PACED impatiently back and forth across the chamber. "How can you say there is nothing to be done?" he angrily demanded of the man seated on the silk cushion by the door. The king strode to the window and leaned out. It was one of those crystalline winter days of Judah, when the sky was a vivid, almost violent blue, and the air felt so fresh and clean one could laugh aloud for joy — that is, unless one lived in Jerusalem. In the streets of his city, Zedekiah's people were starving. Rising in a palpable fog, the miasma of death and rot clogged the air with its reminder of doom.

From this upper story Zedekiah could see a gaggle of youths battling over the carcass of a rat. They fought tooth and nail, snarling like beasts.

The king felt bile rising in the back of his throat. To this he had brought his people — their children fighting in the streets to eat filth. How long, he wondered, before the hunger in the streets penetrated the halls of this palace? How long before his own sons, about the same age as the boys outside, were forced to eat vermin?

"My king," smoothly intoned the courtier Shephatiah from his seat on the cushion, "you must take courage. Pharaoh Hophra has received our delegation very kindly, with great expressions of interest in our cause. Surely he will—"

"His people do not eat rats!" shouted the young king, his

face purpling as he spun to challenge the noble. "We needed him weeks ago! If he is so interested, where is he?" Zedekiah's stare fired bolts of rage at Shephatiah, who finally shifted his eyes away, a slight shrug sliding from his shoulders.

"I don't know, my king, but we mustn't despair," the adviser said, his voice still polished. "How will the people be served if the king surrenders to panic? You must be the strength of David and Solomon to them, my lord; you must set an example—"

Zedekiah turned his head in disdain, and looked out again across his city. He allowed his eyes to roam past the walls, to the valleys and hillocks where the Chaldean vultures waited with calm tenacity — for however long they pleased.

That was the maddening thing — all the options lay on the other side of the walls. Inside, he was reduced to but two: wait for Hophra, and starve; or surrender to Nebuchadrezzar and die. Babylon and Egypt might act; he could only react. He was as helpless as a bird in a cage, forced to watch in impassive silence as Nebuchadrezzar felled his people with the slow, sure weapon of their own stomachs.

"Leave me," said Zedekiah over his shoulder. He did not turn as Shephatiah rustled out of the chamber.

Never had Zedekiah felt more alone than now, in this sun-bright room. He was presiding over the death of a city, yet all the voices around him counseled hope, resolve, steadfastness.

The measured cadences and careful words of Judah's lords and nobles were suddenly repugnant to him. He longed to hear another voice — one which did not depend on his continued good graces to maintain some coveted position.

He strode to the door of the chamber and motioned to the servant standing outside. "Send for the priest Zephaniah. I have an errand for him."

THE DELEGATION from the king found Jeremiah on the city wall near the Gate of the Furnace, staring west across the Gihon Valley at the Babylonian array. The old prophet stood silently with clenched fists, his arms half-raised as if preparing to ward off an attack — or launch one. Hesitantly Zephaniah cleared his throat and began speaking.

"Jeremiah, the king himself has sent us to ask you this:

232

What word comes from Adonai concerning the attack of Nebuchadrezzar? Pray for us, that perhaps the Lord may intercede with wonders as in times past, that we may be saved."

Jeremiah dropped his arms, unclenched his fists, but did not face the royal messengers. His chin dropped on his chest, as if in defeat. The unhindered wind tossed his hair and beard.

His reply could barely be heard. "Tell Zedekiah this: 'The Lord says, "I will turn against you the very weapons you are seeking to use against Nebuchadrezzar. I Myself will fight against you with an outstretched hand and with fierce wrath. I will smite those who live in this city — even the animals — with plague. And you, Zedekiah, son of Josiah, I will hand over to your oppressors — you and all the nobles and princes of your house. You will be shown no mercy."'"

Jeremiah raised his face to them, and they could see the dust-stained tear-tracks on his lined, leathery cheeks.

"And," he added, "Say this to the people: 'Behold,' says the Lord, 'I set before you the way of life'"—he pointed a hand toward the camps of the Chaldeans—"'and the way of death.'" He pointed the other toward the palace and Temple atop Mount Moriah. "'Whoever stays in this city will die by the sword, famine or plague. But whoever goes out to the Babylonians will live. He will preserve his life as a prize of war.

"'I have set My face to harm this city,' says the Lord, 'and not to spare it. I am against you, Jerusalem — you who say, "Who can come against us? Who can enter our refuge?" I will punish you as your deeds deserve,' says the Lord."

"Again, only treason," hissed one of the priests at Zephaniah's side. "He has nothing we can take to Zedekiah!"

Jeremiah leveled his gaze at the speaker. "You need not take it to him. In time he will call me himself, and I will tell him."

"Jeremiah," said Zephaniah, "it is hard for the people to hear such words in a time when their courage so easily fails. Their bellies are empty, their children moan with hunger—"

"Do you think I do not see?" Jeremiah's words were a hoarse wail from the tattered fragments of his soul. Involuntarily his hearers stepped back half a pace, suddenly fearful of this wizened, stooped, mourning old man.

"Do you believe I do not feel every pang, weep for every

death, vomit with every sickness? Can't you understand, after all these years? I have *seen* all this before, and *before*, and *before!*" Jeremiah pounded his brittle chest as the acrid flood of pain poured from his tortured heart. "The Lord has shown me! *Shown* me! Do you know what that means?" His eyes dared them to answer, but they again pulled back uncomfortably.

"The day is come. I have preached about it to the people for almost two score years. I have told them again, and again, and again. But they had no ear to hear!"

His voice screamed, even without the volume his frail body no longer could supply. "The day has come! Now the Lord destroys this city, which has become a stench in His nostrils. And the people cry, 'Save, Lord!'"

His voice now nearly broken, he raised a trembling hand toward the chief priest. "Do you know the worst thing of all, Zephaniah? The crushing thing? It is that I, too, cry out for rescue — knowing He will not hear!"

They all watched helplessly as the grief poured from him like blood from a mortal wound:

"He assures me He will not show mercy...but I cannot help beating my breast before Him...*and begging!*" Jeremiah reached out his arms toward Mount Moriah and the Temple, shining in the morning sun. Slowly his head dropped onto his chest. He covered his face and sobbed into his hands.

Finally he began gathering himself. He looked up, wiping his cheeks with the backs of his hands.

"You see, Zephaniah, how Adonai compels me. We have had such words before, you and I. Tell me: If you felt the hot coals of His will in your belly, what would *you* do?"

Zephaniah could say nothing.

Jeremiah turned to the man at Zephaniah's side: "Treason, you have said. I see, now as always, the Almighty's judgment. Is it more treason to speak — or to keep silent?"

The priest, too, was wordless.

Jeremiah again looked beyond them toward the Temple, a longing gaze aching outward from his eyes. "You asked me for a word from the Lord," he continued. "This I have brought for forty years. If you want pleasing words, you must go elsewhere. I have no comfort to give."

Stooped with a burden they could not understand, the old man turned and began limping toward the stairs leading down the wall. While he descended, a cloud passed under the sun. Zephaniah watched as the shadow shrouded the Temple — and he shuddered.

JABESH AWOKE with a dry ache in his gut, the same gnawing cramp that had kept him constant company for weeks now: He was hungry.

He scratched his face and sat up, putting on the cloak with which he had covered himself during the night. He squinted toward a window — in the gray light he could just discern the mortared joints in the stones surrounding the sill. Time to rouse. They'd be coming for the morning ration soon, and he'd need all his wits to keep the most desperate ones from slipping around him and getting an extra portion.

To clear his head, he walked outside in the crisp air. In better times he would have automatically breathed deeply and waved his arms to get the blood flowing. But now, unknowingly, his lessening strength kept even the thought of such exertion from occurring.

He worked from a storehouse set against the wall near the Fish Gate, just below the Tower of Hanameel. In the gradually widening light the tower loomed ahead. Despite the weak emptiness in his middle, he decided again, as he did every morning, to climb the tower steps and go out on the wall.

Once upon the top, he decided to sit down today instead of walking. He sat facing the city, stretched his legs, rubbed his eyes, and let the growing light gradually reveal to him the structures below. He looked out on them without emotion, without any remembering, without any dreaming — and again unaware that the dullness of his mind was another manifestation of his vacant belly.

Getting light by now, he told himself several moments later. He rose. *Better get down to the post and prepare for the onslaught.*

He turned to look in the other direction — out, as was his habit, toward the Chaldean lines, to pronounce his daily curse on the oppressors who starved him and his people. As he looked, his mouth came open, but no sound came out.

His eyes swept the terrain, reddening in the long shadows of dawn. No sign of the Babylonian camps!

Again he rubbed his eyes and slapped his face, thinking himself still asleep. He peered outward — still no Babylonians. Their tents, which had dotted the rocky hillsides and valleys in a continuous ring about the city for months, were gone. Also absent were the smudges of the morning cooking fires. The countryside beyond the walls was as empty and still as if the siege had been no more than a dream.

He struggled to suppress the wild hope hammering in his chest. Not daring to believe the evidence of his eyes, he bounded up the steps to the tower — to find the two guards asleep.

"Wake up, you fools!" he shouted, grasping them roughly by the shoulders and bouncing their heads against the stone walls where they leaned. "Wake up and look!"

The guards, snapping awake in wide-eyed panic, grabbed immediately for their weapons. "Sound the alarm!" one shouted groggily. "We are beset!"

"No, no you fool!" said Jabesh, gripping the fellow's tunic and hauling him upright. "Look out there, and tell me what you see — or what you don't see!" The stout Jabesh swung the still-limp guard about until he looked outward. After a moment of silence, the guard asked in a bewildered tone, "Where are the Babylonians?"

"Where indeed?" echoed Jabesh, the excitement in his breast bubbling uncontrollably upward. "They're gone, that's where! Vanished! Absent! Swallowed up by the earth, for all I know!" Clapping his hands like a child, Jabesh looked at them with manic glee tumbling from his mouth in a cascade of laughter. Then he spun and raced down the tower steps, two at a bound, shouting, "They're gone! They're gone! We're saved!" In the quiet dawn, his shouts echoed across the streets below.

Behind him, two guards looked again where the Chaldeans had been, then at each other. Their jaws were slack in helpless amazement.

32

THE CROWD DANCED jubilantly in the square before the Benjamin Gate, hugging each other and laughing in a mass hysteria of relief. For the first time since the beginning of winter, the gates of Jerusalem stood open. Many people had already gone out of the city, to gather from their kin in the countryside such provisions as could be spared for the relief of the hungry capital city. The warm spring air rang with the shouts of unhoped-for deliverance.

Jeremiah wound his way through the crowd, unnoticed in the general frenzy. As he passed a street preacher, he heard the fellow retelling the story of King Hezekiah, in whose day Jerusalem had been saved from a besieging army. The implication was clear: As God spared Jerusalem then, so He has spared her now. The grinning folk gathered about the preacher tossed coins at his feet.

Jeremiah shook his head in helpless discouragement. Still they saw only what they chose to see. In the days of Hezekiah, a king sat on the throne who truly and earnestly sought the face of the Lord. But Zedekiah's head was turned by whichever voice he heard last. Hezekiah had restored the worship of the Lord to the land. Zedekiah allowed the people to pour out libations to worthless gods, so long as it made no trouble for him.

This city was doomed, despite the frantic hilarity it now enjoyed.

The prophet gradually made his way to the gate. Guards flanked both sides of the opening, watching the throngs hustling in and out — those entering bearing provisions upon their backs from the outlying areas, those leaving with empty baskets and jars to bring back the desperately needed supplies.

Jeremiah was passing through the gate when someone

grabbed his clothing from behind, roughly yanking him backward. Hands gripped his shoulders and spun him around, slamming him roughly against the wall of the gate.

"You! Old man! Where do you think you are going?" The commander of the detail barked the questions at the shocked, blinking Jeremiah. There was something about the angry young man's face — something oddly familiar, though Jeremiah knew he had never seen this fellow before.

"I...I was on my way to my village to gather a portion..." he stammered, vainly trying to understand why he was being detained.

"What is your name, old man?" demanded the commander harshly.

A curious crowd of bystanders began to develop, as they heard the odd interchange occurring in the gateway.

"I am Jeremiah. Of Anathoth. I was just on my way—"

"On your way where? To desert to the Chaldeans, perhaps?"

Jeremiah stared back, astonishment numbing his face. "No! Of course not! I was going to my home village—"

"You were deserting to the Chaldeans! Aren't you the old fool who has been standing in the streets for years, preaching about how Nebuchadrezzar will destroy this city?" His fierce eyes accused Jeremiah, but something other than patriotic fervor blazed in his face — something familiar.

"Yes, you're the fellow. You love the Chaldeans so much, you've decided to go find them and join them! Isn't that so?"

"No, no! I am a prophet of the Lord, and I speak—"

"Yes, a prophet," sneered the young man, leaning forward as if to spit in Jeremiah's face. "A jealous prophet, one who cannot abide being humiliated in public by a wiser man..."

In a flash it came to him. The face — it was so much like that of Hananiah, who had been dead for almost seven years now. This soldier; was he...?

"I am Irijah," spat the commander, his mouth twisted in a malevolent grin, "son of Shelemiah, son of Hananiah." He leaned close, and said in a low, grating voice, "I know of your witchery, and how you killed my grandfather. His blood will not go unavenged." His eyes were twin daggers dripping with hate. Then he leaned back. "Take this traitor away," he snapped at his men.

Two soldiers grabbed the old man roughly under the arms and dragged him away, to the house of Jonathan, a scribe of the royal court.

The house had been converted during the siege into an impromptu prison. The two guards flung Jeremiah onto the floor of the house's main chamber. Seated on cushions on a raised dais in the hall were a handful of Judah's nobles, who sat in judgment on those brought to this place. On this particular day, Shephatiah sat in the center of the tribunal, acting as its spokesman.

At once Shephatiah recognized Jeremiah. This was the gloomy old fellow who, for all of Shephatiah's adult life, had haunted the streets and marketplaces of Jerusalem. It seemed to him that Jeremiah's religious ranting had little relation to the pressing problems of the day. Judah's needs had less to do with gods than with shifting political currents. If the fellow wanted to help, Shephatiah thought, he might start by motivating the people to greater loyalty to the king. Shephatiah considered himself a pragmatist — something sorely needed in the court of Jerusalem just now. He had little patience for those who were not useful.

"What is your name, old one?" he asked in a bored voice.

Jeremiah painfully crawled to his knees and rose to his feet. He tottered a moment, then gained his balance.

"I am Jeremiah, of Anathoth, a prophet of the Most High."

Shephatiah's expression did not change as he heard what he already knew. "Why are you here, Jeremiah of Anathoth?"

"We caught this old fool trying to desert to the Chaldeans," interjected one of the guards.

"That is not true," asserted Jeremiah. His voice was low. "I was on my way to Anathoth, to receive a portion from my kin, when I was beset by these—"

"Tell me, Jeremiah of Anathoth," interrupted another of the magistrates, seated to Shephatiah's left, "aren't you the one who preaches the destruction of this city by Babylon, and who says — let me see if I can get it right: 'Surrender to Babylon and live; stay in Jerusalem and die'?"

Jeremiah did not deign to reply to the mocking questioner, but his silence was answer enough.

"Jeremiah of Anathoth," said another, "where are your beloved Babylonians now? What will you preach, now that they have gone away and left Jerusalem still standing?" The questioner gave a snicker, not troubling to hide it.

Jeremiah locked Shephatiah's jeering eyes with his, and said, "In the streets of this city, and in her squares and market-places, I have already spoken of you. You say in your heart, 'Where is the Lord? He does not see; He will not do harm, nor will He do good.' Yet I say to you that His arm is not shortened nor His anger abated as long as you despise Him in your heart. It is because of the wickedness in your soul that He will utterly destroy this place."

For a moment, the black inferno of his holy wrath awed them into silence. Then the spell was broken.

"Give this old fool the forty stripes!" said Shephatiah, angrily. The arrogance of Jeremiah had gotten his hackles up, and he forgot, in his ire, to consult with his fellow jurists. Their murmurs of agreement as the soldiers bared the old man's back told him he had no need to.

"I TELL YOU, this proclamation will cause havoc!" insisted the courtier angrily, raising his voice as much as he dared before the king.

Zedekiah sat quietly, wishing he were somewhere else, but attempting now to sustain his point. "In light of our deliverance from the siege, I felt it fitting to show a sign, an appropriate expression. I thought freeing the slaves would be such a gesture, a way of raising hope among the people—"

"But it has not done so!" asserted the indignant courtier. "What will we do without our servants? All the best household in this city will be thrown into an uproar. And that, you must know, cannot be good for the orderly continuation of society."

"Do you threaten me?" demanded Zedekiah, half-fearful of the answer.

"Oh, no, my king," said the noble quickly. "I do not threaten. I merely point out realities to be considered."

Zedekiah was weary of this conversation. It had been repeated scores of times since he made the proclamation, only two days before. The assembly of Judah's nobles had publicly indicated support for the measure, but since then they had paraded before him one by one, privately cataloging the reasons why it was bad for the nation. Perhaps the symbolism was not, after all, worth the ill will it had engendered.

"Very well," the king said finally. "I will reconsider my proclamation..."

HOPHRA WAS LIVID. This adventure had indeed been ill-conceived. He had relied on the intelligence brought to him by the wretched Hebrews — who, in retrospect, could hardly be relied upon to give an accurate assessment of pertinent strategic considerations.

Egypt had been humiliated — that was the long and short of it. Acting upon the belief that Nebuchadrezzar's forces were deployed in a widely scattered fashion among the walled towns of Judah, the Egyptian host slipped across the Wadi-el-Arish, intending to carve out a foothold in Judah in a series of quick strikes against inferior numbers. It was a sound plan, with but a single flaw: Nebuchadrezzar had the country so well in hand that he was able to confront the Egyptians at Kadesh-Barnea with almost his entire strength.

The carnage had been terrible and swift — over almost before it began. Ruefully, the Pharaoh again remembered the words of Sakhri, which now echoed mockingly in his memory.

STANDING ATOP the barren dome of Jebel Hallal, Nebuchadrezzar watched in grim satisfaction as the decimated army of Pharaoh Hophra limped back toward Tahpanhes. Again the old lion had had her teeth pulled. One day soon he would come to her lair and finish the job.

But for now: He must deal with Jerusalem, once and for all.

JEREMIAH CROUCHED in the dank cellar of the house of Jonathan. The only light in this dismal place seeped weakly around the cracks in the overhead door through which his captors had tossed him.

The cellar was small — it had originally served to store

foodstuffs — and he could not stand upright. Nor could he fully extend his legs to sit comfortably. In the cramped, chilled darkness, his back a blazing, raw network of welts, the prophet thought he would surely die. He felt his spirit beginning to slip within him, felt his dignity and hope being peeled from him as a hunter strips the pelt from a slain marmot.

He didn't know how long he had been in this miserable hole. The ache in his gut told him it was something more than a day. He had had no food since before the beginning of the ordeal at the Benjamin Gate. Perhaps they intended to leave him here until he starved.

"O Sovereign Lord," he began to pray, "do not forget Your promises. Do not abandon me in this pit, but let me again see the light of Your blessed day..."

His thoughts began to fade into an unknown blackness...

Suddenly the door above slammed open and light flooded into his cell, blinding him. Hands reached in and hauled him roughly out of the earthen vault. They shoved him toward the door of the room. Still disoriented, he smashed against the wall by the door. Coarse voices laughed and jeered.

"You'd better open your eyes, old man. If you run into the king like you just ran into that wall, your head will part company with your shoulders."

As his head began to clear, a hand took him by the arm and guided him through the house of Jonathan, then outside into the streets.

Then it was back inside. Gradually he realized he was walking the corridors of the palace.

The king, they had said. Had Zedekiah really summoned him? With a sinking sensation, Jeremiah realized why he was being beckoned. He knew what Zedekiah would ask, and he also knew what his answer would be.

For a fleeting moment, he wished again for the cellar.

33

JEREMIAH WAS USHERED into a small chamber in the heart of the palace. The room was lit by tallow lamps, hanging in brackets fastened into the stone walls. The king sat in the center of the room in a chair fashioned from mahogany, in the style of the Egyptian court.

"Leave us alone," he commanded

The soldier who had brought Jeremiah left, closing the door quietly behind him. Jeremiah remained where he was, barely inside the doorway.

"Come and sit down," said Zedekiah, motioning to an empty chair facing him.

Slowly Jeremiah made his way to the seat. He was still weak with hunger, and his hands shook as he reached for the arm of the chair and lowered himself carefully into it.

The young king and the old prophet studied each other in the flickering glow of the lamps on the walls.

Finally the king began: "This is the first time I have seen you face-to-face, since—" He halted, shifting his eyes uncomfortably away. "Since the day of the founding of the alliance."

Jeremiah sat wordlessly, his eyes never leaving the king's face.

"My father worshiped Adonai," the king began again, hesitantly, "and caused the altars of the other gods to be pulled down—"

"Those are no gods," interrupted Jeremiah bluntly. "There is but one God."

"I agree with you," said Zedekiah. "And yet...the people... even some of the princes..." His eyes pleaded with the prophet for understanding, for commiseration. But the face of the old man was like stone, his eyes as hard as diamonds.

"You are a holy man — this I know," began the king once more, after another tense pause. "Will you pray for us, that Adonai might save us?"

"My king, I have not ceased praying, night and day for forty years, for the deliverance of this people. Yet the Lord will not suffer it to be so. He has turned His face from this city. Even Moses returned from the dead would not be able to turn the present wrath of the Almighty."

Zedekiah put his fingers to his forehead, and blew out a breath of frustration. Then he dropped his hands, clasped them, shifted forward in his chair, and made a final attempt: "We are expecting quite soon," he said in a lower voice, "the report of a great and most interesting confrontation. The tidings are that Hophra has come out of Egypt against Nebuchadrezzar. Perhaps—"

"How many times," Jeremiah blurted out, "have the kings of Jerusalem sought to brandish Egypt like a blade against another foe, only to have her break from the haft and rend them instead? Even if Nebuchadrezzar's entire army was a host of wounded men, they would break down the walls of this place and burn it with fire. Neither you nor Egypt will avail against the Chaldeans!"

The king's nerve snapped like a frayed cord. "You are a stubborn and ill-tempered old man!" He lunged up from his chair and paced rapidly to the far wall. Spinning to face Jeremiah, he aimed an accusing finger. "I have a mind to throw you back in the hole from which I had you taken!"

"You punish *me*, my king. And yet what have you done to all those prophets and counselors who told you, 'Babylon will not come against you…the Pharaoh will protect you'? They have lied to you and to the people, and they go unmolested. I have spoken only the truth. Everything I say has and shall come to pass, for the Lord has shown it to me. Yet it is I whom you smite and throw in the dungeon."

The image rushed upon him of the dark cellar, his cramped body, his darkening mind — and he was filled with sudden dread. Leaving the seat he fell to his knees, pleading with Zedekiah. "My king, please listen to me. I beg of you: Do not send me back to the house of Jonathan, or I will die there!"

Zedekiah viewed with wonder the pathetic figure looking up from the floor, fear and hunger contorting his face into a mask of anguish. At once his heart was smitten by the helpless, uncompromising purity of this prophet, this old man — a man the age of his own father, had he lived...

At last the king looked away and said, "I will give my men orders concerning you. You'll be kept in the court of the guards, under my protection, and fed from the ration of the soldiers."

Jeremiah bowed his head in relief.

"But you may not leave this city," the king ordered, sternly. "You will stay in Jerusalem, come what may. Do you understand?"

"My king," answered Jeremiah sadly, "such has always been my intention, come what may..."

LIKE AN AVENGING WIND from the desert, the Chaldean army came roaring up from the south, bringing a brutal halt to Jerusalem's jubilation. By the first days of autumn the city was again clenched in the mailed fist of siege.

Nebuchadrezzar served quick notice that his patience was at an end. As soon as his positions surrounding Jerusalem were consolidated, he launched a fierce assault on the Ephraim Gate, sending in a company of infantry. They came against the gate with a battering ram, their bullhide shields raised over their heads like the carapace of a beetle. The huge, iron-clad wooden gate shuddered again and again under the crashing onslaught. Only with great difficulty did Judah's archers on the walls and towers blunt the determined sortie.

The Chaldean commanders sent a near-continuous rain of flaming missiles into the city. They were launched from the siege towers which stood like the skeletons of great beasts on the high places surrounding the walls. Buildings within were constantly being set ablaze.

Soon the faces of both soldiers and citizens acquired a drab, dull patina of fatigue. There was always a fire to fight, an assault on the gates to withstand — and never enough time to rest.

NEBUZARADAN WAITED in his pavilion. A deserter — an important one — was being brought to him. Found last night, he was a fairly high-ranking official of the palace, Gedaliah by name. Supposedly his father and grandfather had been influential in the courts of previous kings of Judah. Nebuchadrezzar had given strict orders: Deserters from Jerusalem were to be protected, especially those who might later prove useful. This Gedaliah appeared to be such a one.

The guards brought him in. A bedraggled fellow, his eyes burned with the urgency of hunger. Gedaliah dropped to his knees — less from respect, Nebuzaradan thought, than from weakness.

The man stared with ravening intensity at the sweetmeats Nebuzaradan popped leisurely into his mouth. It was just as the commander intended; the prospect of filling their bellies often freed their tongues.

"Who are you?" asked Nebuzaradan, beginning the interrogation.

"I am Gedaliah, son of Ahikam, chief scribe of the royal court."

"Why are you here?"

For a moment the cleric's eyes wavered from the food on the board. His voice came from a great distance as he said, "I am here because...because the Lord has turned His face from Jerusalem."

"Well said, Gedaliah," observed the commander. "Your lord Nebuchadrezzar has indeed— "

"No, that is not what I meant," interrupted Gedaliah earnestly. "Adonai, the Lord God, who established this city for our father David, has turned His favor away from us. We are doomed."

More of that strange, pessimistic Hebrew religious jargon, mused Nebuzaradan.

"The princes have turned the ears of Zedekiah away from the word of the Lord. They fill him with vain notions of deliverance, and they block those who do not agree with their folly. I cannot get a word alone with him, for they know that I heed the words of the holy prophet Jeremiah and will urge the king to—"

"Who is this Jeremiah?" asked the commander, his memory suddenly jolted by something Gedaliah said.

"He is a prophet of the Almighty Lord. It is he who has announced, for the past two-score years, the coming of your master and the downfall of this city."

"For forty years this prophet of yours has preached the destruction of his own people?"

Gedaliah nodded.

The commander remembered the strange, intense man who had stood with Jeconiah just before the king was taken away to Babylon. Again Nebuzaradan found himself mystified by this strange people. Their kings staged ill-advised and foredoomed rebellions against clearly superior armies, yet within the walls of their own capital they tolerated a preacher proclaiming disaster — for forty years!

"This prophet — he still lives?"

"Yes, my lord."

"And still preaches?"

"Yes, my lord. Every day, in the courtyard of the king's guard, he proclaims the words which the Lord has given him."

Astounding!

"And he is unhindered?"

"Oh, there are those of the king's council who hate him and would slay him, if given the opportunity. But I believe the Lord protects Jeremiah, because he speaks the words of the Almighty."

"Very interesting," reflected the commander. "Sheshbazan!" A servant materialized from the rear of the pavilion. He kneeled before the commander, head bowed. "Bring food for my guest," instructed Nebuzaradan. Gedaliah's face slackened with relief and anticipation. "You will stay here for now," said the commander, turning again to the Hebrew. "I wish to hear more from you of this Jeremiah."

ZEDEKIAH STOOD in the bedchamber of his sons. The two boys slept upon their couches, their chests rising and falling in slow rhythm. The full moon shone through the windows of the room, falling upon the dark profusion of curls spilled out upon their pillows. The king felt his heart choking with anxiety for the fate of his children.

He had kept them as safe as he could from the uncertainties swirling about them. He had not permitted them outside the palace compound, nor allowed their teachers to give them true tidings of the city's desperate situation. When he was with them, he maintained a forced cheerfulness, downplaying the gravity of the siege. And he fed them from his own portion, depriving himself that his children might not feel the pinch of hunger.

Again, with a shudder, he remembered the waifs fighting over the rat. A sob swelled inside his throat, threatened to burst from his lips. Quickly he hurried from the room and closed the door.

Shephatiah was waiting impatiently for him in the corridor. "My king," whispered the prince urgently, "I must speak to you at once."

Wearily Zedekiah nodded. They proceeded to a small side chamber.

"My king," began Shephatiah, as soon as the door was closed, "it is about that crazy old prophet, Jeremiah."

Zedekiah waited, knowing what was coming.

"He is sapping the will of your loyal subjects with his inane ramblings about surrender to Babylon. Day after day he harangues any who will listen..."

Zedekiah looked away from the noble's complaining face and into a dark corner of the chamber. A look of tired resignation tugged at his countenance.

"It is enough that the soldiers and people are subjected to the lies and distortions uttered by the traitors who have gone over to the enemy," continued Shephatiah, "but you must not allow this old fool in your very household to dishearten the people with his vain and subversive prattle."

Against his every wish, Zedekiah turned his gaze upon Shephatiah. "What would you do to better the situation?" he asked in a voice drained of emotion.

"He should die," said the prince, simply.

"You don't think it bad luck to kill a holy man?"

"My king," said Shephatiah, his teeth clenched, "I beg you to remember the loyalty of your servants who have held together this city in the face of all the troubles, both inside and outside the walls. If this loyalty should be withdrawn..." The courtier left the sentence unfinished, but the implication hung in the air as clearly as a spoken threat.

Fatigue and frustration pulled at Zedekiah like coursing hounds at the heels of a deer. He did not have the will, especially now, to breast the current of spite directed against Jeremiah.

"Very well," he said at last. "Do with him as you wish. I will not oppose you." The prince nodded curtly and left.

Zedekiah, alone in the darkened room, had a sudden urge to wash his hands.

"'THE HOUSES of the princes of this city — the fine, great houses which are being torn down to build engines to fight the Babylonians — these will be the houses of dead men,' says the Lord..."

Jeremiah sat on a pile of dirty goatskins, half-reclining in the weakness of his hunger. Still his voice today was strong and its cadences possessed a harsh majesty, enfolding the attention of the soldiers and others who sat in a semicircle before him. His eyes lanced each of them in turn as he spoke.

In a strange way, the intense old man with the searching eyes had become the master of his jailers. He fascinated them with his odd, unpredictable actions and pronouncements. Only yesterday they watched in amazement as a fellow claiming to be a kinsman of Jeremiah came into the courtyard and asked the prophet to buy a parcel of land from him, in keeping with the customs of inheritance among the clans. They all snickered, scoffing at the notion of anyone investing in Judean land now, when Nebuchadrezzar laid the country waste.

Yet Jeremiah seemed to take the proposal quite seriously. Indeed, he acted as if he had been fully expecting his cousin to come to him and make this preposterous offer. Gravely he pulled an old, moth-eaten wallet from beneath his clothing and carefully weighed out the purchase price the cousin demanded — seventeen shekels of silver. The deed was signed over before the amazed witnesses, and Jeremiah summoned a scribe friend to verify the terms and conditions of the agreement. The scribe took the documents with him for safekeeping. Jeremiah had said to them, "The Lord says, 'Though the Babylonians will destroy this city and burn it with fire, I will one day have mercy, and restore My people. Again will fields be purchased in Benjamin and Judah, and the voice of the bride and bridegroom will once more be heard in this land."

Now Jeremiah was speaking to them again along the same lines. "The Lord says this: 'You may say this place is deserted, desolate, a wasteland without men or beasts to inhabit it. Yet one day in the towns of Judah and the streets of Jerusalem the sound of joy and gladness will again be heard.'"

He raised his eyes to the sky and lifted his shaking hands in a gesture of adoration. "Give thanks to the Lord Almighty, for He is good. His love endures forever!"

"What is this ravening old idiot saying now?" sneered Shephatiah, entering the courtyard with two companions. His face in a grimace, the prince stalked toward the prophet. "What is this talk about love and restoration from the vulture of Anathoth? Now that you've softened the fists of the fighting men of this city, do you seek to soften their heads as well?"

As the menacing trio came nearer, Jeremiah saw the clenched slashes of hatred in their mouths — he knew the sign too well. Shakily he tottered to his feet. "I am in this place," he began, "by the word of the king—"

"So am I," grinned Shephatiah. "Seize him!" he barked to the two accomplices, who roughly grabbed Jeremiah, jerking him off his feet. They turned to drag him away.

"Stop!" shouted a high, strong voice. Ebed-melech, a Cushite eunuch of the king's house, thrust himself in front of Shephatiah. "You must not do this evil thing!" he warned. "This is a holy man! You cannot—"

Shephatiah slashed a forearm across the eunuch's face, knocking him to the ground. "Get out of my way, stoneless one," he cursed. "I am a prince of the house of David, not one of the lesser concubines, to be ordered about by the likes of you." He glanced back at his two allies, jerked his head toward the gates, and continued on. Jeremiah, too weak to resist, was dragged between them, his feet scraping twin trails in the dust.

JEREMIAH STOOD in the mire at the bottom of an abandoned cistern, leaning weakly against the wall of the dank hole. He looked up helplessly at his captors. They were grinning down at him, two man-lengths above his head.

"This is the perfect place for you, old man," laughed Sheph-atiah. "The little bread left in this city should not be wasted on useless mouths. Stay here and rot in the mud."

He leaned over and spat at the prophet, then walked away, laughing with the others.

34

JASIEL WATCHED CAREFULLY as the small party made its way along the western rim of the Kidron toward the Sheep Gate. It appeared to be a bodyguard of infantry surrounding some potentate or other. Quickly he scanned the ridges and hollows to his left for any sign that this excursion might be a feint to draw his attention from the real threat.

"Watch closely," he admonished his men in his detail. "Watch for your very lives." He checked his station. A catapult was on top of their tower; the stones were in place.

He turned and again squinted at the bodyguard and the concealed one whom it shielded from his view.

Gedaliah trod carefully in the center of the small ring of infantrymen, a chill washing over him despite the warmth of the early summer day. Nebuchadrezzar had ordered him to speak to the defenders of the city, and he did not relish the task. Too well he knew the curses — and perhaps worse — that would be directed at him.

They stopped some seventy paces from the Sheep Gate. Any closer would be foolhardy; any farther away and the speaker would not be heard.

The bodyguard parted, their practiced, wary eyes ceaselessly roving the walls and towers for the first sign of attack. There had been many attempts to silence the propaganda speakers — several infantrymen had been felled by covert archers finding a lucky mark.

From between the guards, Gedaliah cupped his hands in front of his mouth, took a deep breath, and began.

"Men of Jerusalem! I am Gedaliah son of Ahikam, the scribe..."

On the wall, Jasiel felt his face grow numb with shock.

Gedaliah! None so influential and respected as he had yet gone over to the Chaldeans. Were matters so grievous that the cream of the nation now forsook their heritage among the tents of the oppressors?

"I come before you today not to heckle or threaten, but to plead," Gedaliah continued. "I beg of you — do not turn your hearts away from the words of the Lord, who says to you, 'I am giving this city to Nebuchadrezzar.' Through the mouth of His prophet, Jeremiah of Anathoth, He proclaims to you that you must not attempt to withstand His purpose for this city. Look deep within your hearts — do you not know it is so?"

Gedaliah's last phrase hung in the air before the gates of the city like the wail of a mourning woman. Jasiel, bound to his post by duty and oath, nevertheless felt the truth in the scribe's words burning a hole in his chest. He clenched his jaw and felt his grip tighten on the haft of his sword.

From somewhere below and to his right, among the parapets of the wall, he heard a bowstring thrum. The bowman's aim was true, but the vigilance of the bodyguard bettered him. The shaft ended quivering in the bullhide shield of one of the infantrymen. Quickly they surrounded Gedaliah again, backing carefully away from the gate, pursued by the shouted imprecations of the hungry, desperate defenders of Jerusalem.

NIGHT FELL over the city, spangled with thousands of stars. But only a few shone on Jeremiah, crouching miserably at the bottom of the cistern. He had huddled here for two days, delirious with hunger, wracked by humiliation and fear.

The nights were the worst, when the vermin crawled into the hole, seeking the moisture left in the muck. Shuddering, Jeremiah felt them crawling over his legs, his hands. But he was too weak to cast them away. He barely had enough strength remaining to pray.

During the day he could remember the song of David:

> *"I waited patiently for the Lord;*
> *He turned to me and heard my cry.*
> *He lifted me out of the slimy pit,*
> *out of the mud and mire...."*

But as the dark, crawling night descended with its quiet horrors, he felt despair whisper witching words into the whimpering silence of his dread. Again he was alone and oppressed. Again the Lord's call had landed him in a filthy place, had made him the object of hatred and loathing.

Soon it was all he could manage to clench his teeth against the wail of hopelessness luring him with seductive, useless promises of release. *What harm?* the voices murmured. *You are as good as dead, no matter what happens. Why go on? Put an end to your misery. Stop trying. Give in, give in...*

As the curses began pressing again irresistibly, something slithered down on him from above.

He felt the dry scratching of a new rope against his arms. Bewildered, he looked up against the tiny circle of stars. A dark place moved against the greater darkness, at the edge of the cistern's opening. A voice spoke.

"I'm dropping some old rags down to you. Put them under your arms, then pass the rope around your waist and tie a loop."

Was this another trick? Was he about to be shamed once more, taunted with deliverance, then thrust again into the blackness of abandonment and misery?

"Old man," the voice said, "it is I — Ebed-melech, the Cushite. I've come to get you out. Tie the rope about you."

Still he squinted upward, afraid to believe.

There was a quiet exchange of voices above him, and another figure leaned over the edge of the cistern to look down. Jeremiah looked carefully at this second man, for even in the silhouette there was something familiar...

The Cushite spoke again: "Can you do it?"

Denying his hesitation, Jeremiah put the rags beneath him, pinning them with his arms while he looped the line around his waist. He looked upward. "I am ready."

The line tightened, and he felt his feet and legs sucking loose from the muck at the bottom of the hole.

The men above grunted as they hauled him up the side of the cistern in jerks and starts. While he gradually came nearer the top, Jeremiah eyed the second man again. The face was a pale blur, the head smooth, with no hair. A black slash cut across the countenance.

"Squint!...Is that you?" Jeremiah's voice quavered with fatigue and emotion.

"Yes," came the terse answer from above.

When he reached the top, hands gripped his arms, hauled him out, and supported him as he staggered weakly on his feet.

"Go now," whispered Squint, when the prophet had gained his balance.

"I'll take you back to the court of the guards," said Ebedmelech, "but I'll hide you from Shephatiah and his ruffians. I'll see that you have food."

Jeremiah looked deeply into the two starlit faces. With a shudder, he recalled how near he had come to losing the dark battle in the pit below. He put his hands on their shoulders. "My friends, you have delivered me from more than starvation and indignity. I will remember this night."

A moment more their gazes were joined. Then the eunuch turned, taking the prophet's arm. "We should go," he said.

GEDALIAH STUMBLED from the chariot, his knees almost buckling with exhaustion. Nebuzaradan had ordered him to accompany this party north, to Riblah in the territory of Syria. He was to appear before Nebuchadrezzar himself. They had driven at a madman's pace for a day and a half, stopping only when the lack of light made it dangerous to force the horses onward.

The emperor had spread a huge pavilion of silk on the western shore of the Orontes. He reclined on a linen couch, the breezes wafting across the water to cool him in the shade.

Gedaliah approached cautiously. Reaching the threshold of the pavilion, he dropped to his knees and placed his face atop his hands, spread flat on the ground.

"Enter," commanded the emperor.

He rose slowly and approached Nebuchadrezzar, eyes lowered in subservience.

"You are Gedaliah, son of Ahikam." It was not a question. "Lord Zaradan has told me things about you, Gedaliah. I have wished to speak with you because of his reports."

Nebuchadrezzar studied the silent, still form of the Hebrew, then continued.

"You know that I will destroy your city."

Gedaliah nodded.

"What did you imagine you might gain by deserting your kindred and coming to me?" queried the emperor.

Gedaliah's breathing quickened. He almost raised his eyes to those of the emperor before checking himself. "My lord," he replied at last, "I left the city because I do not believe my God wishes me to remain there."

"Indeed," said Nebuchadrezzar drily. "And starvation and death had no part in your decision?"

"I risked death in leaving. I left behind me all privilege, all position. I came out into the unknown. There are worse things than death, my lord."

Nebuchadrezzar weighed the Hebrew's response for several moments as he looked down on his contrite form. A grudging appreciation dawned in his eyes.

"When you first spoke to Lord Zaradan, you mentioned a holy man, a prophet whose teachings prompted you to take the course of action you chose. What is this fellow's name?"

"Jeremiah, my lord. His name is Jeremiah."

"Yes…" drawled the emperor, rubbing his chin. He had heard his young Hebrew boys mention the man.

"And what is his message?"

"He says, 'Surrender to Nebuchadrezzar, and live — oppose him, and die.'"

"Is this prophet of yours so sure of my good graces that he advises such actions?"

After a long pause, Gedaliah raised his eyes resolutely to those of the emperor. "He is sure of the words that Adonai, the Lord God, has given him." A faint flicker of challenge glimmered in the Hebrew's gaze before he dropped his head once again.

Once more Nebuchadrezzar mulled the strangely proud words of this defeated nation. His city was hopelessly beset, yet Gedaliah insisted on seeing these circumstances as the workings of this enigmatic, unnamed deity of his. In all his other conquests, a victory for Babylon had been a victory for Marduk — a defeat and dishonor for the opposing nation's gods. Yet this god of the Hebrews seemed positively bent on dishonoring himself, to hear Gedaliah tell it.

Altogether a strange and riddlesome people, these Hebrews. He had observed the same trait in the young boys at his court. An odd mixture of pliancy and resolve, of loyalty and independence.

Again he looked directly at this one he had summoned. "Gedaliah, son of Ahikam — I wish you to remain with Lord Zaradan until I have finished my business with Jerusalem."

Gedaliah shuddered, then nodded, not looking up.

"I may have plans for you," he added, tapping his cheek with a jeweled forefinger.

LOOKING SWIFTLY up and down the corridor, Ebed-melech opened the small door. He ducked into the unused closet, and quietly secured the door behind him.

Jeremiah glanced up at him. The prophet was crouched in a corner of the tiny room. Huddled in a ball, he appeared to have been holding his face in his hands. A single small tallow lamp offered grudging illumination.

"Are you ill?" asked Ebed-melech.

The old man shook his head. "No, my friend. Not with any illness of the body."

Quietly the eunuch set down the small bundle he had brought, concealed under his clothing. "I am sorry I could not bring more," he said. "There is so little food to be had."

A vague smile crossed the old man's face. "Ebed-melech, you, of all people, have no reason to apologize to me."

Ebed-melech stirred uneasily. "I bring word to you — from the king."

Jeremiah stiffened, his face a silent, fearful question.

"He wishes to speak again with you. He sent me to bid you come to him."

"What of Shephatiah and the others?" demanded the prophet warily.

"I am to bring you tonight, in the darkness, to the king's entrance to the Temple. No one else is to know of the meeting."

"But the priests—"

"We will avoid them," he answered quickly.

Filled with misgivings, Jeremiah nodded his head only slightly.

"I know of secret ways," the Cushite offered brightly. "No one will see us!"

The prophet slowly let himself smile again, then absently picked up a hard, stale crust and began to chew laboriously. After several moments of silence, he fixed the eunuch with an intent stare.

"What is it?" asked Ebed-melech, uncomfortably.

"The Lord has shown me something." The prophet's voice had suddenly changed. No longer was it the weak, rasping whisper of a hungry old man. Though still quiet, it had acquired a resonance, a presence it lacked only moments before. The eunuch straightened involuntarily, as if about to receive orders from a superior.

"What do you see?" he asked.

"The Lord says this to you, eunuch of the house of Zedekiah, king of Judah: 'I am about to destroy this city, as I foretold. Your own eyes will see the things come to pass which I have spoken. But I will rescue you on that day,' says the Lord, 'and you will not fall by the sword, or be delivered over to your enemies. I will save you, and you will escape with your life, because you place your trust in Me,' declares the Lord."

His words concluded, something seemed to pass out of him. He slumped, looking momentarily at the floor. Then he raised his face, a smile blooming tentatively on his parched lips. "I praise the Lord," pronounced the prophet in an awed whisper, "for He has mercy on His faithful ones."

The eunuch's eyes were round with awe. "It is truly so, isn't it?" he breathed gratefully. "The Lord God will have pity on me, and spare me!"

LIT ONLY by the distant flames from a building set ablaze by Babylonian missiles, the Temple courtyard was eerily quiet.

True to his word, Ebed-melech brought Jeremiah — cloaked and shrouded against chance eyes — to the palace entrance without mishap. A lone figure waited at the doorway. It was the king. Silently he motioned Jeremiah toward a small, dark hallway. Ebed-melech melted away into the night as the king and prophet entered the passage together.

They climbed a small, well-worn flight of stone steps and

came to a small room with a single window looking out on the Temple courtyard. From the angle of the view, Jeremiah surmised they must be somewhere on the northern end of the palace.

There was no lamp: the room was lit only by the same flames that lit the courtyard. From this elevation they could hear the faint cries of townfolk and soldiers as they fought the blaze. Jeremiah saw the faraway tongues of flame, but they did not seem real to him, did not touch him.

Zedekiah went to the window, looked out a moment, then sighed and turned away.

"Is there any word from the Lord?" the king asked in a hopeless voice, his face averted from the prophet's.

"If I tell you, I fear for my life. And at any rate, what is the use? You will not heed me."

With the last dregs of conviction he possessed, the king turned and placed his hand on Jeremiah's forearm, staring into his face. "As surely as the Lord lives, the God who has given us breath, I will not kill you or allow you to be killed."

Jeremiah looked at the king's hand on his arm, then into his eyes. What he saw in Zedekiah saddened him deeply. His face was that of a man who had lost all hope — the face of a condemned criminal. Through Jeremiah, the king was pleading with God, pleading for a reprieve which would never come — and he knew it. Zedekiah was snared by his own follies. They twined about his legs in a tangle of false ambitions, a knot of failed plans, a twisted mass of futile gestures. This was what the sin of Judah had at last produced: a king who was an object of pity.

Jeremiah looked away. It was not seemly for the king to see the condescension in his eyes.

In a dead voice the prophet said, "I have told you the word of the Lord: 'Surrender to the king of Babylon and you will live, nor will this city be burned. But if you do not surrender to the officers of Nebuchadrezzar, this place will be handed over to them. They will burn it down and you will not escape them.'"

Zedekiah turned away. "But what of our people who have gone over to Babylon?" he asked. "Will they not kill me, if I go out voluntarily to Nebuchadrezzar?"

"The Babylonians will not hand you over," asserted Jeremiah firmly. The king still stood with his back to the prophet. "If you will obey the Lord, your life will be spared, and that of your family. But if you refuse, the Lord has shown me that your wives and women will be given over to the officers and men of Babylon. You will be deserted by those you thought to be your friends. You will be mired in the mud of your own disobedience — alone and without aid." Jeremiah paused. "I would not wish such a fate even on a dog," he finished, with quiet vehemence.

Zedekiah reluctantly faced the prophet. "Don't tell anyone what has been said here," he commanded, "or you will die. If some of my officers come to you to ask why you spoke with me, say that you were pleading with me for your life."

The situation had actually been the opposite, and a silent look between the two men showed their tacit knowledge of this. Jeremiah folded his hands, and brought them to his lips. He had a sense that this was the last time his words would fail to persuade Zedekiah. After this, it would be too late.

"You may go," said the king, needlessly.

Jeremiah turned and walked forever out of the palace of the king of Judah.

PART IV

The
Exile

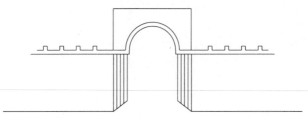

35

JASIEL STRUGGLED manfully at his post on the Tower of Meah. The assault on the gate below was well-advanced. The catapult was of little use now, for the enemy swarmed at the very foundation of the walls. He and his men pushed the stones over the edge of the tower onto the heads of the teeming hordes. Screams and cries of pain told the effect of their efforts, but for every Chaldean foot-soldier they killed, three pressed forward to take his place.

Hunger made their arms tremble, but fear spurred them on. When the stones were exhausted they began firing arrows into the roiling mass. Jasiel could hear the booming crash of the battering ram above the confused shouting of combat. He reached again into his quiver — his last arrow. He turned to order a re-supply. "Runner!" he shouted into the avalanche of noise. "Runner!"

No use. Everything was chaos, every soldier fighting his own disorganized war.

His heart pounding in his chest, Jasiel looked again down at the swirling tidal wave of helmets, torches, and curses. He could hear the Sheep Gate's timbers splintering as the battering ram pounded mercilessly home, again and again. He thought of his wife, cowering in their house, hugging their daughter's head tightly to her breast, trying vainly to keep the dreadful clamor from frightening the child.

Simultaneously with the next battering blow of the ram came a blindingly clear vision, like a mauling slap across his unprotected eyes. He saw overwhelmingly what he had so often willed his mind never to see: his family's obscene, certain fate at the hands of these Babylonians.

Despair rose like a black fountain in his throat. He stood

and hurled his javelin uselessly into the attacking mob below. Drawing his sword, he stood on the parapet, looking back a last time on Jerusalem, lit now by raging flames in every quarter of the city. A raw, ragged scream tore out from him. Holding high his sword in both hands, he threw himself forward, plunging like a catapult stone onto the heads of the foe.

JABESH STOOD before the Corner Gate, gripping his sword in a clammy fist. The infantry regiment to which he was assigned stood in battle array, preparing to meet the onslaught which threatened at any moment to come pouring through the already rupturing gate. For the first time in months, all thought of the ache in his belly was gone, swept away in the rush of fear flaring through his veins.

The battering ram crashed once more against the gate, and he saw gate-beams peeling, shredding, splintering, then lost behind a rising dust-cloud.

He watched and listened. The dust veil thinned. Despite the wild clamor of battle all around him, Jabesh heard nothing. The gate became his entire world, as he waited for one sound only — one final, finishing blow.

It came, pounding, screeching, cracking endlessly, shrieking at him as a thousand unleashed demons might sound. The gate was shattered, but the noise did not diminish. With a terrible, roaring battle shout, the Chaldeans surged inside and fell upon them. As the bristling wave of mayhem bore down upon him, Jabesh felt his bowels and bladder empty in a warm gush down his legs.

Their fury was irresistible. Jabesh grunted and gasped, forcing his unstable sinews to parry the furious blows rained on him. He caught the swordstroke of a Chaldean fighter on the hilt of his blade, grimacing with the effort. For a moment, their eyes locked, and they were bound together in the fierce embrace of hand-to-hand battle. Then the Chaldean thrust Jabesh from him with a savage push. Growling like a wolf, the Babylonian struck at him. Jabesh caught the first blow on his buckler, parried the second with his sword. The Babylonian feinted. Too late Jabesh realized he had left his side exposed. His hunger-slowed reflexes had betrayed him. He felt the icy edge of the

Chaldean's blade slicing into his abdomen. The metallic taste of his own blood filled his mouth. The world went dark.

ZEDEKIAH RUSHED into his sons' chamber. "My sons, awake!" he called urgently. The boys, already roused by the tumult in the corridors of the palace, rushed to their father, their eyes stricken with fear. They buried their faces in his chest, sobbing uncontrollably.

"There, there," the king soothed, with a confidence he did not feel. "Come. We must go now." They hurried from the room and down the corridor.

A bodyguard was waiting at the end of the passageway. As Zedekiah approached, the guards quickly surrounded him and fell into step. The party turned into a narrow, seldom-used hallway. At the end was a small, plain wooden door. A guard held his torch to illuminate it, and Zedekiah brought out a bronze key hanging from a chain about his neck. He inserted it in a slot in the door, turned it, and the door swung open upon a musty passageway, hung with cobwebs. The party passed through the doorway, a rear guard closing the door behind them.

The small tunnel opened into a garden, near the wall by the Ophel Tower. Silently they passed along back ways into the Old City, coming at last to the Tombs of the Kings. As they walked among the sepulchers of the ancient kings of Judah, Zedekiah's sons clung closer to him in dread.

Beside the doorway of one of the crypts stood another troop of guards. Approaching the entrance, Zedekiah again took out the bronze key. They went inside the vault.

Going to a far wall within, one of the guards slid back a stone panel. A dark hole led down into the ground. Zedekiah glanced at his men, then remarked lightly, "A strange way to escape, isn't it — by means of a tomb?" He gave a short, false laugh. None of the other faces returned his smile. One by one, they clambered down into the darkness.

BARUCH AND SQUINT hurried through the melee in the streets, trying to reach the court of the guards. Crowds rushed by in delirium. A merchant, his arms full of hastily gathered wares, elbowed his way through the clogged streets. A wild-eyed woman stopped everyone she passed, grasping at them and shouting, "My children! Have you seen my children?" Soldiers, most of them wounded and unarmed, rushed in harassed confusion back and forth.

The two old men shouldered their way through the tumult. Rounding a corner they hurriedly pulled back as a squad of Babylonian infantry came marching down the street from the opposite direction, preceded by screaming, raving citizens. Ducking into a side way, they made a quick detour and continued on their way to the place where Jeremiah was imprisoned.

The court of the guards was empty. Squint stationed himself outside to watch while Baruch rushed into the barracks buildings, shouting, "Jeremiah! Jeremiah, where are you?" The prophet was nowhere to be found. Baruch raced through the empty chambers, left in a state of random disorder by the soldiers' hasty departure. No Jeremiah.

Leaving the barracks, Baruch began searching the storage buildings, calling the name of his friend again and again. As he wandered the dark hallways, a door creaked open behind him. Cautiously, the head of Jeremiah peered from behind the panels. "Baruch?" the prophet called quietly.

The scribe hurried to his friend. "We must go! The Chaldeans have broken the gates, and the city is aflame! Come! Squint is outside."

Still confused, Jeremiah peered questioningly into the scribe's face. "Go? Now?"

"Yes, and hurry!" said Baruch, pulling Jeremiah's arm and hustling him toward the courtyard. "There is no time to lose!"

They emerged into the courtyard just as a troop of Babylonian soldiers marched through the gate. Seeing the three old men, the commander barked an order, and they were swiftly surrounded, their hands bound behind their backs, their ankles shackled one to the other. "Come along," the leader said in broken Hebrew. "You will go join the other prisoners."

Yanking the chain which bound them together, their guard led them out into the street.

THE THIN EDGE of dawn traced a pale line along the eastern horizon as the chariots pounded toward the Plain of Jericho.

Zedekiah looked down at his feet, where his sons crouched, huddled against his legs as they drove furiously onward. For the thousandth time he looked behind him — still no pursuit.

They had threaded their way through the ravines and recesses of the Kidron after emerging from the secret opening of the tunnel. The chariots and horses were waiting, undiscovered, exactly as planned. In the confusion and uproar of the city's collapse, Zedekiah, thirteenth king of Judah since David, had fled the city of the Name, seeking to save his life and the lives of his sons.

If they could reach the valley of the Jordan they might elude Nebuchadrezzar's minions. The dense foliage and twisting course of the river could give them cover — for how long, Zedekiah preferred not to think. Now the only goal was to reach the hiding place. After that, longer-term considerations might be pondered.

They were within a bowshot of the walls of Jericho when the driver of Zedekiah's chariot cried out and fell limply across the side of the chariot. Zedekiah looked in confusion at the man, and saw the feathered shaft protruding from his neck. He stared about in panic, and saw the Scythian on horseback, suddenly racing along beside them, drawing his short, sharply curved bow for another shot. Close behind galloped a patrol of some thirty armed riders.

The chariot team, confused by the strange tension in the reins, swung to the left in a wide arc, taking them nearer to the pursuing horsemen.

The king grabbed at the reins. Tugging in a frenzy at the dead driver, he managed to pull the corpse away from the side of the vehicle, allowing it to fall limply behind. He barely heeded his sons, now whimpering as they clung to his knees. All about him the cries of his men in the other chariots could be heard above the pounding of the horses' hooves.

He pulled the team to the right, looking over his shoulder at the Scythians, who seemed to be gaining every instant. He looked back to the front, just in time to see one of the warriors from the steppes leap from his mount's back onto the withers of the near horse of his team. The animal shied, yanking the chariot violently back and forth, but the hardy Scythian held on, grabbing at the bit. He managed to grasp the reins of both horses, and pulled them forcefully to a rough halt. Instantly his chariot was surrounded by ten of the riders, arrows notched and pulled back. Zedekiah looked desperately for his men, but the other chariots were careening out of control, driverless. Hebrew corpses littered the plain.

The ring of Scythians parted to admit one who appeared to be their commander. He dismounted and approached Zedekiah with the curious rolling, bow-legged gait of the lifelong horseman. In Hebrew heavily accented by the coarse, guttural tongue of his people, he said, "You are the king. You will come with us."

He turned to his men and barked several short commands. One of the soldiers pulled a horsehair rope from a kit slung across his mount's back. He made a loop in the rope, and with a practiced gesture flicked it over the head of the king of Judah, pulling it snug about his neck. At the same time, two of the others yanked his sons by the arm and pulled them onto the backs of their horses, holding the screaming boys in grips of iron.

The Scythian with the rope turned his horse, and began walking in the direction their commander had set. Zedekiah followed, stumbling along in the dust, the Scythian tether half-choking him.

36

NEBUZARADAN STRODE OUT of his pavilion, stopped for a moment, and looked about.

The commander had chosen this town of Ramah as the staging-ground for transporting the Hebrew captives to Babylon. It was the third day since the walls of Jerusalem had been breached, and his men were still in the process of ferreting out those who had hidden among the ruined buildings or tried to escape to the countryside. Several regiments of the Hebrew army were still unaccounted for, but the Babylonian generals had decided these posed no serious strategic threat, and had begun the mopping-up operations.

Before him now Nebuzaradan could see the Hebrews chained together in long lines. At intervals, their chains were stapled to the ground with long stakes. Guards patrolled the pickets, and scribes hurried up and down the lines, pausing at each prisoner to ask again and again the same series of terse questions: "Name? Father's name? Occupation?" The scribes would rapidly scribble the monosyllabic replies onto rolls of papyrus and scurry on to repeat the endless inquiry.

Nebuzaradan walked along the lines, looking thoughtfully at the captives. Here and there mothers wailed for children either dead or missing. Old men sat tossing handfuls of dust on their heads, their faces streaked with dirty trails of grief. In every face Nebuzaradan read absolute hopelessness and dejection. After a lifetime of service in Nebuchadrezzar's host, he should have been inured to such scenes. But somehow, he could never quite forget the moans of the conquered.

As he strolled past one of the questioning scribes, he heard an old man answer with his name. The commander stopped.

"What is that one's name?" he demanded, grasping the arm

of the scribe. The questioner nervously glanced down at his tablet, then back at Nebuzaradan.

"He says his name is Jeremiah, son of Hilkiah. But what—"

"Unchain him," ordered Nebuzaradan to the nearest guard, who quickly approached.

"My lord," the scribe protested, "why—"

"It is no concern of yours," snapped the commander, turning back threateningly. "Go back to your work!"

The scribe meekly hastened to the next prisoner along the chain. "Name...?"

Nebuzaradan gently raised the old man to his feet. Jeremiah stood, rubbing his wrists and looking quizzically into the face of the commander. "Why have you shown me special attention?" he asked in a wheezy voice.

"You are the prophet Jeremiah, are you not?" inquired Nebuzaradan.

"I am," answered Jeremiah, his face still clouded by confusion.

"My lord the emperor has had word of you, and of how you urged the people of this land to submit to his rule. Though he does not understand it, he is grateful for your loyalty to him. He has commanded me, should I find you, to set you free, and do for you whatever you ask."

Jeremiah stared at Nebuzaradan as if he had uttered nonsense. "My loyalty is to Adonai, the Lord of Hosts. That your master happened to be His chosen vessel is a matter entirely beyond my ability to approve or disapprove."

Nebuzaradan stiffened with a momentary indignation. "Indeed, old man, since I saw you in the courtyard with Jeconiah, I would have thought time and events had abated the tartness of your tongue."

Jeremiah stared back at him with eyes too scarred by misery, too seared by pain to be cowed. Nebuzaradan relented. "Ah, well...the emperor has commanded, whatever his reasons. I can do nothing else than obey him."

"And I can do nothing else than obey my Master," inserted the old man.

Nebuzaradan glanced sharply back at the prophet's leathery face. Slowly a smile dragged its way across his face. "Very well. We both have our orders. What would you have me do for you?"

Jeremiah looked askance at the commander, as if still not quite able to believe Nebuzaradan's words. Finally he looked about him and said, "If what you say is true, my first desire is that you release my two friends here." He pointed at the two old men seated on the ground to his right, still chained together. Baruch and Squint looked up, waiting avidly for the commander's next words.

"Release these, also," he snapped, and the guard hastened to obey.

The three former prisoners stood together, rubbing their wrists and ankles, hardly daring to accept this turn of events. Presently Baruch said, "Where will we go now?" Jeremiah shook his head, then turned again to peer inquiringly at Nebuzaradan.

The commander smiled at them. "You are free. You may come to Babylon, under my protection, if you wish. Or you may go anywhere else you like. The decision lies with you." After a moment's hesitation, he added, "If I were you, however, I would seek out Gedaliah, son of Ahikam."

Jeremiah cocked his head, curious as to how Nebuzaradan knew the name of one of his former protectors.

"The emperor has made Gedaliah governor over this area," the commander explained. "The hand of Babylon is upon him, for the good of those who will be left behind in this place. He has set him up at Mizpah, a half-day's journey to the north of here." Nebuzaradan pointed over their heads, indicating the direction. "If I were you, I think I would go to him. He will need wise counsel in the days ahead."

Jeremiah responded slowly, "Perhaps you are correct. Perhaps we should go to Mizpah. Come, my friends," he said, turning to go.

"Wait," said Nebuzaradan, placing a hand on Jeremiah's shoulder. "Do not leave just yet." As the three released captives looked on, he turned and whispered something to a page nearby. The boy raced away, and in a few moments came back holding a linen-wrapped bundle. He bowed and offered it to the commander.

"Here," said Nebuzaradan, in turn offering the bundle to Jeremiah. "Take this. It contains food and a talent of silver."

Jeremiah reached out to accept the gift. Incredulous still, he bowed respectfully to the Babylonian. "I have been treated with greater kindness by a stranger," he said, "than by the king and princes of my own people. May Adonai bless you for your generosity."

Nebuzaradan, made uncomfortable by the old man's eyes and earnest benediction, turned his head away. Moving quickly on, he cleared his throat and called back. "You should go now."

THE SUN BURNED hot at Riblah — a molten bronze disk in the merciless sky. Not even a breath of wind stirred this day, and the summer heat over Syria was like a blanket of hot lead.

The nobles and princes of Judah — those who had survived the battle of Jerusalem — were assembled in lines, shoulder to shoulder, as if about to receive homage from an adoring multitude. But they were naked, and their ankles were chained together with sun-heated shackles that scalded their skin. Their heads hung in abject shame. Their wives and children had for the most part, been sent to Ramah, and would undergo the long forced march to Babylon. But for these, the march was ended.

The officials of Nebuchadrezzar's court and most of his high command were assembled on a raised platform built by the shackled prisoners. Slightly apart from this dais sat another, more elevated stage, overhung with a canopy of gauzy cotton fabrics and furnished with plush silken cushions of royal purple. Presently the emperor would occupy this vantage point. But now everything was still. The day held its breath.

From one of the mud-brick buildings at the edge of the town, a small party emerged: a man and two boys, guarded by five Chaldean infantrymen. They paced slowly toward the parade ground by the river where the prisoners and the Babylonian nobles were assembled. They were unchained, their steps hindered only by the fear which palsied their limbs and screamed in silent desperation from their eyes. Zedekiah, last king of Judah, was marching out toward judgment. His sons limped beside him, trying desperately, with the tragic courage of children, to appear brave.

When they were in place, facing the long line of the nobles and princes, their garments were ripped from them. Like the others, they now stood naked, their defeat and humiliation displayed bluntly for the ruthless scrutiny of all.

When they had stood so for what seemed hours, the trumpeters stationed beside the entrance to Nebuchadrezzar's pavilion raised their horns and blew a harsh fanfare. The Babylonian officials made obeisance, and the guards roughly shoved the prisoners to their knees. Nebuchadrezzar paced solemnly from his pavilion, surrounded by chanting mages and incense-bearing priests. Gravely the emperor ascended to his stage and seated himself on the cushions. When he had taken his place, the nobles on the other platform reseated themselves.

After inspecting the premises and assuring himself that all was ready, Nebuchadrezzar announced in a clear and commanding voice, "Let it begin!"

Five burly men, stripped to the waist and carrying shining scimitars, stepped to the line of chained prisoners, accompanied by a band of the priests of Marduk, waving incense bowls and chanting in unison a strange, warbling refrain.

Each scimitar-wielder stood before a single prisoner, gripping his weapon in both hands. With practiced eyes they all measured the distance between themselves and their five whimpering victims. Then, in simultaneous, swiftly effective strokes, they disemboweled the men in chains before them. The five mutilated bodies dropped like sacks of wet meal onto the packed dirt of the parade ground, and the executioners moved down the line to face the next five to die. All the while, the priests chanted in implacable repetition the sacrificial hymn to their god.

The slaughter moved slowly down the line five by five, until the bodies of all the princes of Judah lay in a bloody, tangled row in the dust of Riblah. Then the executioners turned and began walking toward the king and his sons.

The boys' facade of bravery broke. They wailed and fell to the ground, grasping at their father's legs. "No! No, father, don't let them do it!" screamed the younger. The older only sobbed incoherently.

Zedekiah turned to face Nebuchadrezzar. "Mercy!" he

begged, kneeling on the ground. "Will you not slay me, and let my sons live? Why should my children die because of my actions? I beg of you, please!"

The emperor looked on as if not listening, his face an unreadable mask.

The executioners took the boys and bound their arms and legs. The children were too paralyzed by terror to struggle, but they screamed incessantly. When they were trussed up like fowl for market, the executioners placed them in a kneeling position, facing their father, who stared, transfixed by horror. One of the swordmen leaned near to Zedekiah. "Your sons will feel no pain," he murmured, giving all the comfort he could.

Two of the men stationed themselves behind the whimpering boys. The scimitars flashed up in the sun, then down. Silence.

Then the scream of a wounded beast burst from the throat of the king of Judah. And the Syrian sun burned down upon his gaping mouth, unhearing, uncaring.

FAR TO THE SOUTH, at that very moment, Jeremiah was walking the road to Mizpah.

Suddenly he stopped. He turned and stared intently to the north as if listening for a far-off echo. Baruch and Squint looked on, confused.

Suddenly the prophet jerked his hands to his face — and began weeping.

"BECAUSE OF YOUR REBELLION, you have caused the death of your people and of your own sons," pronounced Nebuchadrezzar solemnly, still seated atop his dais. He looked down on Zedekiah, who knelt pitifully on the ground, great, wracking sobs wrenching from his tortured body. "And now, you shall never again see the light of day."

The emperor nodded to the executioners. Two of them yanked the king to his feet, pinioning Zedekiah's arms behind him. A third grasped a handful of the king's hair, pulling his head back so that he stared upward. From behind the emperor's dais, a fourth brought an iron rod, sharp-pointed and heated to a white glow.

He approached Zedekiah, glancing a final time at the emperor, who gave the signal to proceed.

He jabbed the white-hot spike first into Zedekiah's right eye, then the left, then back again into each. Smoke hissed up, and the odor of burning flesh hung in the air. The smell was so strong it almost diverted the attention of the witnesses from the victim's ghastly, high-pitched screaming.

At last the spike was withdrawn, and the men allowed Zedekiah to fall limply to the ground, sobbing and clawing at his eye sockets.

"Bind him and bring him to Babylon," commanded the emperor. "As for the others — leave them to the birds and the jackals.

"So let it be done."

37

WITH FURTIVE GLANCES and animal stealth, the small band of men crept among the crags and gullies until they came at dusk to the cave. The day's take had been fair. They had managed to scrounge some grain from a broken bin on the outskirts of Bethel. Most of it was edible. And the oil, though slightly rancid, would also be welcome.

Almost a hundred men were banded together in the cave, ragtag remnants of the host of Judah. Some had deserted from units stationed in the outlying cities; others had fled from the sack of Jerusalem, somehow escaping amid the chaos. Together they survived as roving scavengers in the hills of Ephraim and northern Judah.

To a surprising degree the old disciplines and loyalties still held forth in the strange, orderless world they now inhabited. Johanan, their leader, had been an officer in the infantry. He had been at Jerusalem. It was he who had patched together a semblance of order among the escapees, and given assignments and duties. In the societal vacuum, anything familiar was to be grasped, clung to. This slight comfort was all they had left.

Word had lately come, trickling through the valleys and down the byways, of other bands. Like Johanan's men, they were loosely organized groups that had eluded the Babylonian search-and-destroy sweeps. A rudimentary network between the bands was being formed, new alliances forged. The kingdom of Judah was a charred tapestry, but — cautiously — stray threads were being collected together once again.

Those on watch near the cave entrance greeted the returning reconnaissance party with nods and quiet monosyllables. The inside of the cave smelled of animal grease and smoke. While the others carried the provisions to a storage area at the rear of the main chamber, Jaazaniah, the leader of today's scavenging party, sought out Johanan where he squatted just inside the entrance.

Johanan was staring out absently across the broken, rocky ravine which faced the hillside where the grotto was located. Evening shadows had already climbed the flinty slope. Only the topmost portion reflected the orange light of the setting sun.

Jaazaniah squatted beside him. Without ceremony, Jaazaniah passed on the intelligence he had gathered that day.

"A ragpicker in Bethel says the Chaldeans have made Gedaliah, son of Ahikam, governor."

Johanan made no reply, no sign he had heard. After several more moments of silence, Jaazaniah continued.

"His place is in Mizpah. Quite a few have gathered to him." More silence.

"It will be winter soon," Jaazaniah observed.

The orange light thinned atop the opposite ridge, withdrawing slowly before the advancing shadows of night. When the entire hillside was cloaked in darkness, Johanan looked for the first time at Jaazaniah. In the graying light of dusk, he nodded slightly at his aide.

"Gedaliah is a fair man," said Johanan.

His companion nodded in agreement. Across the ravine, stars began to blink in the night sky.

NIGHT FELL at Mizpah. Jeremiah and Baruch sat in the doorway of the small, single-roomed, mud-brick hut which sheltered them. Perhaps a handful of words had passed between the men over the last few days. They partook of each other's silence with an understanding beyond speech. Words were superfluous to the tacit strivings in the deep quiet places of their spirits. It was enough to be together, to know without speaking.

Baruch raised his eyes to the sky for a moment, then started to his feet, staring intently.

"What is it?" asked Jeremiah, rising slowly to stand beside his friend. Wordlessly, Baruch pointed to an orange glow waxing on the southern horizon — from the direction of Jerusalem.

Softly came the prophet's voice: "Zion will be a plowed field; Jerusalem will become a heap of rubble…"

"Surely Micah wept, to have foreseen this day," said Baruch.

"I must go there," said Jeremiah, decisively.

"But...why? What is left that you should—"

"I must bear witness," said the prophet firmly. "For all those who shared the vision of this abomination, this destruction. For all those who drank the bitter cup of the Lord's calling, and felt the scalding oil of His anointing on their heads. For Micah, for Hosea, for Obadiah, for Habakkuk..." He looked intently at Baruch. "For Isaiah, and for Mahseiah, his scribe..."

Baruch dropped his eyes to the ground.

"I stand in a long line, Baruch. For all of them — I must go. I must see."

THE RUBBLE WAS STILL burning two days later when they arrived. The summit of Zion, once the glowing jewel in the signet ring of God, was now a charred heap. Here and there carrion birds pecked at flesh which had escaped the flames. Even above the smell of burning, the stench of death lay thick on the place like flies on a corpse.

Nebuzaradan's troops had been thorough. Scarcely one stone had been left joined to its mate. The walls of the city — once her pride and the boast of her kings — had been broken asunder. Not a house was left standing, not a cistern unfouled, not a street left clear. Jerusalem, born in the days of David some nine generations ago, was dead.

As Jeremiah picked his way among the debris, he felt a grief roiling within him that could not be named in words. A dirge tolled in his mind, called forth from the lifelong pain of his avocation by the scene of total desolation which lay before him:

> "How deserted lies the city,
>   once so full of people!
> How like a widow is she,
>   who was once great among the nations.
> She who was queen among the provinces
>   has now become a slave.
> Bitterly she weeps at night,
>   tears are upon her cheeks.

Among all her lovers,
there is none to comfort her.
All her friends have betrayed her;
they have become her enemies.
After affliction and harsh labor,
Judah has gone into exile.
She dwells among the nations,
she finds no resting place.
All who pursue her have overtaken her
in the midst of her distress..."

They climbed Mount Moriah. The walls of the Temple courtyard lay open like gashes in the chest of a murdered man. The Temple was a black, charred derelict.

"I have heard them say the Chaldeans took everything back to Babylon — even the Bronze Sea and the pillars of Jachin and Boaz," said Baruch, gazing at the sacrilegious waste that was once the House of the Eternal.

Jeremiah, son of the line of Aaron, could not stay out of the Temple, even in its ruined condition. Almost in a trance he stepped past the tumbled, wrecked wall, across the courtyard, and slowly up the steps. He walked through the gaping hole that had once been the doorway to the Outer Sanctuary.

Inside was the scene from a nightmare. The cedar paneling, so renowned for its exquisite joinings and seamless workmanship, clung here and there to the walls in charred fragments. Some of the tapestries and drapes had been left behind, and these too were now a smoldering ruin. The interior of the chamber was soot-blackened. Great burnt-edged holes gaped in the roof, and every so often half-consumed pieces of the support beams gave way, spilling a clattering cloud of masonry down into the room. The prophet's eyes, however, were fixed on the west end of the sanctuary, on the blackened remains of the wall which delineated the boundary of the Holy of Holies. Slowly he approached. Even in its present state, after having been utterly despoiled by pagan hands, the place evoked awe in Jeremiah's heart. Here was the place where God Himself showed His glory to the high priest on the Day of Atonement. His soul resonating with the enormity of the act, Jeremiah went inside.

But he found only another, much smaller, burned room. The glory and terror had departed. God had renounced Israel, and no more would He hear the call of the high priest. The final Day of Atonement had come on the edge of the swords of Babylon.

Jeremiah looked down. A small pile of burned wood and ash was all that remained of the Ark of the Covenant. Presumably, the gilding and ornamentation had been pried loose and taken to Babylon, a trophy for Nebuchadrezzar. Tears drained from his eyes as the dirge groaned again from the tortured darkness in his soul.

> *"The enemy laid hands*
> *on all her treasures:*
> *She saw pagan nations*
> *enter her sanctuary —*
> *Those You had forbidden*
> *to enter Your assembly...*
> *Is it nothing to you,*
> *all you who pass by?*
> *Look around and see:*
> *Is any suffering like my suffering*
> *that was inflicted on me,*
> *That the Lord brought on me*
> *in the day of His fierce anger?"*

A numbness creeping into his chest, Jeremiah left the Temple and went out to the courtyard where Baruch waited.

They passed through the rubble-strewn streets like restless shades through a valley of tombs. A pack of wild dogs, growling over some prize, was frightened by their approach and skulked away, tails between their legs. Their backward glances at the two men had a look of guilt, as if even the dumb beasts knew they feasted in what had once been a holy place.

Drawing closer to where the dogs had been, they saw the carrion on which the animals had gorged — the torn, burnt body of a child. A sob tore from the prophet's throat.

> *"My eyes fail from weeping.*
> *I am in torment within.*

My heart is poured out upon the ground
because my people are destroyed,
Because children and infants faint
in the streets of the city.
They say to their mothers,
'Where is bread and wine?'
as they faint like wounded men
in the streets of the city;
As their lives ebb away
in their mothers' arms..."

He felt the yawning chasm of sorrow threatening to overwhelm him, to swallow him in its endless blackness. He stood, swaying, as the world seemed to twist away from him. Baruch grasped at his shoulder, trying to steady him.

"Come," the scribe said. "We should sit down awhile. You are tired, my friend. Let us rest in the shade of this wall."

Baruch helped him sit down and lean his back against the partially standing wall of a building that might once have been part of the palace. Jeremiah panted with an exhaustion that was more a fatigue of the soul than of the limbs. As he looked about him, he realized they sat in the courtyard where he had delivered his oracle against the alliance of Zedekiah. He remembered the strident crowing of the streetcorner preachers, each one hastening to be the first to congratulate the king on his political coup. Jeremiah felt a tide of anger rising in him — indignation at the false voices who had led astray those who were only too eager to believe their fair words.

"The visions of your prophets
were false and worthless;
they did not expose your sin
to ward off your captivity.
The oracles they gave you
were false and misleading..."

The anger blunted the sharp edge of grief which had almost bettered him. Jeremiah felt some of his strength returning. "Let us go," he said, reaching out to take hold of Baruch's shoulder.

"Come — help me up." The two men levered themselves to their feet, and resumed their doleful inspection.

They left the abandoned city by what had been the Horse Gate, and descended into the Vale of the Kidron. Halfway up the opposite slope, Jeremiah stopped. He stared ahead at the olive groves surmounting the eastern heights above the Kidron. The heat of summer was giving way to the cool breezes of autumn, and the trees were in their fruit-bearing phase. He could plainly see the olive berries clustering in rich profusion among the pale silvery-green leaves.

Then he looked back, from where he had come. The derelict city lay behind him, across the ravine. In front, life and sustenance. Behind, death and emptiness.

The contrast bore in on him with the force of an epiphany, and again he felt words struggling for birth within his spirit. But these were words of hope — of the gleam of light following tedious darkness.

> "I remember my affliction and my wandering,
>   the bitterness and the gall.
> I well remember them,
>   and my soul is downcast within me.
> Yet — this I call to mind
>   and therefore I have hope:
> The steadfast love of the Lord never ceases;
>   His mercies never come to an end.
> They are new every morning.
>   Great is Your faithfulness.
> 'The Lord is my portion,' says my soul,
>   therefore I will hope in Him…
> For men are not cast off by the Lord forever.
>   Though He brings grief, He will show compassion —
> so great is His unfailing love.
> For He does not willingly bring affliction
>   or grief to the children of men…"

"My friend," said Jeremiah after several more moments of quiet contemplation, "I have suddenly a desire to see again the place of my birth."

"Are you sure?" asked Baruch in a concerned voice. "Surely after what you have witnessed here—"

"Ah, my friend," soothed the prophet, "after this, what harm can come?" He gave Baruch a look of calm assurance. "Besides," he continued, "I have bought a field there. Should I not go and inspect my property?"

Baruch nodded. "Very well," he assented.

They started north along the rim of the ravine, picking olives from the trees as they went.

38

TOWARD NIGHTFALL they came winding down the dusty road from Jerusalem to the village. Some of the outlying villages had suffered less than the main walled towns. Anathoth was one of these. The houses crouched silently — intact, but seemingly vacant. No lamps illumined the windows, no cooking fires curled upward into the purple dusk. The place had a furtive feel, as if trying to avoid notice.

Jeremiah involuntarily dropped his voice to a murmur as he spoke to Baruch, pointing out landmarks. "There was the house of Jephaniah, my boyhood friend. Our house was on the other end of the village — just beyond this rise."

They passed the jagged, broken stump of a long-dead tree. "This," commented the prophet, "was the gathering place of the town's elders. It was a mulberry..." He fell quiet, remembering a long-ago day of hard words and wounded eyes.

"Where was I?" he resumed after a moment's thought. "Oh, yes. This was the potter's house — I used to love to come here and smell the wet clay! — and there was my favorite climbing tree. After all these years, that tree is still alive! And there lived— " Again his voice fell silent, ambushed by a memory so strong it took the breath from his body.

"What? You were saying?" prompted Baruch. He looked at Jeremiah. The prophet stood staring at a house not much different from any of the others. His mouth tried helplessly to frame words, to explain, to tell...but no sound came out. Confused, Baruch looked from the house to his friend — attempting to understand, unable to guess.

It was the house of Gershom the miller — and of Hannah his daughter.

Jeremiah turned away, resumed the walk. "Come," he said.

"The night falls. Let's find some shelter." He trudged away into the quiet darkening, toward the dwelling of his youth.

They spent the night in the hushed halls of the house of Abiathar. To their surprise, the ashes on the hearth were warm, though they could find no other sign the place had been recently occupied. Baruch managed to dig about in the ashes and find a weakly glowing coal. Soon they had a small but comforting blaze kindled.

As they sat before the fire and pulled pieces of dried meat from the supply in their kit, Jeremiah said to Baruch, "Tomorrow I will show you the place where your grandfather lived."

Both of them stared quietly into the heart of the flames, each wrapped in his own reminiscences.

During the night, Jeremiah awoke, feeling sure he had heard footsteps. He looked about in the darkness, but saw nothing, heard nothing. Lying before the hearth in this house, he heard faint whisperings of the past, voices just beyond the edge of his hearing: loving voices, stern voices; taunting voices, pained voices. They crowded about him now, murmuring mute questions into the echoing caverns of his soul. He felt as if he were being examined, spied upon. Again he imagined the remote scuffing of surreptitious feet. Again he saw nothing. At last he slept.

In the morning they walked out into the fields — once immaculately husbanded by Joash, now overgrown with weeds and clumps of scrub oak. Apparently the Babylonians had pastured some of their livestock in this field, for piles of dried droppings were scattered about, the ground cover gnawed down to the dust, as if by sheep. Here and there the stone dividing walls had fallen haphazardly, leaving gaps. It appeared to matter little, since no one tended the fields of Anathoth anymore, and all the cattle had been slain to feed the armies of Nebuchadrezzar and Zedekiah.

Behind them they heard the click of stones striking together. They turned around.

An old woman stood there. Her foot had inadvertently tumbled one loose wall stone against another. She looked as if she were about to turn and flee. Then Jeremiah recognized her.

Hannah.

Baruch looked from the woman to Jeremiah. Then back. "You know her?"

Dumbly Jeremiah nodded.

Her words floated down to him on the breeze, coming from years and miles away: "Jeremiah? Son of Hilkiah?" The words sounded raspy, weak, but he heard the lilt of a maiden's voice. Again he nodded.

For another moment she regarded them warily. Cautiously she said, "I...I have wine and oil hidden in the house. Come." She turned and led them back inside.

As they entered again where they had slept, she was coming from the back rooms of the dwelling, carrying a skin of wine and an urn. With a grunt she set down the urn on the rough-hewn plank table. She offered them the skin.

"When the Babylonians came," she said, "I hid some provisions in a place in the wall outside," she said. "They used this house as a barracks for their herdsmen. They made me serve them food and drink. I was able to stay out of their way — most of the time.

"Then when the Chaldeans left, the bandits began coming. That is why you found no one in the village last night. The nights are worst. Many of the people sleep in the ravines and copses, for fear of the wandering marauders. I thought that's what you were at first. So I hid. Then I heard you talking, and I started to wonder..." She paused, glancing at Jeremiah, then away. She took a little meal from a clay pot in the corner, mixed it with some oil from the urn, and began to knead bread.

Since he had first seen her, the prophet had not uttered a sound. He sat spellbound, staring at her as if at an apparition.

Her hair, once raven-black, was now a dirty gray. Her jowls were heavy and loose, and skin hung in folds from her neck and the backs of her arms. And her face — the wrinkles and liver-spots of age had not changed it so much as the weight of the years that dragged at her eyes and the corners of her mouth. Time had broken her; diminished her from what he remembered her to be. Time and sorrow. He was surprised now that he had ever recognized her at all.

Finally he was able to speak — a single word.

"Lemuel?"

Again she glanced sideways at him. "Dead. Years ago." She made it sound as if he should have known. And perhaps he had. Not a shadow of grief showed on her.

"Your children?"

Her hands stopped their restless motion as sadness dragged a long, shuddering breath from her. Then she resumed kneading.

"My sons died in the fighting. My daughter was taken by the Chaldeans."

Baruch felt his heart bleeding toward this woman. She was pressed like dough between the swift, uncaring hands of circumstance.

"You should come with us to Mizpah. A friend of ours has gone ahead of us there. And Gedaliah is there, the appointed governor. He is a good man, and a wise one. Many people are coming— "

"No." Her answer was curt, decisive. She did not look up at them as her hands pressed and folded the dough. "I'll remain here. This is where I was born, and where I grew to womanhood..."—her voice flickered with a momentary sadness, as a breath of wind from the past blew by—"and where I shall die." She turned from them, spreading the dough onto a long, flat stone, and went to the hearth to rekindle the fire for baking.

When she left the room, Baruch looked at Jeremiah, seeking some explanation for the bitterness which was the constant, unspoken backdrop to this woman's life. Something inexplicable hung in the silences between her and his friend — something unresolved which had bound them through all these years in an invisible tether of melancholy. Baruch's face was creased in perplexity and concern as he looked at Jeremiah, who sat, head bowed, at the plank table.

In answer, the prophet rose and slumped outside, as if he dragged a millstone. Baruch found Hannah to tell her they would soon return, then stepped out to follow Jeremiah.

They walked wordlessly up the main path of the village. When they had gone a stone's throw away from the house, Jeremiah cleared his throat. "Would you like to see the place where your grandfather lived?"

"Yes, I would like that very much," answered Baruch. He

could feel other words straining for birth around the edges of his friend's restless quiet — words which Jeremiah could not yet say.

They turned from the main path down a side trail, overgrown and disused. Descending a gradual slope, the trail wound around a bend and past a small, young stand of scrub oaks. Jeremiah paused, looking about in momentary confusion.

"This is the place, but...these trees — they have grown up since..."

Baruch was peering intently among the tangled growth in the thicket. "I believe I see the remains of woodwork."

Jeremiah looked where Baruch pointed. "Yes," he agreed after a moment's study. "Yes, this is it." Parting the branches of the squat saplings, he stooped and entered the thicket, Baruch following.

Among the branches and undergrowth, the remains of a small mud-and-wattle hut slowly crumbled into dust. The two men looked about them in quiet reverie — the one remembering, the other wishing.

"Look there," said Jeremiah, pointing at a small, rudely fashioned oaken table standing off to one side. Made of sturdier stuff than the house which had contained it, the table reared up amid the decay of the dwelling, stubbornly resisting the erosion of the years. It stood like a sentinel — as if guarding some treasure which gave it immunity to the passing of time.

"Beneath this table he concealed the scrolls," explained Jeremiah. "The same ones you now have." The prophet mused quietly for a moment, then said, "How well I remember the first day I came here. He pulled from beneath this table the scroll of the prophet Isaiah..."

Unbidden, the words of the prophet whispered in Jeremiah's ear — a voiceless sound as dry as old parchment:

"A man will seize one of his brothers at his father's home and say, 'You have a cloak — you be our leader! Take charge of this heap of ruins!'

"But in that day he will cry out, 'I have no remedy. I have no food or clothing in my house; do not make me the leader of the people...'"

No remedy. No remedy…

Baruch's voice intruded into his musing.

"Who is she?" the scribe asked gently. "Why does a bond of pain stretch between you?"

Hesitantly, the prophet looked at his old friend, then away. In a voice that echoed from long, tired years, he said, "She was Hannah, daughter of Gershom the miller. I… Once I…"

He swallowed several times. "We had planned to marry," he finished, simply.

Brushing the branches aside, he left the thicket.

39

JUST PAST MIDDAY they prepared to leave Anathoth. Hannah sat quietly, staring out a window as they gathered their meager bundles. Baruch would not look at her; Jeremiah could do nothing else.

At last he could keep quiet no longer. He went to her, squatted in front of her, and looked earnestly into her face.

"Hannah..." He said it gently, as a mother sings a lullaby. Her lusterless eyes turned from the window to him, their depths blank as slates.

"Hannah, won't you come with us? Soon you will have no food. You will starve." He begged her with his eyes to answer, to relent.

In a lifeless voice that cut him like a lash, she replied, "I am dead already. I died while still a maiden — along with my dreams. You consigned me to the life of a slave — I was scarcely more than a childbearing drudge to Lemuel. He took me to wife only to spite you.

"Isn't that odd?" she went on. "Even in your rejection of me, you were responsible for bringing me into this house." She looked about her, at the sagging roof beams, the cobwebbed corners. "Everything that was precious to me, I lost here. My love...my hope...my children... Don't you see, Jeremiah? This house has always been my tomb. I cannot leave it."

He tried once more, in a voice barely audible through the grief that stifled him. "Why? Others in the land have lost as much as you — yet they do not abandon life. Why has your bitterness chained you to this darkness?"

For the first time, emotion showed on her. Her nostrils flared and her eyes widened in anger as she glared at him. "Well might I ask you the same question, prophet," she spat.

"Why," she grated, "after all the curses you rained down upon the people of this land, including your own flesh and blood — after the trail of malice you have trodden for so many years, after seeing all your hateful words come true — why do you come here to gloat over an old woman you killed long ago? Why must you come again before my face? Why can't you let me die in barren obscurity, just as I have lived, thanks to you?"

The venom in her voice yanked a gasp from him. He stared at her, panting in horror at the self-portrait she had painted on the canvas of her life — a bleak scrawling of dark colors and hateful images, drawn in acrid desperation from the forced solitude of her own despair.

Finally he was able to answer.

"All my life," he said, half-choking, "I have listened to the voice of the Eternal..."

She snorted, looking again out the window.

"I have listened to Him," Jeremiah went on, "and I have tried, with all that is within me, to heed. The cost has been terrible. I have known pain. I have seen more death than any man ought. I have lost the love of almost every person who was ever dear to me." She glanced quickly at him, then away.

"But one thing He has never taken completely from me," continued Jeremiah, his chest heaving with the effort of controlling his voice, "and that is hope. I have not been able to afford the dry comfort of bitterness."

Slowly, unwillingly, she turned again to look at him.

"The tiny spark of belief, which not even the burning of the Temple could quench, has kept my heart vulnerable to pain." His eyes glistened as he looked into hers. "When the heart can no longer feel pain, then hope is truly gone. And with it, life.

"I did not come to gloat, Hannah. In your heart of hearts, you know this. I came to remember. And to grieve. And..." He struggled over the next words. "...And to hope for what is yet to come." Hannah shook her head uncertainly.

"This," he said, "is what your bitterness has caused you to forget: that affliction and faith are sisters in the same house." He pulled himself painfully to his feet. "And know it as truth, Hannah: Bitterness and despair are thieves who worship at the altar of Self."

He stood leaning on Baruch, still looking upon her. For a few breaths she returned his gaze, a war being waged across the terrain of her soul. But the darkness had mastered her too long, and her face closed, never to reopen.

She turned and stared again out the window, seeming to dwindle before their very eyes.

Sadly they turned and left the house, leaning upon each other as they limped toward Mizpah.

ONE DAY in the early autumn a shout came from atop the ancient stone watchtower for which Mizpah was named. A small armed band trooped toward the place from the east. Hastily those in the fields dropped their gathering-baskets and rakes and rushed to the town, grabbing their swords and homemade weapons. They assembled in front of the closed gates, reinforced by the handful of Babylonian regulars still stationed in Judah. Nervously Gedaliah stood at their head.

The men who marched in haphazard order toward them had the same patched-together look as most of those who had come to Mizpah from out of the surrounding countryside. Their eyes shifted this way and that, taking in the assembled militia, the walls, the fortifications, the looks of those who barred their way into the city. Here and there the odd piece of equipment or patched armor showed the Judean military origins of the small squadron.

At the head of them strode one with a wolfen, hungry look. Gedaliah instinctively mistrusted him, but resolved to offer this company the same hospitality he had extended to all the others who had ingathered to the land of their birth. He hailed the chief, taking two steps out from the front of the militia.

"Greetings, brother! I am Gedaliah son of Ahikam, appointed governor of the province of Judah by the Emperor Nebuchadrezzar. Be welcome. You may live here without fear under the protection of the emperor and his governor. There is room for all who will take the land to live in and work upon. How are you known?"

The leader of the newcomers made no immediate reply. Instead, he slowly looked Gedaliah up and down, a sneer on his lean, dusty face.

"So... A scribe rules in the emperor's place! How amusing! I had heard the tale, but I did not believe it until now." A low, evil chuckle rattled from his chest.

Standing with his men behind Gedaliah, Johanan felt his grip tightening involuntarily on the hilt of his sword as the amused troubler gave his name: "I am Ishmael, son of Nethaniah, son of Elishama." The prince quoted his semi-royal lineage with a haughty lift of the chin. And by the look of him, the rumors were true that said the former prince had hired himself and his men out to Baalis of Ammon. The signet ring on Ishmael's left hand seemed to confirm the tale. Johanan asked himself why this one, untrustworthy even in better times, had survived the sack of Judah.

Now Ishmael spoke again to Gedaliah. "These," he continued, motioning to the ten men behind him, "are my servants. We have returned to Judah. Just in time, it would appear," he finished, with a sardonic smirk.

Gedaliah ignored the barely veiled barb. "Come in, then, Ishmael! You are in the homeland of your fathers, and are welcome."

Johanan stared unbelieving at Gedaliah. Was the governor blind? The bad blood in this surly renegade would be obvious to a child — yet Gedaliah greeted him with open arms. Johanan resolved to speak sternly to the governor at the first opportunity.

Gedaliah continued the ritual greeting by inviting Ishmael to his house two evenings hence to sup and discuss events in the surrounding countries. Until that time, he was to feel free to inspect Mizpah and the surrounding country, with an eye to selecting an agreeable place to settle.

The prince made a mocking bow, and accepted. At a signal from Gedaliah, the ranks of the militia grudgingly made way as Ishmael and his band slouched into the town.

As the militia disbanded to return to the harvest fields, Johanan drew up beside the governor and whispered urgently in his ear. "Gedaliah! Are you mad? Can you not see this one is evil? He has blood on his mind as surely as the sun rises tomorrow. And if I don't miss my guess, he intends to replace you as leader in Judah."

Gedaliah walked stolidly onward, as if he had not heard the desperate warning. "That will not happen," said the governor quietly. "The emperor has appointed me as his regent here. Ishmael cannot undo that."

"What are you saying?" insisted Johanan, his voice rising and his legs moving faster to stay up with Gedaliah. "When you are dead, what difference will it make what Nebuchadrezzar has decreed? Don't you understand— "

"I have no proof of what you allege," Gedaliah interrupted calmly. "I will not judge Ishmael on the basis of unsubstantiated rumors."

"And why not?" shouted the soldier, losing patience. "What I say is true! Ishmael was worthless on the day of his birth, and he has gotten worse with age!"

Gedaliah stopped and turned slowly to the red-faced Johanan. Fixing a firm stare, he said slowly, "They said that also about me when I left Jerusalem. They called me traitor, coward, and worse. Yet some of those same ones now live under my protection, and they learn firsthand the error of their earlier opinions.

"I will not judge Ishmael by what others say he may have been," Gedaliah continued. "Until he acts in a way that forces me to do otherwise, I intend to receive him in good faith." The governor turned and resumed walking. Johanan caught up with him, and made one more desperate try.

"Tomorrow morning my men and I leave Mizpah to go on patrol," he began. "Let me eliminate this threat to the security of the people of this place."

Gedaliah halted again. Now it was he whose face was crimson with anger. "Has there been insufficient bloodshed in this land that we must now turn our swords on our brethren?" His jaw clenched. "If you do this thing, I myself will order you killed! Do you understand?"

Johanan stalked away in frustration, the governor staring sternly at his retreating back.

IN THE AUTUMN AIR, sound carried farther. Gedaliah heard his guest coming long before he could see him striding out of the early evening shadows.

The governor stood, took a deep breath, and carried a lamp outside to greet his visitor by the front door.

Ishmael came alone, without his henchmen. Gedaliah was relieved. Johanan's warning still rang in his ears, but any symbol of accommodation on the part of this latest arrival was a welcome contradiction to the soldier's ominous assessment.

The prince made a bow as he approached. Gedaliah thought the gesture lacked the cynicism of the display at the city gates two days before. And Ishmael's next words convinced him even further.

"I must bow twice, brother Gedaliah," said the prince meekly, making a second obeisance. "Once for gratitude at your hospitality, and a second time to beg your forgiveness for my indelicate manner of two days ago. Please, let me explain—"

"No, no..." began Gedaliah.

"I must insist," interrupted Ishmael firmly. "My men and I have seen difficult days, my brother. Difficult indeed, since..." The prince's voice wavered. Taking several deep breaths he went on: "...since the destruction of our home. Our people have lived in this land for hundreds of generations, Gedaliah. Hundreds! And now, it is gone. All gone."

He finished in a dismal voice: "So I was somewhat overwrought. It is a poor excuse, I warrant, for the harsh words I gave you, but it is my only defense. Please do not hold this moment of poor judgment to my charge." The prince bowed his head humbly, awaiting Gedaliah's response.

"My brother! Of course I will not blame you," replied Gedaliah warmly, laying a hand on Ishmael's shoulder. "Who in these last years has not felt the lash of desperation? Who has not been driven by necessity to means previously unthinkable? No, I will not count your words against you. Come inside. Food is prepared."

With a grateful glance, Ishmael entered the governor's house.

By the standards of the days since the exile, it was a sumptuous repast. On the board were bowls of boiled lentils, *chamets* bread made with yeast, the unleavened *matzoh*, roast fowl, and even dried figs from the last harvest.·

"I am sorry I cannot offer you wine with your food," said Gedaliah as they seated themselves. "This past year was a poor one for the vines. But there is plenty of water." He motioned to a large urn in the corner.

"Please!" protested Ishmael. "With such an excellent board, how can I cavil over drink?" The two men grinned at each other, and began to eat.

Later they took council together, reclining on plainwoven woolen rugs in a corner of the room.

"So you see," Gedaliah was saying, "Nebuchadrezzar has left us largely to our own devices. He does not expect large tax levies from us for many years to come. It is his desire that the people cultivate the land, become settled, and — What is it?"

Ishmael was peering over Gedaliah's shoulder, out a window which opened onto a darkened street of the town. Quickly he looked back at his host. "Nothing — forgive me. I thought I saw someone walk past your window, but it was nothing."

"The hour grows late," observed Gedaliah. "Perhaps I tire you with my constant talking— "

"No, no!" protested Ishmael. "It is I who tire you! You have many duties other than entertaining latecomers to Mizpah. I should leave, so that you can rest."

"Well...perhaps we might continue our discussions at another time."

"Yes, of course." Ishmael stood. "Brother Gedaliah, I must thank you sincerely, once again, for hospitality undeserved. I want to give you a gift."

"You need not do such a thing!"

"Oh, but I think I must," said Ishmael. He reached into his linen girdle, smiling at the governor, and drew a small dagger, displaying it upon open palms, as if offering it for Gedaliah's inspection. With a puzzled expression the governor leaned closer.

Catlike, Ishmael plunged the dirk into Gedaliah's throat. The governor fell to his knees, then onto his back at Ishmael's feet, his life draining in a pulsing red tide from his severed flesh. As he died, his face still wore the puzzled expression.

Ishmael motioned toward the window, and three of his men leaped from the darkness into the room. "Is everything quiet?" he demanded in a low voice.

One of them nodded. "Most of them sleep. The streets are empty."

"Very well," said Ishmael. "We will start with the Babylonians. Once they're gone, the rest should be easy."

"Will we kill them all?" asked another of the henchmen.

"All — except some of the women," said Ishmael with an evil grin. "We will make an example of this miserable dung heap of a village. They will think twice before resisting, when we return at the head of Baalis's army."

WITH A START, Squint awoke. He stared at the ceiling above his pallet, then all about, blinking from side to side. The other two were asleep. He could hear their heavy breathing on both sides of him in the darkness.

What had stirred him so suddenly from sound slumber, without the usual prelude of a dream? Squint was too much a creature of instinct to remain in bed. There was an explanation, and he would not be able to sleep until he found it.

· Odd — it had seemed to him that someone in the room had spoken his name. With a soft grunt of perplexity, he rose from his pallet and walked quietly through the small house.

The light from the moon lay in pale oblongs on the packed-clay floor. He walked to a window and looked down the narrow, quiet midnight street — and stiffened.

A shadow had just slipped soundlessly from the window of a dwelling a stone's throw away, and then behind a corner, out of his sight. As he continued to scan the street, a similar figure furtively opened the door of a house on the opposite side of the street. As the dark silhouette sidled through the opening, Squint saw the silver flash of moonlight on steel.

He had seen enough. Quickly and silently he went to the others. The violent shaking woke them quickly. Just as quickly they rose to follow Squint as he glided to a window concealed from the street by the wall of a neighboring building. They made no noise as they went through the window and into the stillness of the night.

They passed the hours until dawn nervously crouching under an overhanging rock in the hills above the town.

40

JOHANAN AND HIS MEN had been on patrol for three days. They topped the final rise before coming into Mizpah, and the first sight greeting their eyes was a column of circling carrion birds. The grim sight sent a chill down Johanan's spine, and he began jogging down the path toward the town.

The guardpost at the entry of the town stood open and untended. "Halt!" commanded Johanan to his men, and with quick, practiced motions he deployed them in a defensive formation. Nostrils flaring, ears and eyes tuned to the keen intensity of impending attack, they slowly edged toward the streets of Mizpah, eerily silent in the midmorning sun.

Johanan motioned to two of his nimblest scouts to reconnoiter the Babylonians' barracks, a large house just beside the main road into the town. The two scampered off and returned scarce moments later. Gravely, they signed to their commander that all inhabitants of the barracks were dead.

House after house told the same grisly tale. Whole families had been slain, apparently in their sleep. They lay in dried pools of their own blood, with throats slashed or stab wounds in their chests. Caution began to give way to dread — fear that they would find not a single survivor of this horrible, as yet unexplained massacre.

When it became evident they would not be ambushed, Johanan divided his troops into three parties. They would search the town and meet back before the guardpost when the sun had just passed its zenith.

"Josiah, Elihu, Jachin, Benjamin," Johanan commanded, "you come with me. Let us examine the quarters of Ishmael and his ruffians," he mumbled. "I would wager my right eye we will find no casualties there."

They gathered back at the appointed time.

"We found no one living," reported Jaazaniah, "but some appear to be missing from their dwellings — some women, and a few elders."

Grimly Johanan nodded. "It was Ishmael, that's certain. Not a drop of blood anywhere about his area. And Gedaliah was slain — in a most treacherous fashion."

The men clenched their jaws, appalled and deeply saddened by the loss of the fair-minded, if too trusting, governor.

Just then, the third search party returned, with three extra members in tow.

"We found these three in hiding just above the town," explained Keriah, the lieutenant in charge. "They were here the night it happened. I thought you'd want to talk to them."

Johanan approached the elders, carefully looking them up and down. He peered closely at Jeremiah, then asked, "aren't you the prophet from Anathoth? The one who kept preaching about the fall of the city?"

Mutely, Jeremiah nodded.

"How did you escape with your skins?" queried Johanan, suspicion poking through the silences between his words.

"I was awakened by my friend," explained Jeremiah, pointing with his chin at Squint, who stared at Johanan with a one-eyed scowl.

"And what was it that roused you, Patch?" pressed Johanan.

Squint shrugged and made no other answer.

"Surely you cannot think we had any part in this slaughter," interrupted Baruch. "Think, man! What gain would three old men such as we have in murdering an entire town, then hiding nearby until caught? We feared for our lives. We hid, and would have continued hiding, fearing the possible return of the murderers, except that your patrol found us."

Johanan pretended to mull these thoughts, but had already decided for himself the innocence of the three. "Perhaps what you say is true," he muttered. "Then tell me: Did you see anything or anyone which might tell me where to start looking for the killers?"

"Yesterday," said Jeremiah, "a group of pilgrims came up

from Samaria. There were...perhaps four score. They went into the city, but only ten came out, and these with a handful of armed men — presumably those who did the killing. Some time later, the armed ones came back, carrying bags of provisions. I don't know what happened to the ten pilgrims."

"You didn't see the armed men leave?"

The three shook their heads and shrugged. "Perhaps they left during the night — I don't know," said Baruch.

A scout came running up. "Commander, I have struck the sign of a large party, leaving the city within the past day! Their track leads south — toward Gibeon."

"Gibeon! You are certain?" asked Johanan. The scout nodded solemnly.

"Perhaps Ishmael thinks to gain an advantage by going in an unexpected direction," mused the commander. "But soon or late, he will try to get back to Ammon. And I will be waiting for him"

The commander pivoted about, motioning to his men. "Eliezer! Jacob! Run about and gather such provisions as remain! The rest of you, prepare to march. And you three," he finished, turning his attention once again to the old men, "come with me. I want to ask you more questions about what you saw..."

ISHMAEL WIPED HIS MOUTH with the back of his hand, tossing the last crumbs of the barley cake into the glowing coals of the cookfire. He stood, wiping his hand on the back of his leg, and leered at the captive women huddled fearfully in the darkness beyond the ring of light, under the watchful eyes of three of his henchmen. Slowly Ishmael stalked toward them as they cowered away from the malice in his eyes.

"Yes, I believe Baalis will be pleased with you," he smirked. "Such delicacies as these are rare enough in Ammon, eh, fellows?" He grinned at his men, who guffawed in approval. He leaned over and seized a handful of the hair of the nearest woman, roughly pulling her head backward, so that she stared, her eyes rolling in fright, up into his jeering face.

"You're a fine piece of merchandise, aren't you? What is your name, girl?"

Her mouth moved in fright, but terror froze her voice. Angrily he yanked her head about. He shouted at her, "I asked your name, wench! Loosen the tongue in your head or I'll cut it out!"

"Miriam!" came the frightened wail. "My name is Miriam."

"Ahhh... Miriam." In his mouth, it sounded vulgar. "I like that name. Perhaps I should sample the wares I bring to Baalis, hmmm?" His hand slid down her neck, even as she cringed away from him.

A muffled shout came from the darkness, a cry of warning cut brutally short by the thud of a blade and the sound of snapping gristle. Ishmael jerked around, his hand immediately going to the hilt of his sword, his voice calling the guard. "Gazzam! Gazzam! Speak, you fool!"

An arrow struck the chest of another of Ishmael's henchmen with a hissing thump, and he fell dead into the laps of the shrieking women.

Johanan and his band raced out of the shadows, yelling and whirling their swords above their heads. Seeing Ishmael, Johanan drove straight for him, eager to avenge the shameful death of Gedaliah.

Ishmael reached down, and with a grip of iron dragged Miriam to her feet. Violently he shoved her in front of him, toward the charging Johanan. The hapless girl collided with the soldier, and they fell in a tangle of arms and legs. By the time Johanan extricated himself, Ishmael had melted away into the night, with his eight remaining lackeys.

WITH A GRUNT of weariness, Johanan placed the last stone atop the cairn marking the mass grave of the victims of Mizpah. It had taken them three days of back- and heartbreaking labor to cover the bones of the murdered ones. He and his men had arrived back at Mizpah on the day after they left in pursuit of Ishmael, and drearily began the grim task, assisted by the rescued hostages and the three old men who had escaped the carnage.

As sunset pushed its long shadows across the plains, the survivors of Mizpah gathered about the stark pile of stones. Instinctively they looked toward Johanan, by default their new leader, to explain or at least enunciate the dismal burden of grief that bore upon them. But he was not given to eloquence. Uneasily he shifted the duty to Jeremiah. "Holy man, can you give us words for our dead?"

The prophet closed his eyes, reaching within himself, trying to get his fingernails under the edge of this fresh pain, so lately and unexpectedly cast upon them after all that had gone before.

What came to him was a lament — a mournful wail for these slain and for their annihilated nation, the murdered spirit of a people, killed by their own hand. It was an elegy for them all — the dead, the exiled, and those who struggled on in this present misery in a world where there was no escape.

With bowed head, the tall old man began speaking, swaying slowly in time to the doleful rhythm of his dirge.

> *"Remember, O Lord, what has happened to us;*
> *   look, and see our disgrace.*
> *Our inheritance has been turned over to aliens,*
> *   our homes to foreigners.*
> *We have become orphans and fatherless,*
> *   our mothers like widows.*
> *We must buy the water we drink;*
> *   our wood can be had only at a price.*
> *Those who pursue us are at our heels;*
> *   we are weary and find no rest.*
> *We submitted to Egypt and Assyria*
> *   to get enough bread.*
> *Our fathers sinned and are no more;*
> *   and we bear their punishment.*
> *Slaves rule over us, and there is none to free us*
> *   from their hands.*
> *We get our bread at the risk of our lives*
> *   because of the sword in the desert.*
> *You, O Lord, reign forever;*
> *   Your throne endures from generation to generation.*
> *Why do You always forget us?*
> *Why do You forsake us so long?*
> *Restore us to Yourself, O Lord, that we may return;*
> *   renew our days as of old —*

Unless You have utterly rejected us
and are angry with us beyond measure."

THE LAST PLAINTIVE phrases of the prophet's funeral hymn floated away on the breeze, and the people were about to go back into the city, when Jeremiah's words halted them.

"This," he said, pointing at the cairn, his voice like a whip, "this is what Israel has done to Zion." His fiercely glowing eyes swept the circle, pinioning each of them in place as he continued. "A prince of Judah has, with foul hands, slain his own brethren, and you have angrily sought revenge. With loud wails you have mourned those slain by their own kindred.

"Yet look what you have done to the nation! Is your guilt any less than that of Ishmael? For years the Lord sent prophets among you; prophets who cried out against the persistent evil in your hearts — a plague of lust, of adultery, of idolatry and dishonesty — which throttled the soul of Israel just as surely as the sword of Ishmael has slain those buried here. But it was a slow poison, a lingering death which Jacob's children died. You would not see it. You preferred sickness to health, and now Jerusalem lies atop ruined Zion like stones piled on a grave.

"Look at Jerusalem," he shouted, pointing his finger like a blade at the cairn. "Behold the monument you have built to your own sin!"

No one stirred. The breeze blew silently past, sighing drily among the stones of the tomb. Slowly they began to drift away, back toward the empty houses of Mizpah.

And then it was night.

Jeremiah leaned against the wall of the house, staring upward into the night sky. The three stars which made up the belt of Nimrod the Hunter twinkled merrily down at him. At this time of year, the Hunter stalked the southeastern quadrant, his bow pointed across the sky to the west — toward Egypt.

Baruch walked up quietly behind him, laying a hand on the prophet's shoulder. "It is late, my friend. You should rest."

Jeremiah sighed. "There is a weariness which denies sleep."

The scribe moved along beside Jeremiah. His eyes traced the path of the prophet's stare, up into the radiant host of the heavens. "The Hunter is brilliant indeed, tonight."

"His bow is aimed toward Tahpanhes and the land of Hophra," commented Jeremiah. "Even across the night sky, Babylon harries Egypt..."

Baruch carefully studied his friend's face; etched in shadow by the dim light of the stars. "Something troubles you — something besides the latest tragedy."

Jeremiah looked down at the ground. "I thought His wrath would be spent by now, Baruch," he groaned. "But still He has not emptied the deep vats of His anger. Yet once more He will punish us — even this tiny remnant which gasps for breath among the dregs of the destroyed land — because the people still harbor evil in their hearts."

Wordlessly, Baruch looked away, down the nearly deserted street. Upon a rooftop at the far end of the dusty avenue, a tiny flame flickered. A dimly lit figure made obeisance before the blaze, spreading arms upward, toward the starry host of heaven.

41

THE NEXT MORNING Johanan knocked on the door of the prophet's house. Squint opened the door, then walked away, leaving the commander to enter or leave as he wished. Jeremiah and Baruch squatted before their small hearth, tearing pieces from a loaf of *matzoh*. Johanan thought the prophet wore a knowing look, as if the strange old man who now beckoned him had been expecting his visit.

"Come and be seated, Johanan," said the prophet. "Have some bread."

The commander took a small portion from the loaf, holding it nervously in his hand. Jeremiah made him uncomfortable. Johanan always felt that the old man's eyes stared directly through him. He shifted in his place, then said, "Holy man, I have come to ask your advice."

Jeremiah studied him, thoughtfully chewing his bread and waiting for the soldier to continue.

"Ishmael has slain the Babylonians — not to mention Gedaliah, whom Nebuchadrezzar himself appointed to govern this territory. I...I fear that the emperor will be angered by this, and will come and destroy us."

"Why should he do this? You are not to blame for the deaths of the Chaldeans. Why would the emperor kill innocent men?"

Diffidently the commander looked away from the prophet's face. "Perhaps he will not believe in our innocence. Perhaps he will wish to make an example of us for others to learn by. Gedaliah stood before him, and won his favor, but I... I was in Jerusalem when the city fell. I saw what the emperor does to those who oppose him. I cannot speak well, as did the governor..." His fingers shredded the bread as his hands twisted in his lap.

Jeremiah place a hand on Johanan's shoulder. "Commander, you must listen to me. The Lord has shown me that we will be safe if we stay here. Here the people can build a new life; here they can stay in the land of their inheritance and learn again the ways of the Eternal. The emperor will not harm you, as you believe, if you will trust in the words the Lord has given me.

"But if you turn your face toward Egypt"—Johanan's face came up sharply; he had not mentioned where he intended to flee—"and if you go down to the Land of Bondage," continued the prophet, "it will not go well with you. How many times has the promise of Egypt proven false to our people? Think, Johanan: Since the days of Moses, the Pharaohs have afflicted the children of Abraham. From Rameses to Shishak, and so with Psamtik, Neco and Hophra, the rulers of Egypt have been a curse upon our people.

"And what is worse, Johanan, if the people go down to the land of Egypt, they will forget the Lord and His commands. In this place they might turn again, and learn to rely upon His promises. But if they go down there they will see the golden images of Egypt, and will be drawn ever more into the worship of worthless idols. You must not lead them down there, Johanan. To go there is to die." His eyes glistened with intensity as he waited for Johanan's reply.

The soldier stood and walked to the nearest window. His back to the disturbing eyes of the holy man, he said, "I know little of such things as you say. I am a soldier, not a seer. You claim to see things that yet may be..." He turned and faced Jeremiah. "But I see only what is — here and now. And I fear for my life and for the lives of the people for whom I am now responsible." He held Jeremiah's eyes a moment, then strode from the house.

Jeremiah exchanged a look of disappointed resignation with Baruch, then slowly tore off another piece of bread, his eyes on the doorway where Johanan had exited. Squint stepped over and closed the door.

SQUINT WALKED back and forth across the small room, making bundles and tying packages together. "Squint," called Baruch, busy at the back of the room, "do not forget the scrolls." The scribe motioned toward the leather satchel he had made for his treasures; lighter to carry than the clay pot. Squint nodded and turned again to his work.

The order had come only a day after Johanan's visit to the prophet. The leader sent word that the remnant of Mizpah should gather their belongings and prepare to leave for the south. He sent a special envoy — Jaazaniah, his second-in-command — to advise Jeremiah that he would not be allowed to stay in Mizpah. Though the prophet's words might not be pleasing to the ear, Johanan was loath to incur the anger of Jeremiah's god by leaving the holy man behind. He would come with them. Perhaps he would bring them luck.

Jeremiah sat glumly by the door of his house, taking no notice of the hurried activity of the other two. He knew he would never again see the borders of Judah. After all the indignities he had suffered, he would not even be allowed the austere solace of dying in the land of his birth. The thought of this last affront galled him sorely. In his mind, he wrestled with the Lord.

"Why, Sovereign Lord?" he moaned silently. "Is it not enough that I have carried Your words to an unwilling people for these two score years and ten? Have I flagged in my devotion to Your calling, that You now carry me from the land of Judah to a country of strangers and strange gods, to die there?"

The confused, wounded questions twined endlessly in his mind, but no answers came.

THEY SET OUT at midday, a long, straggling line of dejected refugees escorted by the small band of Johanan's men. They carried with them pitifully few possessions. Few of them looked back.

They camped that night near the remains of Bethlehem, the ancient birthplace of King David. As the embers of the cookfires faded, Johanan once again sought out Jeremiah.

"Will you not pray to your God for us?" he beseeched. "It may be that He will hear you, and for your sake will give us guidance. Seek a word from Him..." The soldier's unspoken wish was plain to Jeremiah — he wanted a blessing pronounced upon this misbegotten undertaking. The prophet's eyes turned away from the commander to stare into the darkness.

Johanan persisted. "I beg you, holy man. Pray to your god.

And I… In return," he said hesitantly, "I will do as He directs you. I will listen to his words, and do accordingly. Will you not do this for us?"

Jeremiah sighed, and bowed his head. Enough silence crawled by that Johanan thought the old man had fallen asleep. Then Jeremiah turned to him.

"Very well. I will seek a word from the Lord. But you must wait here until He has spoken to me. I will go up into the hills to seek His face…"

"I will come with you," said Baruch.

"No!" said Johanan, quickly. He glanced from Baruch to Jeremiah, evaluating. Perhaps the holy man and his friend would use this as an opportunity to leave the party. He could not allow this. "No," he said again, "Baruch, you may not go. You will wait here, with the rest of us, for the return of the holy man."

Baruch looked at Jeremiah, who nodded slowly. Then the prophet got wearily to his feet and trod off into the night.

The Voice was within him that very night:

"If My people stay in this land, I will build them up and not tear them down. I will plant them, not uproot them, for I am grieved over the disaster I have inflicted upon them. They should not fear the king of Babylon, for I am with them and will deliver them from his hand. Because I have compassion on them, he will have the same, and will restore them.

"But if they persist in going to Egypt, thinking to escape war and the battle trumpet's call and hunger, the very sword they fear will come down to Egypt and overtake them, and famine will come upon them. Just as My wrath was poured out even upon Jerusalem, the city of My Name, so shall My anger be kindled against them in the land of Egypt."

Even as he heard within his spirit the very word he expected, Jeremiah strove with the Lord.

"Sovereign Lord," he moaned, "do not make me go back to the people with this word. All my life I have been an object of cursing and loathing because of the hard message You have placed on my lips. Now, in my old age, I beg of You, my God — do not place this burden upon me. Let Your servant die, and know an end to the conflict!"

For ten days he contended with the Almighty — pleading for rest, for a halt to the grinding, endless turmoil. But the answer was the same.

The Eternal's will was adamant. He could rebel if he chose, but he could not win amnesty from the pain of his call. And so, at the end of the tenth day, Jeremiah arose from the ground, wiped the dust from his face, and went down from the hills to Bethlehem — to face Johanan and the people.

Baruch was the first to see him coming. He hobbled out and gripped the arms of his friend. "You have not eaten anything for all this time!" he gasped, looking into the haggard features of his friend. "Before anything else, you must take food..."

Slowly Jeremiah shook his head. "I will not die — not yet," he said sadly. "I must go to the people."

"What will you tell them?" asked Baruch, knowing the answer.

"I will tell them...what the Lord has said," said Jeremiah simply.

THE CROWD CIRCLED about, coughing, shifting, growing quiet. The strange old man stood, leaning on the shoulders of his two friends in the center. Just inside the ring stood Johanan, who now addressed the prophet.

"Tell us, then. What word has come from the Lord?"

Before answering, Jeremiah looked slowly around the gathering. As his gaze rested on each face, most of them glanced away, discomfited by his piercing eyes. A few returned his look, pity, and confusion sketched on their brows. All were silent.

At last he spoke. "O remnant of Judah," he said in a voice surprisingly strong, given his appearance, "you made a fatal mistake when you asked me to inquire of the Lord!" Now the prophet's eyes locked with those of Johanan. "You said, 'We will follow the word of the Lord, whatever it may be!' Very well. Hear then, what the Lord, the God of Heaven, says to you:

"'Do not go to Egypt. Stay here in this land, and I will establish you, and have mercy on you. Nebuchadrezzar will not harm you, for I will be with you,' says the Lord.

"'But if you go to Egypt, against My word, I will seek you out, and slay you with the sword and with famine—'"

"You are lying!" hissed Johanan, stung by humiliation at having his leadership belittled in front of all the people. "You!" he shouted, pointing angrily at Baruch, "you have told him to say these things! You wish to stay here, and so you poison the people against me! You want us to die at the hand of Nebuchadrezzar!" An angry buzzing rippled among the throng, following the harsh words of the leader.

"Go back to your places, and prepare to march!" commanded Johanan a moment later. "We have heard enough of the dodderings of these two old ones! They are addled with age! Go, all of you!" His face flushed with fury, Johanan stared about at them until the crowd slowly began to break apart and wander away, each one muttering quietly to his neighbor.

When they had all left, Johanan turned again to Jeremiah. "You will not speak again to the people, as long as we are on this journey," he said. "You will remain silent, or I will have you bound and gagged."

The soldier turned on his heel and strode away.

42

TWO WEEKS LATER they staggered into Tahpanhes, on the northeastern frontier of Pharaoh Hophra's domain. The pitiful troop stared around them in wonder at the fine stone buildings, their courtyards festooned with date palms and other greenery. The richly hued murals of Egypt swarmed across the walls in brilliant grandeur. Everywhere stood obelisks and statuary, raised to the glory of the gods and of Pharaoh, the son of the sun.

A handful of Hebrews had fled to Egypt during the siege, and these were able to offer shelter to some of the refugees. The others did the best they could. Those who had some skill or trade set up makeshift shops and booths in Tahpanhes and the other cities of Upper Egypt. Within six months the immigrants had gained a foothold in the land.

As she had for so many millennia, Egypt began the absorption of yet another layer of humanity, the latest of so many which had washed up on the shores of the Nile. And the descendants of Israel had, at last, come full circle.

Jeremiah's eyesight was failing. Squint still managed to find work to do, and Baruch acquired a few students. The three old men leaned against each other in these waning days. They had few other friends.

BARUCH DISMISSED his last pupil of the day. The boy was named Isaac. He was the son of one of Johanan's band and a woman who had been one of the royal consorts abducted by Ishmael. The lad was bright — Baruch had entertained thoughts of teaching him the scribe's art, once he had mastered the fundamentals of reading and writing. He fancied the boy had some small interest in the prospect. As he closed the door and turned around, Jeremiah, who had been dozing in the corner of the small room, started and woke.

The prophet blinked and strained his eyes, trying — in the dim shadows that were all that remained of his vision — to discern the form of Baruch. "Baruch," he called, "where are you? I cannot find you."

"Here, my old friend," said the scribe, gripping Jeremiah's waving hand. "You are awake at last. My last three students could hardly bear the suspense — they were afraid you might stir while they were here."

"Am I become so fearful in my dotage, that young boys dread my awakening?" queried the feeble prophet.

"Ah, but they do," assured Baruch. "You see, I told them you were a prophet. You are rather mysterious to their imaginative young minds."

"Mysterious!" scoffed Jeremiah. "What is mysterious about a blind old man who sleeps in the corner?" They chuckled together.

"Baruch, I had the strangest dream just now," said Jeremiah, after a moment's pause.

"What was it, my friend?" asked the scribe.

"I dreamed I stood on the causeway outside the royal residence, here in Tahpanhes. I had pried up several stones, and dug a hole in the pavement. Then I took large stones and mortar, and set them in the hole I had made, forming a sort of pedestal. A crowd — all Hebrews — was gathered about, watching me.

"And I turned to them and said, 'One day the king of Babylon will place his throne upon these stones, and will spread his canopy above them. He will bring death to Egypt, and he will burn the temples of the gods of this land. So says the Lord of Hosts...'"

His voice faded, and his eyes searched the dimness for Baruch's face. "Could it have been a word from the Lord?" he asked, more to himself than to his friend. "But how can I, an old man nearly blind, go to the royal residence and dig the stones from the pavement?"

"Softly, friend, softly," soothed Baruch. "You will do no stonemason's work today. Wait here and I will fetch my pens."

"Tell me," asked Jeremiah when Baruch returned, "how do the people behave, now that they have been here for awhile? Do they remember anything of the Eternal?"

Baruch answered sadly, "Old friend, they do not. Hardly an evening passes without my seeing some Hebrew wife burning Ashtaroth-cakes in the fire. All the years and all the calamities have not taught them anything."

"Then write this," said the prophet, his voice firming slightly as he pushed himself up, sitting as erect as his stooped shoulders would allow. "This is what the Lord Almighty, the God of Israel, says: 'You saw the great disaster I brought on Jerusalem and on all the towns of Judah. Today they lie deserted and in ruins because of the evil they have done. They provoked Me to anger by burning incense and worshiping other gods that neither they nor you nor your father ever knew.

"'Again and again I sent My servants the prophets...'"

BARUCH SHADED his tired old eyes against the harsh glare of the Egyptian sun. He peered down the dusty village path to see the figure of Isaac striding toward his house. The boy was coming for his lesson.

Isaac walked in, greeting his teacher. "Honored Baruch, I am here." Respectfully he bowed to the ancient scribe, who smiled at his favorite pupil.

For a moment Baruch looked Isaac up and down. The boy was rapidly becoming a man, he thought. How long was it? Three years now he had been coming here. Baruch had introduced him to the intricacies of the written word. Subtly he had tried to pass on the culture, the essence of respect for the written word — and the urgency of keeping a record, a history, that those who came behind might remember...

"Did you bring the scrolls I gave you last time?" inquired the stooped elder.

"Yes, teacher, I have them right here," said Isaac eagerly, producing the documents from the kit he carried on a strap over his shoulder.

"Very well," said Baruch, "and where are your copies?"

"Here, master," said Isaac, nervously displaying his assigned handiwork.

For long moments the old man sat quietly, studying the young man's work. Isaac shifted from one foot to another in an agony of apprehension. He had striven scrupulously to make exact copies; laboriously he had sat by the window in his house, carefully holding his pens as Baruch had taught him, painstakingly etching the ink onto the papyrus in exacting mimicry of the old master's calligraphy. Each time he encountered the representation of the name of Yahweh, he stopped, just as Baruch had taught him, cleaned his pen, wrote the word, recleaned his pen, and continued.

Again and again as he worked, he heard Baruch's ubiquitous admonitions running through his mind: "A scribe's work must be perfect. Each jot and dash must be the exact duplicate of the original manuscript. How else can the words be preserved for our descendants? We have an exceedingly grave trust, we scribes."

Baruch looked up at Isaac, his face unreadable. Isaac felt the hot flush of anxiety rush from his cheeks to the pit of his stomach. Then Baruch smiled at him.

"This is excellent work, my boy," he was saying. "The best I have ever seen."

Isaac's knees felt weak with relief. He allowed himself to smile. "Thank you, teacher. I have tried very hard."

"So you have," nodded Baruch. "Well then, sit down. I have something special for you — something I believe you are now ready to attempt."

Curiosity wrinkled the boy's brow as he sat on the mat facing Baruch. While he arranged his pens and other materials around him, Baruch rose creakily to his feet and hobbled over to a corner of the room. As Isaac watched, the old man carefully raised the lid of a clay pot, reached within, and slowly drew out a scroll wrapped in a soft leather sheath. He flipped open an end of the sheath, glanced at the scroll, grunted in satisfaction, and returned to the mat and his pupil.

Groaning, he seated himself again, then raised his eyes and studied the face of the boy across from him.

"Isaac, I want you to make a copy of this scroll." With an undecipherable expression on his face, Baruch handed the scroll reverently to his student.

Confusion still registering on his face, Isaac unwrapped the scroll. Carefully he unrolled it to the opening lines, his eyes scanning right-to-left as he quickly read the beginning words.

"This Jeremiah; is he—?"

Baruch nodded. "Yes. He was my friend, now dead these two years past."

Isaac looked from the scroll to his teacher. "And this scroll contains his prophecies?"

Again Baruch nodded, waiting for the next questions.

"Was he a very great prophet?"

"Very great," assured Baruch with quiet intensity.

"Did he bring down fire from heaven, or cause floods, like Elijah?" asked Isaac eagerly.

Quietly Baruch smiled and shook his head. "No. The fire he brought was in men's hearts, not in the sky."

Isaac looked slightly disappointed. "But I thought you said he was a very great prophet!"

"And so he was," said Baruch. He peered intently at his pupil, carefully emphasizing his next words. "He was called by the Eternal. And for more than seventy years was faithful to that call. It is his only claim to greatness, my boy, but mark you"—he tapped Isaac's leg with a forefinger—"it is claim enough."

He held Isaac's eyes, then dropped his gaze. "You should begin now. When you have copied two sheets, I will inspect your work."

Looking from Baruch to the text, Isaac carefully spread the scroll before him and reached for his pens and a sheet of papyrus. Baruch laid a hand on his arm.

"Wait. For this, you should not use papyrus." The old man reached behind him, handing Isaac a fresh sheet of vellum. "This task warrants parchment."

Never before had the master allowed him to use the more durable medium, and Isaac felt a thrill of exhilaration. Quietly he smiled, gratefully accepting the warm-smelling sheet from Baruch. He arranged himself and began to write:

The words of Jeremiah, son of Hilkiah, one of the priests at Anathoth in the territory of Benjamin. The word of the Lord came to him in the thirteenth year of the reign of Josiah....

Baruch hoisted himself slowly to his feet and walked over to a window, his back to his pupil. He could hear the boy behind him — the busy scratching of the stylus on parchment. He looked out across the sun-washed landscape to the pile of rocks standing alone perhaps a bowshot from the house.

"Very well, my old friend," he muttered. "It is completed. And begun."